A. Gray.
11F.

Book 4 **Modern Mathematics** for Schools

Book 4 Modern

Mathematics for Schools

Prepared by the

Scottish
Mathematics
Group

Blackie
Glasgow and London

Chambers
Edinburgh and London

Blackie & Son Limited
Bishopbriggs · Glasgow
5 Fitzhardinge Street · London W1

Blackie & Son (India) Limited
103–5 Fort Street · Bombay

W. & R. Chambers Limited
11 Thistle Street · Edinburgh 2
6 Dean Street · London W1

First published 1967
Revised edition 1969

Standard book numbers

Pupil's edition

Blackie 216.89065.9
Chambers 550.75804.6

Teacher's edition

Blackie 216.89066.7
Chambers 550.75811.9

Printed and bound in Great Britain by
Morrison & Gibb Limited
London & Edinburgh
Set in 10 point Monotype Times Roman

Scottish Mathematics Group

Members associated with this book

Aberdeen High School for Girls	**Elizabeth K. Henderson**
Hutchesons' Girls' Grammar School	**Helen C. Murdoch**
Dundee College of Education	**W. T. Blackburn**
Hamilton College of Education	**W. Brodie**
Lenzie Academy	**C. Clark**
Robert Gordon's College	**D. Donald**
Allan Glen's School	**R. A. Finlayson**
Madras College	**J. L. Hodge**
Duncanrig Secondary School	**R. McKendrick**
High School of Dundee	**W. More**
John Neilson High School	**A. G. Robertson**
Grove Academy	**A. A. Sturrock**
St. Aloysius' College	**Rev. J. Taylor**
Glasgow Academy	**E. B. C. Thornton**
Dollar Academy	**J. A. Walker**
Hutchesons' Boys' Grammar School	**P. Whyte**
City Public Secondary School	**H. S. Wylie**

The late **A. G. Sillitto** formerly of Jordanhill College of Education

Preface to Revised Edition

This revised edition is published to meet the need, already met in the later books of the series, for examples using British decimal currency. At the same time the opportunity has been taken to increase the number of examples where metric units appear, while still retaining some British weights and measures. At appropriate points too, chapter summaries have been inserted.

Throughout the book the pagination is the same in the original and revised editions so that for many chapters the two editions may be used in the same class without inconvenience.

Preface

This is the fourth of a series of seven books based on the Alternative Ordinary Grade Syllabus in mathematics introduced in 1965 for the Scottish Certificate of Education. But the series is equally suitable for courses under similar syllabuses leading to the Ordinary Level papers of the General Certificate of Education. Each part has been tried out experimentally with a group of 7,000 children and contains all the mathematics considered to be necessary for approximately half a year's work in school, but references to further reading are given in the teachers' version of the book.

The authors of the course recognize that while *teaching* should be integrated it is undesirable that any text should impose a particular scheme or method on individual teachers. This course is designed for a wide ability range in all types of Secondary Schools and for this reason it is assumed that different teachers will use it in different ways. The aim therefore has been to supply adequate material in a form which can be readily adapted to suit individual schemes and teaching methods.

For this reason each book is arranged under the headings Algebra, Geometry, Arithmetic with, later, Trigonometry and Calculus to allow flexibility in actual teaching. Throughout, however, ideas, material and method are integrated *within* each branch of mathematics and *across* the branches; the opportunity to do this is indeed one of the more obvious reasons for teaching this kind of mathematics in the schools—for it is *mathematics* as a whole that is presented.

Pupils are encouraged to find out facts and discover results for themselves, to observe and study the themes and patterns that pervade mathematics today. As a course based on this series of books progresses, a certain amount of equipment will be helpful particularly in the development of geometry. The use of calculating machines and slide rules is advocated where appropriate, but these instruments are not an essential feature of the work.

While fundamental principles are emphasized and reasonable attention is paid to the matter of structure, the width of the course should be sufficient to provide a useful experience of mathematics for those pupils who do not pursue the study of the subject beyond school level. An effort has been made throughout to arouse the interest of all pupils and at the same time to keep in mind the needs of the future mathematician.

The introduction of mathematics in the Primary School and recent changes in course at Colleges and Universities have been taken into account. In addition, the aims, methods, and writing of these books have been influenced by national and international discussions about the purpose and content of courses in mathematics, held under the auspices of the Organization for Economic Cooperation and Development and other organizations. Publications of OECD to which reference has been made are: *New Thinking in School Mathematics; Synopses for Modern Secondary School Mathematics; Mathematics Today—a guide for teachers.*

Contents

Algebra

Geometry

Arithmetic

Notation

Sets of numbers—Different countries and different authors give different notations and definitions for the various sets of numbers. In this series the following are used:

E The universal set

∅ The empty set

N The set of natural numbers $\{1, 2, 3, \ldots\}$

W The set of whole numbers $\{0, 1, 2, 3, \ldots\}$ or counting numbers

Z The set of integers $\{\ldots, -2, -1, 0, 1, 2, \ldots\}$

Q The set of rational numbers

R The set of real numbers

The set of prime numbers does not include 1.

Algebra

CHAPTER 1 Further Sets

1 Defining sets

We saw in Book 1 that *set* is the term generally used in mathematics for a collection of articles, persons, points, or objects of any kind whatsoever. Mathematics is concerned with the properties common to all sets and the operations that can be performed on them. Our ordinary language has many collective terms, almost every special term denoting some quality of its set as a whole. For example, we have 'watch of nightingales', 'army of ants', 'gaggle of geese', 'team of football players'.

Although a team of football players, dressed in club colours, consists of eleven men who have trained together and have a common interest, and for that reason are called a team, yet the spectator at a match sees eleven different players. He is interested in the moves of each one, and for his benefit the players are often distinguished by large numbers sewn on to their jerseys. A club supporter may even absent himself from a game because a particular player is not *listed* to play. This listing, usually in a newspaper, makes the team a proper mathematical set.

Similarly, in mathematics, we may consider the set whose *members* are all the positive integers, and notice how the commutative law of addition applies to all pairs of members of the set. Seeing the set as a whole we may even hide the identity of two members by saying that if a and b are any two members, then $a+b = b+a$. But the mathematician is as much interested in the individuals of his set as the spectator is in the players. He may say, for example, that zero is not a member of the set of positive integers and, if you want it in your set, you should change to another set, the set of whole numbers.

When a set is named in mathematics, it must be possible to identify every member of the set. To have a set, we must either list all the members *or* we must give a description which will indicate precisely whether any object is or is not a member of the set. In either case we say that the set is *well defined.*

Note.—(i) *No two members of a set may be identical.*
(ii) *The order in which the members are listed does not matter.*

Set Notation

It is customary to name a set by a capital letter and to write its members within curly brackets. $A = \{5, 2\}$ is a set. (5, 2) is an ordered pair of numbers and not a set; it may be represented by a point in the x,y plane. $a \in S$ means 'a is a member of S' and $b \notin S$ means 'b is not a member of S'.

Example. Let P be the set of prime factors of 12.
$2 \in P$, $3 \in P$, and no other prime number is a factor of 12.
Hence $P = \{2, 3\}$. This set is well defined.

Exercise 1

1 Decide whether or not each of the following is a well-defined set. If you think it is, either list the members, or tell how the list might be obtained, or give a good description of the set.

(i) Members of your class who are over 5 feet tall.
(ii) Divisors of 84.
(iii) A flock of starlings.
(iv) Names of people in your town (or county) who had a vote in the last General Election.
(v) Points which are 3 units distant from the x-axis and at the same time 2 units distant from the y-axis.
(vi) Letters in this square array of letters which belong to exactly three different sets of three letters in a straight line.

A	*B*	*C*
D	*E*	*F*
G	*H*	*K*

2 Give two examples of well-defined sets by listing the members.

3 Give two examples of well-defined sets by describing the members.

4 Give two examples of collections of objects which do not form sets because they are not well defined.

5 A is the set of whole numbers from 0 to 10 inclusive.
B is the set of prime numbers between 0 and 10.
C is the set of even numbers from 2 to 10 inclusive.
D is the set of multiples of 3 between 2 and 10.

List the members of the sets A, B, C, and D, and use the symbols $\in$ and $\notin$ to state whether or not the numbers 2, 3, 5, 7, 10 are members of each of the sets A, B, C, D.

2 Equality of sets

Two sets A and B are equal when they have the same elements. This means that every member of A is a member of B *and* every member of B is a member of A. For example $\{\Delta, *, 0\} = \{0, \Delta, *\}$.

If $X = \{0, 3, 2, 5, 4, 8\}$, then the number of members or elements in X is 6. This is written $n(X) = 6$.

Note that if $A = \{5, 8\}$ and $B = \{2, 3\}$, then $n(A) = n(B) = 2$, but A and B are not equal sets.

Exercise 2

1 List the following sets:

$F = \{$the first 7 positive odd numbers$\}$.
$G = \{$the prime numbers from 10 to 24$\}$.
$H = \{$the multiples of 7 between 1 and 50$\}$.
$M = \{$the initial letters of the surnames of the pupils in your row in class$\}$.

Give the values of $n(F)$, $n(G)$, $n(H)$, $n(M)$.

2 If $A = \{1, 2, 3, 4\}$ and $B = \{1, 2, 3, 4, 5\}$, then every member of A is a member of B. Why are A and B not equal sets? Give $n(A)$ and $n(B)$.

3 List the set C of integers between 9,528 and 9,537 which have 3 in the tens place. Find $n(C)$.

4 If $n(A) = n(B)$, must $A = B$? If $A = B$, must $n(A) = n(B)$?

5 List the prime factors of 60 as a set named X.
List the divisors of 60 as a set named Y. Find $n(X)$ and $n(Y)$. Does $X = Y$?

6 The digits 5, 4, and 1 are used to make 3-digit numbers, each digit being used only once in each number.
List this set S of 3-digit numbers. What is $n(S)$?

7 R, S, P, I, T, H are the sets of ways in which a given rectangle, square, parallelogram, isosceles triangle, equilateral triangle, and regular hexagon, respectively, can fit into its outline.
Give $n(R)$, $n(S)$, $n(P)$, $n(I)$, $n(T)$, and $n(H)$.

8 Using only coins in current use, 70p is to be shared equally among x children so that each gets at least 2p. Write out the set of which x is a member.

9 C is the set of pupils in class I C, and D the set in class I D in the same school. There are 28 pupils in each of the classes I C and I D. Are C and D equal sets?

10 P is the set of prime factors of 2,310 and Q is the set of prime numbers less than 13. Show that $P = Q$.

3 Large sets and infinite sets

Any Post Office can show you a directory of telephone subscribers; this contains a large set of names. Can you think of a counting scheme to give an approximation to the number of members in this set? There are two distinct reasons why this set must be listed:

(i) If a page is torn and one name is missing, no argument based on the other names will help you to replace it.
(ii) The set is so large that unless it is listed in some order it would be a very long task to find out whether or not one resident in the area belonged to the set.

A large library of books is another set of the same kind. Name another. Can you think of a much larger set which does not need to be listed? Is your set one which 'builds itself' from element to element? The set of all even integers from 2 to 1,000,000 is of this kind. Call it set A. Whether it is necessary to list all of this even-number set depends on the possibility of answering certain questions about its members:

(i) Is 3,265 a member? Is 14,020 a member? Is 1,273 a member?
(ii) What is the number of elements in the set?

Another description of this set of even integers is

$$A = \{2, 4, 6, 8, \ldots, 1{,}000{,}000\}.$$

A still larger set is the set of all positive even integers. It has no last member, and so we write $T = \{2, 4, 6, 8, \ldots\}$. You may spend a whole day writing out members of this set T, and at the end of the day you will be no nearer the end of the set than you were when you started. T is what we call an *infinite set*. (Note that A and T are different sets.)

Exercise 3

1 Give a description of the following sets by listing the necessary members, using dots to save writing too many.

(*a*) All positive numbers less than 100 divisible by 3.
(*b*) All negative whole numbers.
(*c*) All squares of positive odd numbers.
(*d*) All negative whole numbers greater than -25.
(*e*) All numbers of the form $2n+3$ where n is a whole number.

2 Describe in your own words:

(*a*) $\{2, 4, 6, 8, \ldots\}$
(*b*) $\{2, 4, 6, 8, \ldots, 98\}$
(*c*) $\{1, 4, 9, 16, \ldots, 400\}$
(*d*) $\{5, 10, 15, 20, \ldots, 100\}$
(*e*) $\{1, 8, 27, 64, \ldots\}$
(*f*) $\{2, 4, 8, \ldots\}$
(*g*) $\{1, \frac{1}{2}, \frac{1}{3}, \frac{1}{4}, \ldots\}$
(*h*) $\{1, 0{\cdot}1, 0{\cdot}01, 0{\cdot}001, \ldots\}$

Find the number of members in the sets in (*b*), (*c*), and (*d*).

3 Make up two infinite sets of your own, listing a few members, and see if your neighbour can describe how the set was formed.

4 Describe in words:

(*a*) $\{1, 3, 5, 7, \ldots, 99\}$
(*b*) $\{1, 3, 5, 7, \ldots\}$
(*c*) $\{0, 4, 8, 12, \ldots\}$
(*d*) $\{1, 8, 15, 22, \ldots\}$

Which of the above are infinite sets?

4 The set-builder notation

Example 1.—Consider $A = \{3, 4, 6, 8, 12, 14, \ldots\}$. Whether this definition of A is good enough depends on whether you discover that its elements are prime numbers increased by 1. The irregularity of the members might suggest prime numbers, but it would certainly be much better to have

'A is the set of numbers which are 1 more than prime numbers'

or 'A is the set of integers which immediately follow prime numbers'.

Instead of either of these statements it is better still to say the same thing more neatly in symbols,

$A = \{x : x = p+1, p \text{ a prime number}\}$. This means '$A$ is the set of all x such that x is 1 more than a prime number'. Is '$44 \in A$' a true statement?

Which number between 120 and 130 is selected by '$x = p+1$, p a prime number'? We read $\{x : \quad\}$ as 'the set of all x such that . . .'.

Example 2.—B is the set of all multiples of 3 which are greater than 9 and less than 99. This is written $B = \{x : x = 3y, 3 < y < 33, y \in N\}$.

Exercise 4

1 $A = \{1, 2, 3, 4, 5, 6\}$ $\qquad B = \{2, 4, 6, 8, 10\}$
$C = \{3, 5, 7, 9, 11, 13, 15\}$

List the sets given by

(*a*) $\{x : x > 3, x \in A\}$ $\qquad$ (*b*) $\{x : x < 6, x \in B\}$
(*c*) $\{x : 5 < x < 13, x \in C\}$ $\qquad$ (*d*) $\{x : x+2 = 6, x \in A\}$
(*e*) $\{x : 2x+1 = 6, x \in B\}$
(*f*) $\{(x, y) : x = y, x \in A, y \in B\}$
(*g*) $\{(x, y) : x = 2y, x \in B, y \in C\}$
(*h*) $\{(x, y) : y = 2x+1, x \in A, y \in C\}$

You will remember that we can graph set A on the number line thus:

FIG. 1

Graph each set (*a*) to (*e*) on a number line.
Graph sets (*f*) to (*h*) using x and y axes.

2 List the sets given by:

$A = \{x : x > 2, x \in N\}$, where N denotes the set of natural numbers.
$B = \{x : x < 6, x \in N\}$

$C = \{x: 0 < x < 4, x \in N\}$
$D = \{x: -3 < x < 2, x \in Z\}$, where Z denotes the set of integers.
Graph each set on a number line.

3 Which of the following statements about the sets A, B, C, D in question 2 are true (T) and which are false (F)?

(i) $2 \in A$ (ii) $2 \in D$ (iii) $3 \in A$ (iv) $A = B$
(v) $n(C) = 3$ (vi) $n(D) \neq 3$ (vii) $-3 \in D$
(viii) $n(D) > n(B)$

4 Express, in set-builder notation, the set of natural numbers:

(*a*) greater than 5 (*b*) less than 10
(*c*) between 3 and 11 (*d*) between -3 and 11
(*e*) between -5 and 5 (*f*) divisible by 5
(*g*) one more than a multiple of 5 (*h*) two less than a multiple of 5

5 The universal set

If you hear two people mentioning the names Jaguar, Cortina, Humber, they are probably discussing the merits of different types of motor-cars. For the time being, the *universal set* under discussion is {motor-cars}. Within this universal set there are all sorts of sets, e.g. {British cars}, {Morris cars}, {racing cars}, and so on. These sets are called *subsets* of the universal set.

Exercise 5

1 State some sets you might discuss if the universal set is

(i) whole numbers (ii) ships (iii) all living persons
(iv) plane figures bounded by straight lines.

2 What might your universal set be if your discussion concerned

(i) Kennedy, Johnson, Eisenhower
(ii) Spheres, cones, cylinders
(iii) $5x = 7$, $2x-1 = 9$, $\frac{1}{3}x = 4-x$?

3 The universal set $E = \{0, 1, 2, 3, 4\}$, and x is a variable on this set. Give the solution set of

(i) $x < 3$ (ii) $x+3 = 7$ (iii) $2x+1 = 2(x+1)$ (iv) $x > 0$

4 Complete the following, where in each case x is a variable on the set E:

(i) $E = \{\text{positive integers}\}$. The solution set of $x+\frac{1}{x} = 2$ is . . . .

(ii) $E = \{\text{primes less than } 13\}$. $x^2+11x+11$ is prime. Solution set is . . . .

(iii) $E = \{\text{positive even integers}\}$. $2x+1 \in E$. Solution set is . . . .

6 Subsets

B is a *subset* of A when every element of B is also an element of A. It is agreed that the empty set $\{\quad\}$ or $\emptyset$ is a subset of every set. B is a subset of A, or B is contained in A, is written $B \subset A$.

You can see that all the subsets of the set $E = \{1, 2, 3\}$ are

$$\emptyset, \{1\}, \{2\}, \{3\}, \{1, 2\}, \{1, 3\}, \{2, 3\} \text{ and } \{1, 2, 3\},$$

and that the number of subsets of E is 8.

Exercise 6

1 List all the subsets of the set of colours $P = \{\text{red, white, blue}\}$.

2 How many subsets does the set $\{B, W\}$ have?
How many subsets does $\emptyset$ have?

3 Place the symbol $\subset$ or the symbol $=$ between as many pairs as you can of the following sets:

$A = \{0, 1, 2\}$ $B = \{0\}$ $C = \{1, 2\}$ $D = \{2, 1\}$ $E = \{\quad\}$
$F = \{1, 2, 3\}$

4 (i) A certain set has only 1 subset. What set is this?
(ii) If $A \subset B$ and $B \subset A$, what statement can you make about A and B?

5 Let $A = \{a, b, c, d\}$, a set of four objects from which you are invited to take a selection; you can either select or reject each object.

(i) In how many ways can you deal with each object?
(ii) If you decide to reject each object, one after the other, what is the set chosen by you?

(iii) If you decide to accept each of the objects, what is now the set selected by you?

(iv) Write out all the sets which may be formed. (You should have 16 different sets, each a subset of A.)

Repeat (iv) for the cases when set A has 1 element, 2 elements, 3 elements, and 5 elements and hence complete this table:

A	$n(A)$	Subsets of A	Number of subsets
$\{a\}$			
$\{a, b\}$			
$\{a, b, c\}$			
$\{a, b, c, d\}$	4	$\emptyset$, $\{a\}$, $\{b\}$, $\{c\}$, $\{d\}$, $\{a, b\}$, $\{a, c\}$, $\{a, d\}$, $\{b, c\}$, $\{b, d\}$, $\{c, d\}$, $\{a, b, c\}$, $\{a, b, d\}$, $\{a, c, d\}$, $\{b, c, d\}$, $\{a, b, c, d\}$	16
$\{a, b, c, d, e\}$			

It should be clear from the definition of a subset, and from your answer to question 5, that A is a subset of itself. So, *every set is a subset of itself.*

Can you suggest a formula for the number of subsets of a given set? (You should refer to the numbers in the last column of the table.)

6 Translate into symbolic language, i.e. using the subset symbol and letters for the sets:

(i) Every square is a rectangle. Use set names S and R.

(ii) All prime numbers are integers. Use set names P and Z.

(iii) Symphonies are musical compositions. Use set names S and C.

7 Here is a way to write out all the subsets of the set $A = \{a, b\}$:

Write a to show you are choosing the element a.

Write a with a stroke through it to show you are *not* choosing the element a.

You can now show the choice you decide on for the element a as in Figure 2(i), and you see you have two paths to choose from.

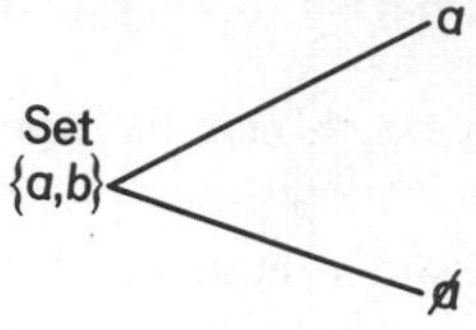

FIG. 2(i)

Now continue on *each* of these paths to show the possible choices for b as in Figure 2(ii).

Notice that there are four paths altogether. The top one gives the subset $\{a, b\}$, the second top $\{a\}$. What do the other two routes give? Now make a diagram giving all the subsets of $\{a, b, c\}$ and of $\{a, b, c, d\}$. Then check the answers given by the routes with the answers in the table of number 5.

Can you see a simple way to find the answers to the last column in that table?

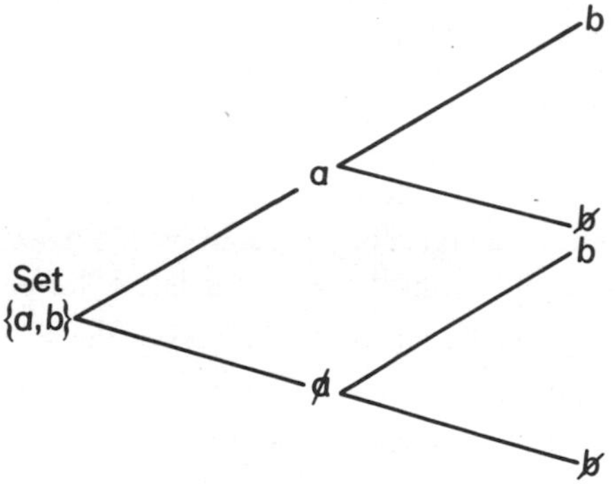

FIG. 2(ii)

7 Venn diagrams

You will remember that it is usual to represent a set of objects as points within a closed region of a plane. The closed region may be a circle, an oval, or a rectangle, or any shape bounded by a closed curve.

Figure 3 illustrates that *p*, *q*, *r*, *s*, *t* are members of set *A*. Points *h* and *k*, being outside the region, represent objects which are not members of *A*. Note that no object is represented on the boundary.

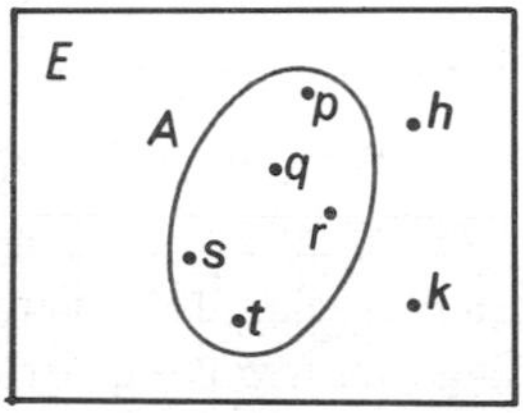

FIG. 3

When the set is a large one it will not be possible to represent all of its elements by named points within the curve. In that case we leave the region within the curve blank, as in Figure 11 later on in this chapter.

The *universal set* is usually represented by a rectangle which encloses all the regions representing the sets that may be discussed.

Figures 3–7 show some examples of Venn diagrams. In each case $E = \{\text{letters of the alphabet}\}$.

Note that in Figure 4 the sets *A* and *B* have no members in common, and are said to be *disjoint* sets; in Figure 5 the two subsets completely make up the set *E*.

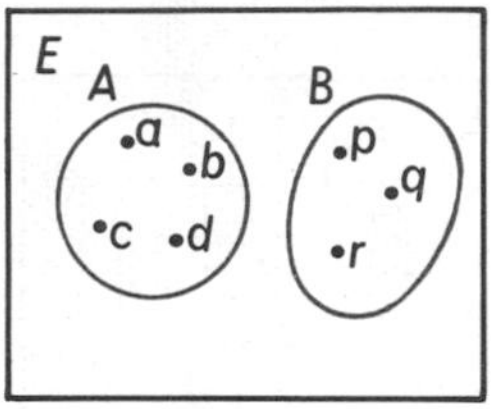

FIG. 4.—$A = \{a, b, c, d\}$, $B = \{p, q, r\}$

Note that in Figure 7 the set *K* is contained in set *H*, so that *K* is a subset of *H*, or $K \subset H$.

John Venn's book *Symbolic Logic*, published in 1881, made diagrams of this kind familiar to students of logic as a method of clarifying their

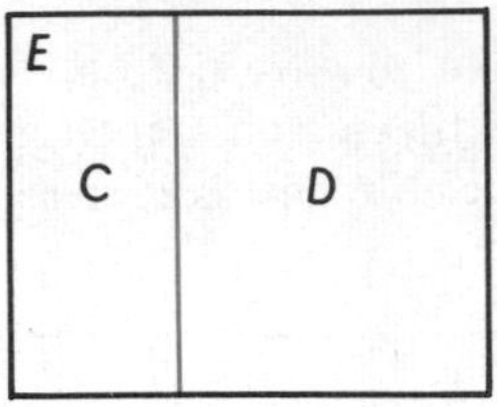

FIG. 5.—C = {vowels}, D = {consonants}

ideas; they are visual aids in reasoning. John Venn claimed no originality for the method. Indeed, diagrams involving circles had been used by the mathematician Euler more than a century earlier. The mathematician

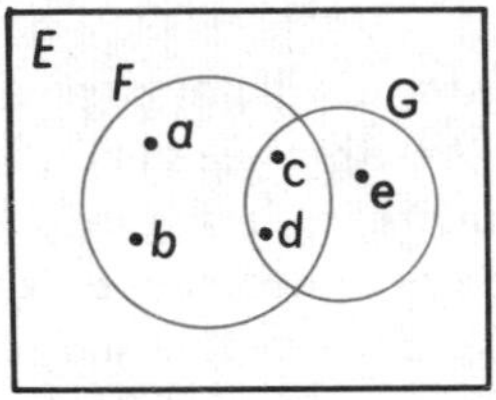

FIG. 6.—$F = \{a, b, c, d\}$, $G = \{c, d, e\}$

Dr. Charles Dodgson, who is better known as Lewis Carroll, the author of *Alice in Wonderland*, used rectangles instead of circles in diagrams like these.

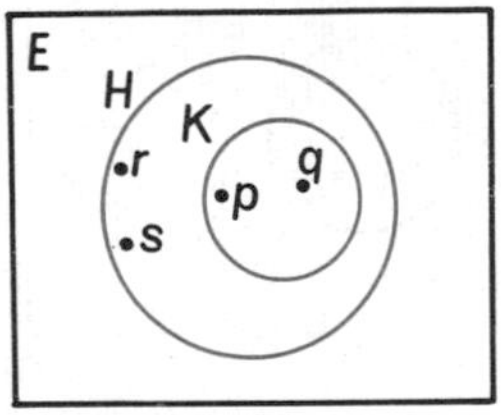

FIG. 7.—$H = \{p, q, r, s\}$, $K = \{p, q\}$

Exercise 7

1 In this question $E = \{1, 2, 3, 4, 5, 6, 7, 8\}$. Draw Venn diagrams to illustrate the following:

(*a*) $A = \{1, 2, 3, 4\}$, $B = \{6, 7, 8\}$
(*b*) $A = \{1, 2, 3, 4, 5\}$, $B = \{3, 4, 5\}$, $C = \{5, 6, 7\}$
(*c*) $A = \{1, 2, 3, 4, 5\}$, $B = \{1, 2, 3\}$, $C = \{4, 5, 6\}$
(*d*) $A = \{1, 2, 3, 4, 5\}$, $B = \{5, 7, 8\}$, $C = \{5, 6, 8\}$

2 E = {all dogs}. Draw Venn diagrams to show
A = {black dogs}, B = {terriers}, C = {household pets}.

3 Let E = {inhabitants of Scotland}, A = {people who play golf},
B = {people who play football}, C = {people who play cricket}

Draw a Venn diagram to show these sets. Explain why you drew it in this way.

4 Draw diagrams to illustrate the following:

(i) E = {all TV programmes}
C = {orchestral concerts on TV}
P = {plays}
N = {news items}

(ii) E = {all TV programmes}
M = {programmes containing music}
S = {religious services}
F = {films}

5 In Figure 8 the sets are defined on page 14 where

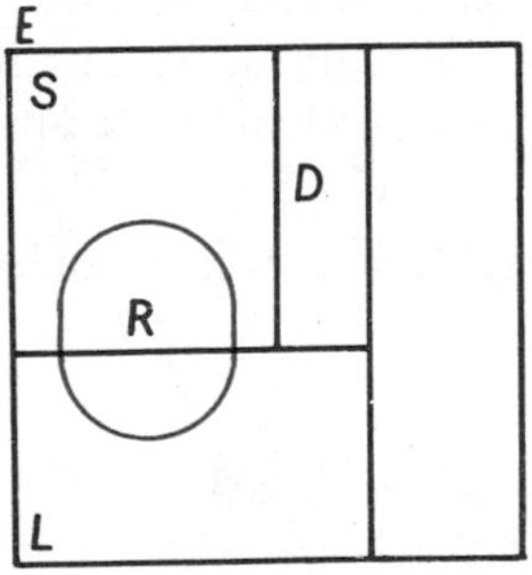

FIG. 8

E is the set of engines in use in Britain in 1946,
S is the set of steam engines,
D is the set of diesel engines,
L is the set of electrically driven engines,
R is the set of railway engines.
Make a diagram more suitable for this year.

8 The intersection of sets

The intersection of the two straight lines in Figure 9*a* is the point common to both. The intersection of the line and the curve in Figure 9*b* is the pair of points common to both.

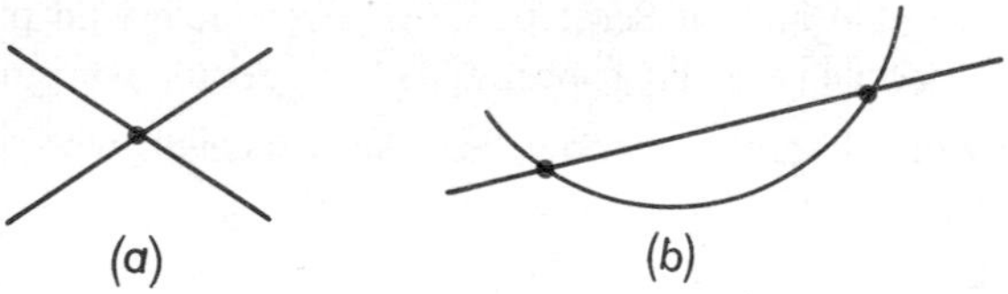

FIG. 9

The *intersection* of two sets A and B is the set of elements which are members of A *and also* members of B; it is denoted by $A \cap B$ ('A intersection B', or 'the intersection of A and B').

Example 1.—If $A = \{3, 5, 7, 9, 11, 13, 15\}$ and $B = \{5, 10, 15, 20\}$, then $A \cap B = \{5, 15\}$.

Example 2.—If S = {quadrilaterals with all their sides equal},
and L = {quadrilaterals with all their angles equal},
then $S \cap L$ = {quadrilaterals with all their sides and angles equal}.

What kind of quadrilaterals are in S, in L, and in $S \cap L$?

Exercise 8

1 $A = \{2, 3, 5, 7, 11\}$, $B = \{3, 5, 17\}$, $C = \{2, 7, 13\}$, $D = \{2, 3, 5, 7, 11, 13, 17\}$.
Find (i) $A \cap B$ (ii) $B \cap C$ (iii) $A \cap C$
(iv) $(A \cap B) \cap (B \cap C)$ (v) $D \cap (A \cap B)$

2 Simplify $[\{1, 3, 5, 7\} \cap \{3, 5, 8\}] \cap \{3, 9\}$. Try interchanging sets here.

3 If S is the set of roses in a flower shop, and if C is the set of yellow flowers in the shop, describe in words the set $S \cap C$.
In what circumstances is $S \cap C = \emptyset$?

4 $E = \{\text{all triangles}\}$, $I = \{\text{isosceles triangles}\}$, $K = \{\text{right-angled triangles}\}$. Represent these in a Venn diagram and explain the reason for showing $I \cap K$ in the way that you did.

5 Let $A = \{a, b, d, e, g\}$, $B = \{a, c, e, f, g\}$, $C = \{b, c, d, e, f, g\}$.

(*a*) Write out $A \cap B$ and $B \cap A$.
What do you notice about these two sets? Draw a Venn diagram and explain in what way it verifies your discovery.
How else could you write $B \cap C$ and $C \cap A$?
You have come across a law like this before. What is this law called?

(*b*) Write out $(A \cap B) \cap C$ and $A \cap (B \cap C)$.
What do you notice about these two sets? Draw a Venn diagram and explain why it verifies your discovery.
Does it make sense to write $A \cap B \cap C$?
You have come across this law before. What is this law called?

(*c*) Do you think that the commutative law is true for the intersection of sets?
Do you think that the associative law is true for the intersection of sets?
Make up examples of your own which verify the commutative and associative laws for the intersection of sets.

6 (i) E is the set of whole numbers. X is the set of divisors of 30. Y is the set of divisors of 42. Draw a Venn diagram to show this. List $X \cap Y$. What is the HCF of 30 and 42?

(ii) Repeat the question for the numbers 36 and 42.

7 Construct all the subsets of three numbers from the set

$$\{1, 2, 3, 4, 5, 6, 7, 8, 9\}$$

such that the sum of the three numbers in each set is 15, e.g. $\{8, 5, 2\}$.
Write in a column four of these subsets which, taken two at a time, have the number 5 in their intersection.
Write out two subsets whose intersection with $\{9, 4, 2\}$ is $\emptyset$.

8 The universal set here is the set of whole numbers and you should graph the given sets on number lines below one another.
$S = \{x : 0 < x < 6\}$, $T = \{x : 0 \leqslant x < 5\}$,
$U = \{x : x > 10\}$, $V = \{x : x < 1\}$.
Find $S \cap T$, $S \cap V$, $S \cap U$, $T \cap V$.

9 The police had three eye-witness reports A, B, and C, stating persons present when a certain incident occurred. Persons are named by small letters. $A = \{a, b, e, g, k, m, r\}$; $B = \{a, c, e, h, g, n, m, r\}$; $C = \{a, b, c, d, h, k, n, s\}$.
List $A \cap B$, $B \cap C$, $A \cap C$ and illustrate the sets A, B, and C in a Venn diagram in which named points represent the elements.
List the set $A \cap B \cap C$. What is the significance of this set?

10 All the pupils in a class of 35 take French or German, or both. 29 take French and 15 take German. How many take both? Illustrate by a Venn diagram.

11 In a survey of 120 pupils it was found that 17 had no liking for music. Of the rest, 88 said they liked 'pop' music and 26 said they liked classical music. How many liked both? Illustrate by a Venn diagram.

12 In a Fourth Form of 20 boys, 15 take mathematics, 12 take science, and 10 take mathematics and science. Show this in a Venn diagram. What further information can you deduce about subjects taken by the 20 boys?

13 A survey of 180 second-year pupils showed that 100 drank tea, 92 drank coffee, 115 drank milk, 43 drank tea as well as milk, 52 drank coffee as well as tea, 57 drank coffee as well as milk, and 25 drank all three. Show this in a Venn diagram.

(i) How many drank coffee but neither tea nor milk?
(ii) How many drank only milk?

14 The following information was obtained from pupils in a certain school:

38 per cent owned a record player.
30 per cent owned a tape recorder.
73 per cent owned a radio.
13 per cent owned a record player and tape recorder.
23 per cent owned a radio and tape recorder.

28 per cent owned a record player and radio.
8 per cent owned all three.

Using a Venn diagram, analyse these data and find:

(i) what percentage did not own any of these instruments,
(ii) what percentage owned exactly two instruments.

9 The union of sets

If A and B are any two sets, the union of A and B is the set of elements which belong either to A or to B, or to both A and B. We denote the union of A and B by $A \cup B$ ('A union B', or 'the union of A and B').

Example 1.—If $P = \{2, 4, 6, \ldots\}$ and $Q = \{1, 3, 5, \ldots\}$, then $P \cup Q = \{1, 2, 3, 4, 5, 6 \ldots\}$, the set of natural numbers.

Example 2.—Suppose that the 21 pupils in a class are asked to declare their liking for music and that this is what we discover (each pupil named by a letter):

Set A = {those who say they like classical music} =
$\{a, c, d, e, f, k, m, p, s, v\}$

Set B = {those who say they like 'pop' music} =
$\{a, b, d, e, h, k, r, s, t, u, v, w\}$

Set C = {the others, who have no liking for music of any kind} =
$\{g, n, q, x, y\}$

Let us see how this appears in a Venn diagram. (It may be necessary to make one or two trial diagrams before getting everyone in place.)

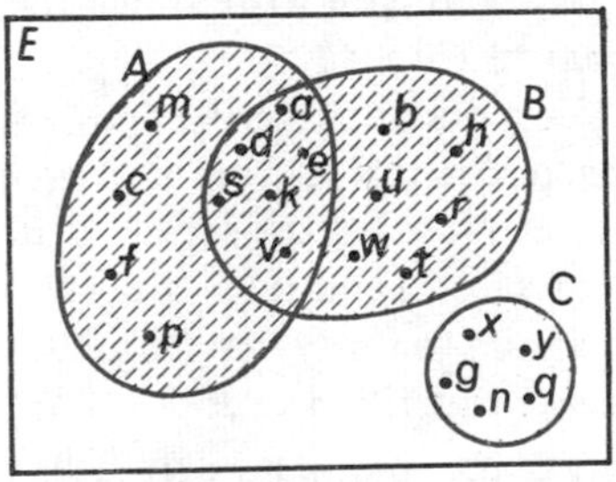

FIG. 10

By definition, *the union of A and B* is the set of all those represented in the *shaded area*. We have then:

$A \cup B = \{a, b, c, d, e, f, h, k, m, p, r, s, t, u, v, w\} =$
{all who like music}

The intersection of A and B, $A \cap B = \{a, e, d, s, k, v\}$; this is the set of individuals who like *both* classical *and* 'pop' music.

Exercise 9

1 $A = \{a, b, c\}$, $B = \{c, d, e\}$. Show the sets A and B in a Venn diagram, and shade in $A \cup B$. What is $n(A \cup B)$?

2 If P = {odd numbers from 1 to 7 inclusive}, and Q = {even numbers from 2 to 8 inclusive}, list $P \cup Q$. Illustrate in a Venn diagram. What is $n(P \cup Q)$?

3 If S is the set of pupils in your second-year class and T is the set of pupils in the other second-year classes in your school, describe $S \cup T$.

4 V = {vowels in the alphabet}, C = {consonants}. What is
(i) $V \cup C$ (ii) $n(V \cup C)$ (iii) $V \cap C$ (iv) $n(V \cap C)$?

5 X = {prime factors of 60}, Y = {the first four prime numbers}.
Is $X = Y$? List $X \cup Y$ and $X \cap Y$.

6 If R = {rectangles}, S = {squares}, what do the following sets represent? (*a*) $R \cup S$ (*b*) $R \cap S$.

7 $A = \{1, 2, 3, 4, 5, 6\}$, $B = \{2, 4, 6, 8, 10\}$, $C = \{3, 6, 9, 12\}$.

(*a*) List the sets $A \cup B$ and $B \cup A$. What do you notice?
List the set $B \cup C$. Can you write down the set $C \cup B$ at once?
What set is equal to $C \cup A$?
By drawing a Venn diagram, verify that $A \cup B = B \cup A$.
You have come across this law before; what is this law called?

(*b*) List the set $A \cup B$. Now list the set $(A \cup B) \cup C$.
Next list the set $(B \cup C)$ and then $A \cup (B \cup C)$.
Draw a Venn diagram to verify that $(A \cup B) \cup C = A \cup (B \cup C)$.
Does it make sense to write $A \cup B \cup C$? What is this law called?

8 (*a*) $n(A) = 50$, $n(B) = 62$, and $n(A \cap B) = 26$. Calculate $n(A \cup B)$.
Enter the number of members in each region of a Venn diagram.

(*b*) $n(X) = 7$, $n(Y) = 11$, and X and Y are disjoint. Calculate $n(X \cup Y)$.

(*c*) $n(P) = 23$, $n(Q) = 25$, and $P \subset Q$. Calculate $n(P \cup Q)$.

9 In each of the following diagrams, A, B, and C represent sets. Describe the set indicated by the shaded region in terms of unions and/or intersections of A, B, and C.

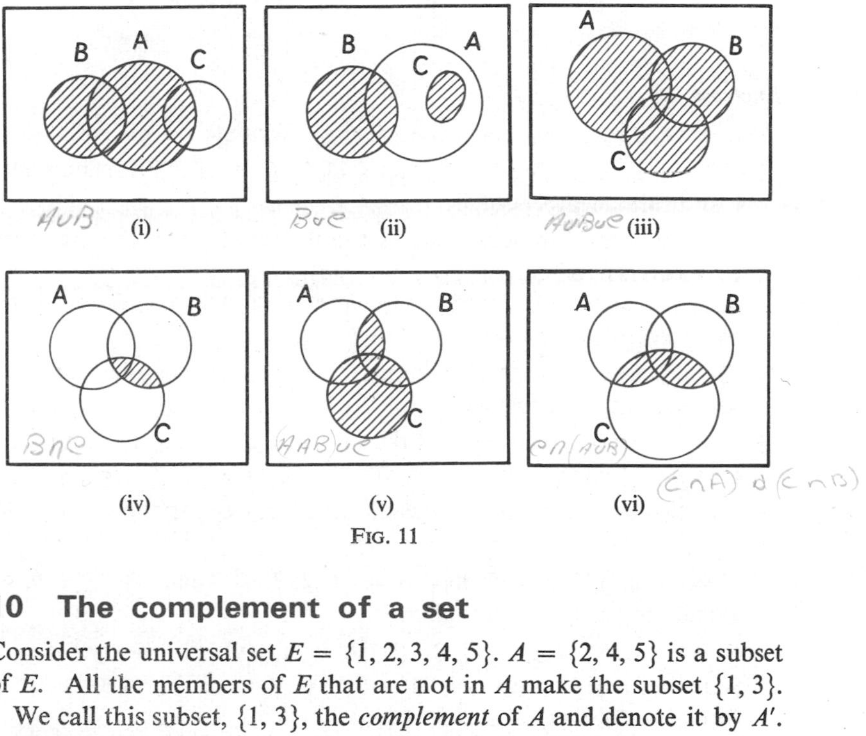

FIG. 11

10 The complement of a set

Consider the universal set $E = \{1, 2, 3, 4, 5\}$. $A = \{2, 4, 5\}$ is a subset of E. All the members of E that are not in A make the subset $\{1, 3\}$.

We call this subset, $\{1, 3\}$, the *complement* of A and denote it by A'. Then clearly (i) $A \cup A' = E$ and (ii) $A \cap A' = \emptyset$.

Here is another example.

Suppose the universal set E is the set of all school subjects taken by a particular boy.

P, the set of certificate subjects taken by him, is {English, mathematics, science, geography, Latin}.

P', the complement of P, is the set of *all other subjects* which make up his whole course.

He may have the set $P' = \{$music, physical education, religious instruction, games$\}$.

Again (i) $P \cup P' = E$ and (ii) $P \cap P' = \emptyset$.

The complement of a set A in the universal set E is the set A' which is such that $A \cup A' = E$ and $A \cap A' = \emptyset$.

A and A' have no member in common, but together they make up the whole of E.

Exercise 10

1 $E = \{p, q, r, s, t, v\}$ and $X = \{p, r, v\}$. Write X' in list form.

2 $E = \{1, 2, 3, 4, \ldots, 20\}$. Subset B of E is the set of prime numbers. List all the members of B'.

3 $N = \{$natural numbers$\}$; this is the universal set in this question. $T = \{$even numbers$\}$.
Give a verbal description, and also a set-builder definition, of the complement of T.

4 The universe is the set of all integers. What is the complement of the set of negative integers?

5 If $A = \{x : 0 \leqslant x < 2\}$ and the universal set is the real numbers, give a set-builder definition of A'.

6 E is the set of all triangles. A is the set of isosceles triangles. Describe A'.

7 $E = \{1, 2, 3, 4, 5, 6, 7, 8\}$, $A = \{1, 2, 3, 4\}$, and $B = \{4, 6, 8\}$. Write out the following sets:
(i) A' (ii) B' (iii) $A' \cup B$ (iv) $B' \cup A$ (v) $A \cup A'$ (vi) $A \cap A'$ (vii) the complement of $A \cup B$, i.e. $(A \cup B)'$ (viii) $A' \cap B'$ (ix) $(A \cap B)'$ (x) $A' \cup B'$ (xi) $(A' \cap B')'$.

8 $E = \{1, 2, 3, \ldots, 10\}$, $A = \{1, 2, 3, 5, 7\}$, $B = \{1, 3, 5, 7\}$ and $C = \{2, 4, 6, 8\}$.
List the sets A', B', and C'.
Select the true statements among the following:
(i) $A \subset B$ (ii) $B \subset A$ (iii) $A \subset B'$ (iv) $B' \subset A'$ (v) $B \subset C'$ (vi) $B' \subset A$ (vii) $A' \subset B$

9 Copy Figure 12 for each of the following questions, and by shading show on it:

(i) A' (ii) B' (iii) $A' \cup B$ (iv) $B' \cup A$ (v) $A' \cap B$ (vi) $B' \cap A$ (vii) $A \cup A'$ (viii) $A \cap A'$ (ix) $(A \cup B)'$ (x) $A' \cap B'$ (xi) $(A \cap B)'$ (xii) $A' \cup B'$

Do the answers to parts (ix)–(xii) suggest anything to you?

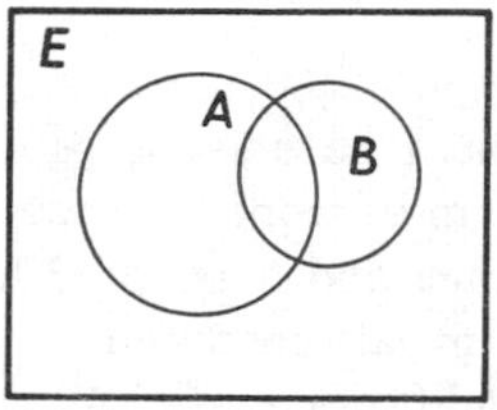

FIG. 12

10 Name the shaded areas in Figure 13 in terms of the complements, intersections, and unions of sets A and B, where the universal set consists of all points inside the large square.

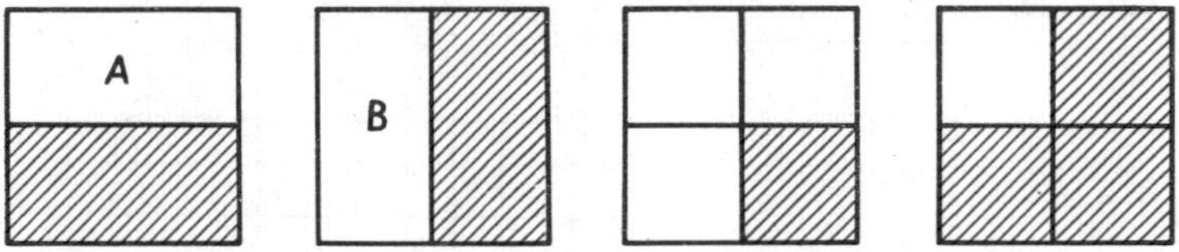

FIG. 13

CHAPTER 2 Linear Equations and Inequations in Two Variables

1 Introduction

Example 1.—Suppose that I have fivepence worth of pence and halfpence. How could this sum of money be made up?

I might have 0 halfpence and 5 pence, 2 halfpence and 4 pence, 4 halfpence and 3 pence, 6 halfpence and 2 pence, 8 halfpence and 1 penny or 10 halfpence and 0 pence.

If h denotes the number of halfpence and p denotes the number of pence, then $h+2p=10$ is a true statement. Let us consider the open sentence $x+2y = 10$.

Figure 1 shows in a table the pairs of replacements for x and y which make this a true sentence, and also the graph of the open sentence $x+2y = 10$.

x	0	2	4	6	8	10
y	5	4	3	2	1	0

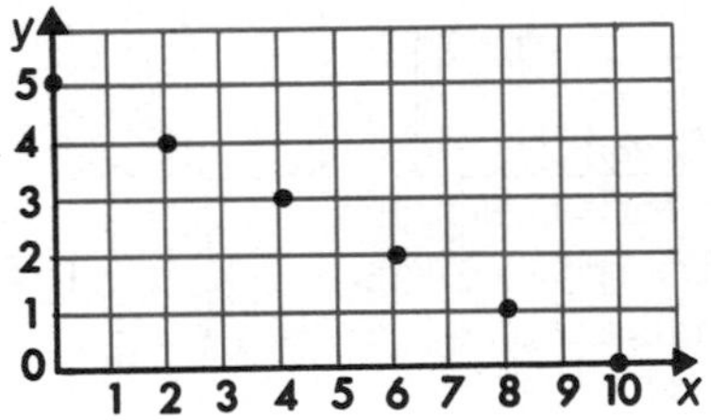

FIG. 1

Example 2.—From Figure 2 you can see that the number of diagonals that can be drawn from a vertex of a polygon is 3 less than the number of sides of the polygon.

Let n be a variable which can be replaced by the number of sides, and d a variable which can be replaced by the number of diagonals. We can write the open sentence $d = n-3$.

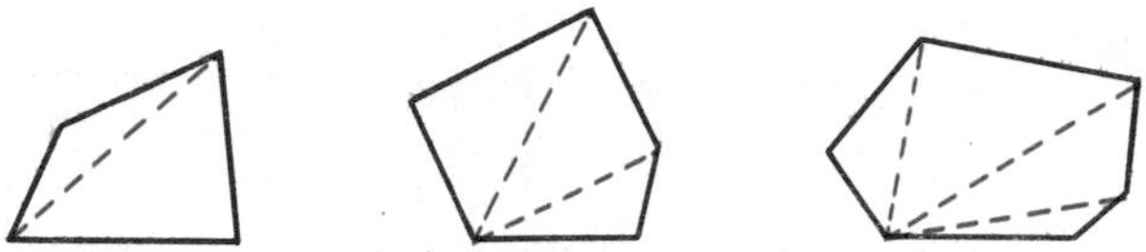

FIG. 2

Figure 3 shows in a table some of the pairs of replacements for n and d which make this a true sentence, and also part of the graph of the open sentence $d = n-3$.

n	4	5	6	7	8	9
d	1	2	3	4	5	6

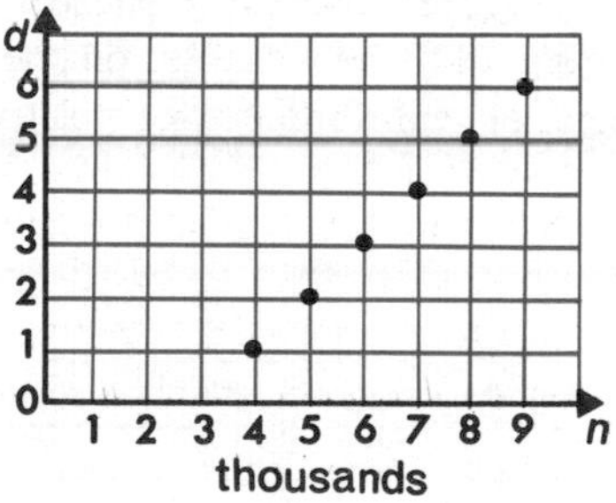

FIG. 3

Example 3.—The cost per annum of running a certain car is £100 plus $2\frac{1}{2}$p for each mile travelled.

Using £C to denote the cost per annum and n to denote the number of miles travelled per annum, we can write the open sentence

$$C = 100+\frac{n}{40}$$

Figure 4 shows in a table some of the pairs of replacements for n and C which make this a true sentence, and also part of the graph of the open sentence $C = 100+\frac{n}{40}$.

Example 4.—Figure 5 shows a variable ray OP meeting a straight line at O.

n	0	2000	4000	6,000	8,000	10,000
c	100	150	200	250	300	350

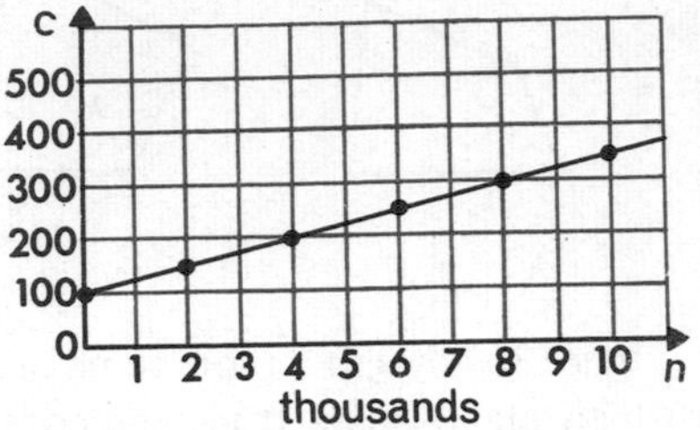

FIG. 4

From Figure 5 we can write the open sentence $x+y = 180$. Do x and y require to be variables on the set of whole numbers, or rational numbers, or real numbers, or positive real numbers?

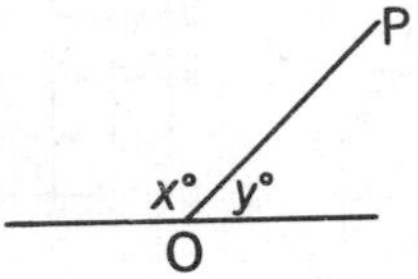

FIG. 5

Figure 6 shows in a table several pairs of replacements for x and y which make the sentence a true sentence, and also the graph of the open sentence $x+y = 180$.

x	0	60	90	100½	150	180
y	180	120	90	79½	30	0

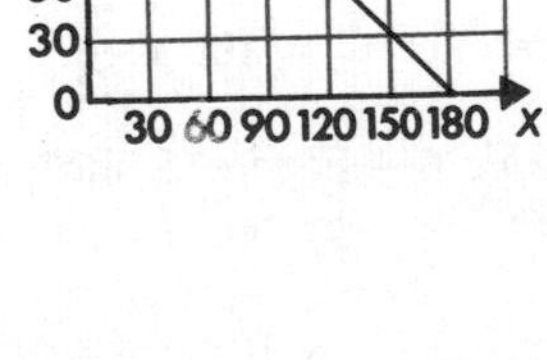

FIG. 6

Exercise 1

1 What do you notice about the graphs and the open sentences in the worked examples above?

2 Why are some of the graphs a set of dots while others are lines?

In each of the following, write an open sentence, make a table of pairs of replacements for the variables which make the sentence true and draw a graph of the open sentence.

3 I have 50p composed of 5-p pieces and 10-p pieces. Use x for the number of 5-p pieces and y for the number of 10-p pieces.

4 Two angles of $a°$ and $b°$ are complementary.

5 The perimeter of a square is four times the length of a side of the square. Denote the perimeter by P units and the length by l units.

6 The cost per annum of running a motor scooter is £20 plus 1p a mile. Denote the cost per annum by £C and the number of miles travelled by n.

7 The sum of the angles of a polygon with n sides is $(2n-4)$ right angles. Denote the sum of the angles by S right angles.

8 A wooden box weighs 1 lb and can hold up to 12 bricks each weighing 4 oz. Denote the total weight of the box with bricks by W ounces and the number of bricks by n.

2 An equation in two variables

In Book 1 we saw that an open sentence containing the verb 'is equal to' is called an equation. We saw that we could obtain the solution set of an equation like $x+2 = 5$, where x is a variable on the set of natural numbers, by finding the replacement for x which gave a true sentence.

Thus when $x = 3$, the sentence $3+2 = 5$ is obtained, and this is true: other replacements for x give false sentences.

The solution set of $x+2 = 5$ is $\{3\}$, and we can show this on the number line as follows:

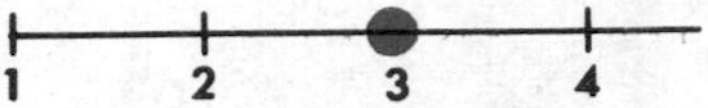

FIG. 7

Suppose we now wish to find the solution set of an equation in two variables, e.g. $x+y = 5$, where x and y are variables on the set of real numbers. Since there are two variables, we have to consider *pairs* of replacements for x and y; you can probably think of pairs which give true sentences. Here are a few: $x = 5$, $y = 0$; $x = 1$, $y = 4$; $x = 8$, $y = -3$; $x = \frac{1}{2}$, $y = 4\frac{1}{2}$.

We can give these in the form of *ordered pairs* in which the replacement for x is written first, i.e. $(5, 0)$, $(1, 4)$, $(8, -3)$, $(\frac{1}{2}, 4\frac{1}{2})$.

All of these are members of the solution set of $x+y = 5$, i.e. are *solutions* of $x+y= 5$. Can you give a few more solutions? How many solutions do you think $x+y = 5$ has?

Exercise 2

1 Which of the following replacements for x and y in the equation $x+y = 3$ give true sentences? $(2, 1)$, $(1, 3)$, $(3, 0)$, $(-1, 4)$, $(5, -3)$, $(1\frac{1}{2}, 1\frac{1}{2})$, $(6\frac{1}{4}, -3\frac{1}{4})$.

2 Which of the following are solutions of $x-y = 10$? $(12, 2)$, $(2, 12)$, $(10, 0)$, $(5, 5)$, $(5, -5)$, $(8\frac{1}{2}, -1\frac{1}{2})$, $(1, 11)$.

3 Give three members of the solution set of each of the following:

(i) $x+y = 4$ (ii) $x-y = 0$ (iii) $2x+y = 11$
(iv) $2x-y = 1$ (v) $x+6y = 13$ (vi) $x-y = 1\frac{1}{2}$

4 $x+y = 10$ is equivalent to $y = 10-x$ as can be seen by adding $-x$ to each side of the equation. In the table, certain replacements for x are given; fill in the replacements for y which give true sentences.

x	0	2	4	6	8	10	12	-10	-8	$5\frac{1}{2}$
y										

5 Repeat question 4 for the equation $x+y = 6$.

6 Repeat question 4 for the equation $x+2y = 18$.

3 The graph of an equation in two variables

An ordered pair of replacements for x and y can be thought of as the coordinates of a point. We can illustrate the solution set of an equation on the coordinate plane.

For the equation $x+y = 5$, i.e. $y = 5-x$, the pairs (1, 4), (2, 3), ($2\frac{1}{2}$, $2\frac{1}{2}$), (3, 2), (4, 1) give true sentences and are shown in Figure 8 by means of the symbol O.

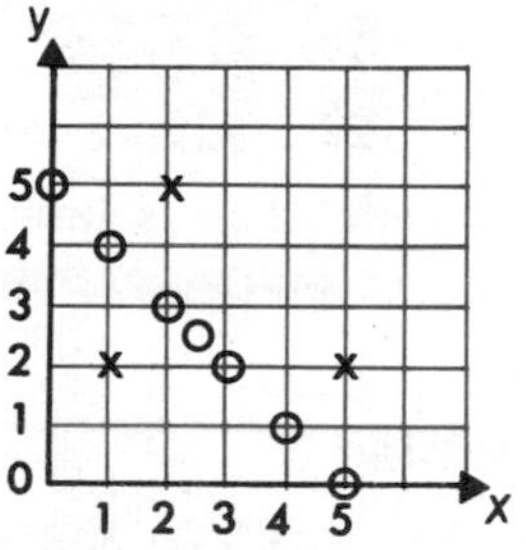

FIG. 8

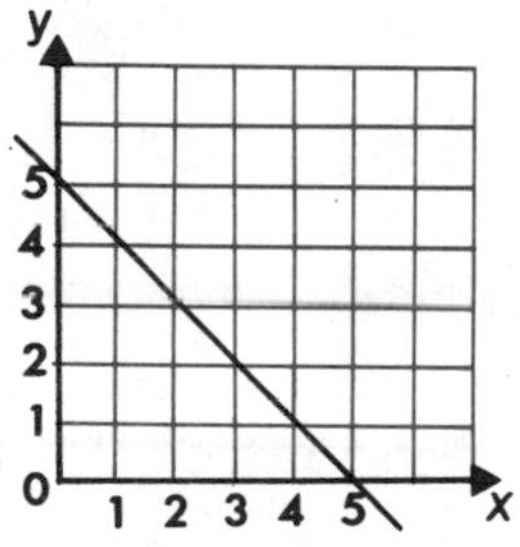

FIG. 9

Some pairs which give false sentences are also shown using the symbol ×, for example (5, 2).

You have already seen in Geometry, Book 3, Chapter 1, that when x and y are variables on the set of real numbers, the graph of an equation such as $y = 5-x$ is a straight line, as in Figure 9. It is for this reason that an equation in two variables in which powers and products of the variables do not appear is called a *linear* equation.

Exercise 3

In questions 1–10, find pairs of replacements for x and y which give true sentences, and draw a graph to show (or, in the case of an infinite set, to indicate) the set of points which have these pairs as coordinates.

W, Z, R denote the sets of whole numbers, integers, and real numbers respectively; the variables are on the sets indicated.

1 $x+y = 6$; W

2 $x+y = 6$; R

3 $x-y = 0$; W

4 $x-y = 0$; R

5 $2x+y = 8$; W

6 $2x+y = 8$; R

7 $y = 2$; Z

8 $y = 2$; R

9 $x = 4$; Z

10 $x = 4$; R

In questions 11–22, x and y are variables on the set of real numbers. Draw the graph of the equation in each case, and try to find quick ways of doing this.

11 $y = x$

12 $y = x+1$

13 $y = x+2$

14 $y = \frac{1}{2}x-1$

15 $y = \frac{1}{2}x$

16 $y = \frac{1}{2}x+1$

17 $y = 2x-2$

18 $y = 2x$

19 $y = 2x+2$

20 $x-y+1 = 0$

21 $\frac{1}{2}x-y+1 = 0$

22 $x-2y+2 = 0$

23 Invent some more equations and indicate their solution sets graphically.

4 An inequation in two variables

Suppose that you had £3 to spend on books which cost 50p or 60p each. What possible selections of books could you buy?

Let x denote the number of books costing 50p, and y the number of books costing 60p.

Then the amount you spend is $50x+60y$ pence.

Since this must not exceed £3 or 300p, $50x+60y \leqslant 300$, which is an inequation in two variables, more simply written $5x+6y \leqslant 30$.

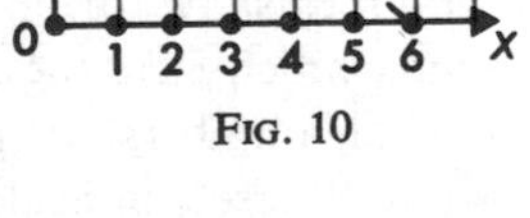

FIG. 10

Assuming $x, y \in R$ we can draw the line whose equation is $5x+6y=30$ (shown broken in Figure 10).

But x and y must be variables on the set of whole numbers. The dots represent the points whose coordinates are the solution set of

$$x \geqslant 0 \text{ and } y \geqslant 0 \text{ and } 5x+6y \leqslant 30$$

So the possible selections of books that you could buy are shown by the following ordered pairs (the first number refers to 50-pence books).

(0, 0), (0, 1), . . . , (0, 5)
(1, 0), . . . , (1, 4)
(2, 0), . . . , (2, 3)
(3, 0), . . . , (3, 2)
(4, 0), (4, 1)
(5, 0)
(6, 0)
(Notice that in some cases you would have money left over.)

Exercise 4

In each of the following write an inequation in two variables and draw a diagram to illustrate the answer to the question:

1 Find the selections of books costing 50 pence and 80 pence that can be purchased with £4 or less.

2 Toffee apples cost 5p and candy floss 4p. In how many ways can 40p or less be spent on them?

3 A diesel engine can haul a load of 200 tons. Carriages weigh 50 tons and trucks 30 tons. In what possible ways could the train be made up?

4 A ferry boat has space for 100 feet of vehicles. What possible loads could it take, made up of cars 12 feet long and lorries 20 feet long?

5 What selections of records costing 40p and 50p can be bought with not more than £2?

6 In how many ways could a sum of money that is not more than 45p be spent on 2-p ices and 3-p bars of chocolate?

* * * * * * *

In the same way that the coordinate plane can be used to show the solution set of an equation in two variables, it can be used to indicate the solution set of an inequation.

Example 1.—Show the solution set of $y < 5-x$ as a graph, where x and y are variables on the set of whole numbers.

As before we indicate points whose coordinates belong to the solution set of $y = 5-x$ by O (see Figure 11).

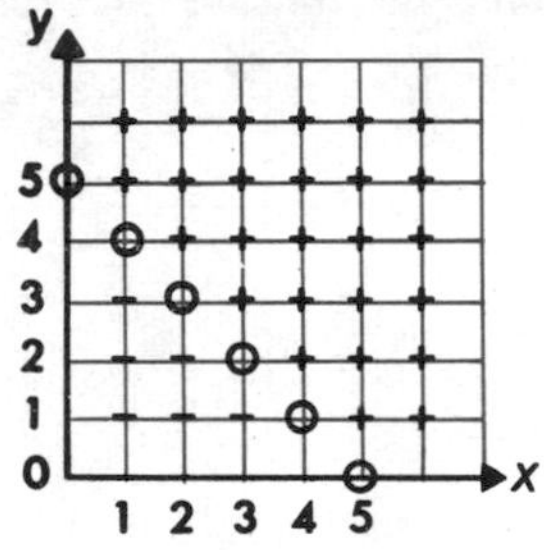

FIG. 11

We first draw the graph of $y = 5-x$, i.e. $x+y = 5$ which we saw in Section 3, by plotting pairs of replacements which give true sentences, e.g. (5, 0), (3, 2), (1, 4). Then we plot some other pairs of replacements, this time marking the points with a plus sign if $y > 5-x$, or a minus sign if $y < 5-x$.

The solution set of $y < 5-x$ consists of all the ordered pairs giving the points marked $-$.

Notice that the line divides the plane into two *half-planes*: one illustrates $y > 5-x$ and the other $y < 5-x$.

Example 2.—Draw a graph of the solution set of $y < 5-x$, where x and y are variables on the set of real numbers.

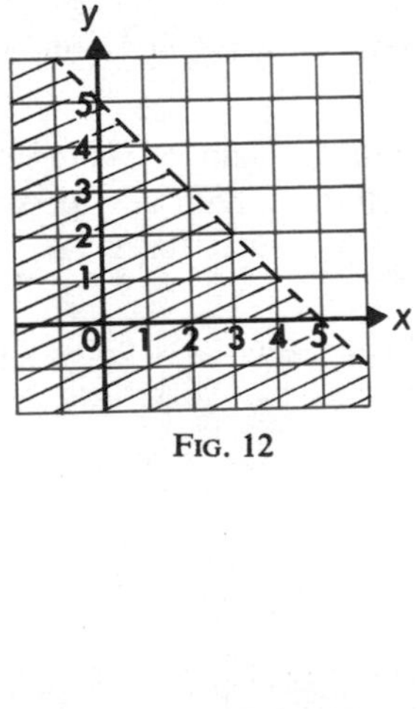

FIG. 12

We know that for points on the line in Figure 12, the coordinates belong to the solution set of $y = x-5$. From Example 1 we can see that the solution set of $y < 5-x$ consists of the pairs of coordinates of the points to the left of (or below) the broken line, as indicated by the shaded part of Figure 12. We can easily check that this is the correct half-plane by considering the origin (0, 0).

Exercise.—Show the graph of the solution set of $y \geqslant 5-x$ in a diagram similar to Figure 12, using a coloured pencil to shade the region.

In this case the boundary line belongs to the set and should be shown as a full line.

Exercise 5

Illustrate the solution set of each of the following inequations on the coordinate plane; x and y are variables on the set stated.

1 $y \geqslant 5-x; R$

2 $y < x; W$

3 $y < x; R$

4 $y < 2; W$

5 $y < 2; R$

6 $x \leqslant 3; W$

7 $x \leqslant 3; R$

8 $y-x > 5; R$

9 $y-\frac{1}{2}x \leqslant 0; R$

10 $2y-x < 0; R$

11 $x-2y \geqslant 0; R$

12 $x-2y > 3; R$

13 $x+y \leqslant 5; R$

14 Invent some more.

CHAPTER 3 Systems of Linear Equations and Inequations in Two Variables

1 Intersection of solution sets—inequations

Do you remember how to show the intersection of two sets on a Venn diagram? See Figure 1.

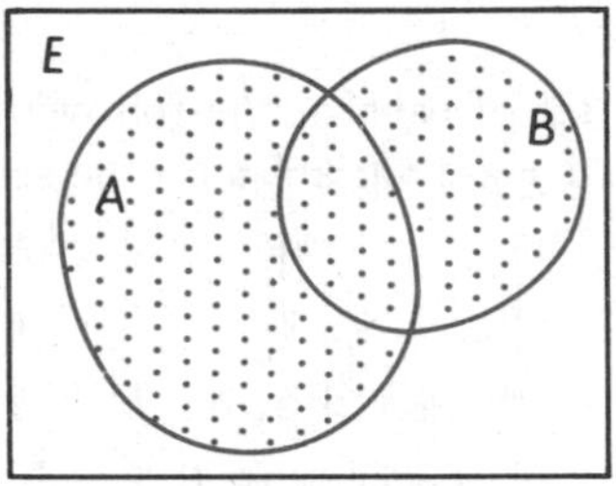

FIG. 1

We will now apply the same idea to show the intersection of two or more solution sets, using the coordinate plane.

Example 1.—Show the intersection of the solution sets of the inequations $y > 0$ *and* $y < 5-x$.

Figure 2 shows the solution set of the first of these and Figure 3 shows

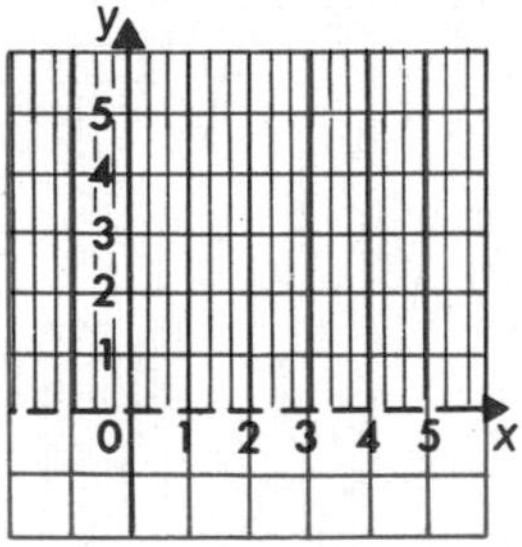

FIG. 2

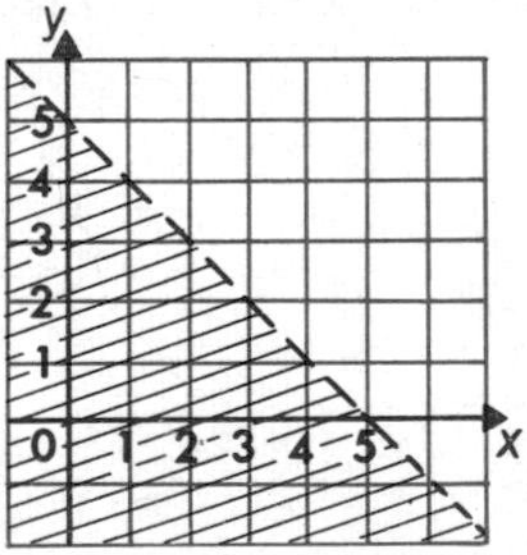

FIG. 3

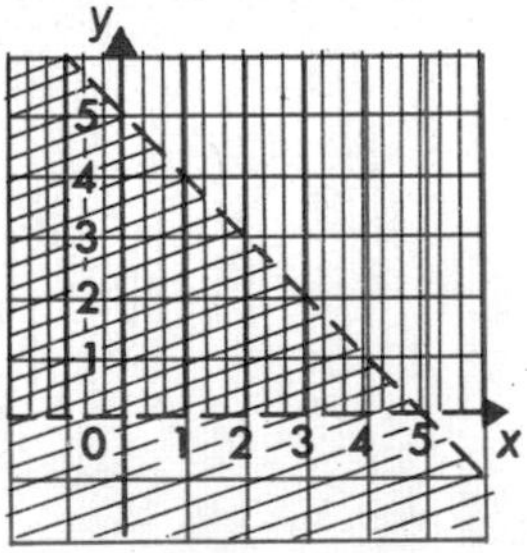

FIG. 4

that of the second. Figure 4 shows these two drawn on the same diagram; the intersection is shaded two ways.

Example 2.—Show the intersection of the solution sets of the inequations $y > 0$ *and* $y < 5-x$ *and* $x > 0$.

Figure 5 shows the solution set of $x > 0$. Figure 6 shows Figures 4 and 5 drawn on the same diagram. You can see that the intersection of the three sets is the interior of the triangle OAB, which is shaded three ways. (Different colours can be helpful.)

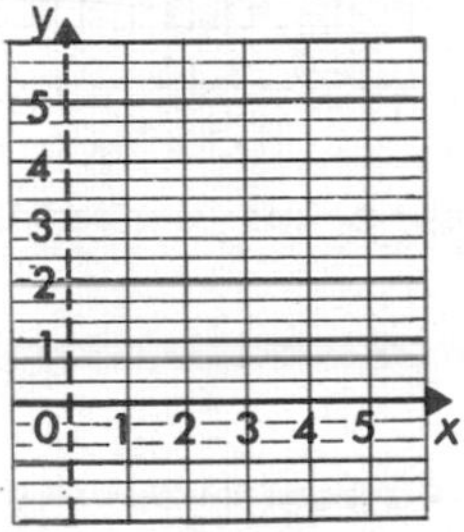

FIG. 5

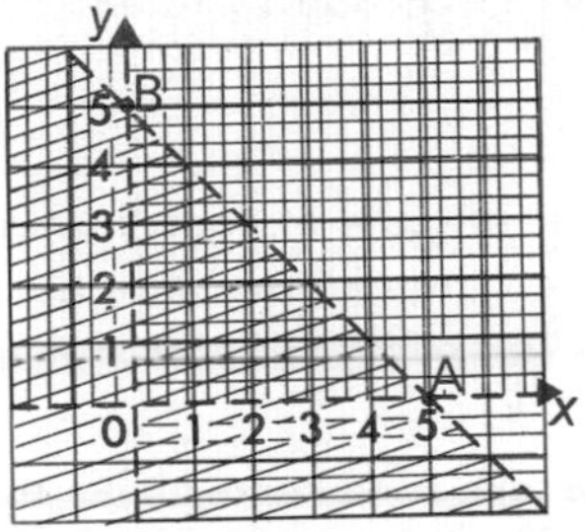

FIG. 6

Instead of shading the region corresponding to the solution set, you may prefer to shade the region corresponding to the complement; this allows the intersection of the solution sets to be clearly seen in Figure 7.

Note.—A pair of replacements for x and y is said to 'satisfy' an inequation if it belongs to the solution set of the inequation. Thus Figure 6 shows the set of points whose coordinates satisfy *the inequations* $x > 0$ and $y > 0$ and $y < 5-x$.

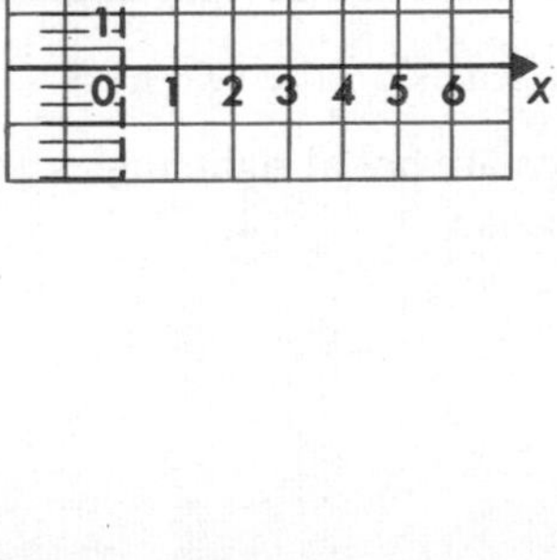

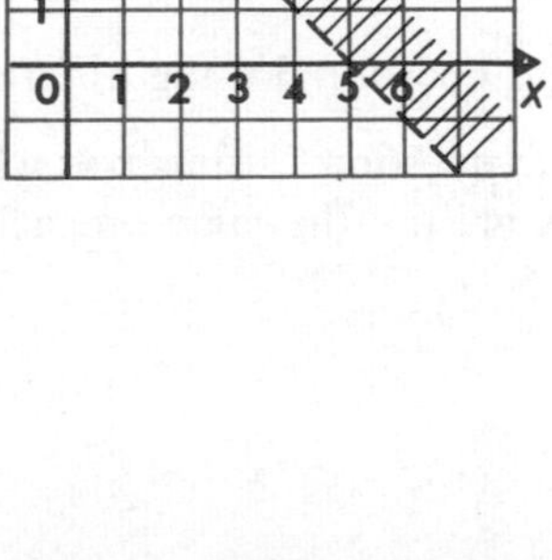

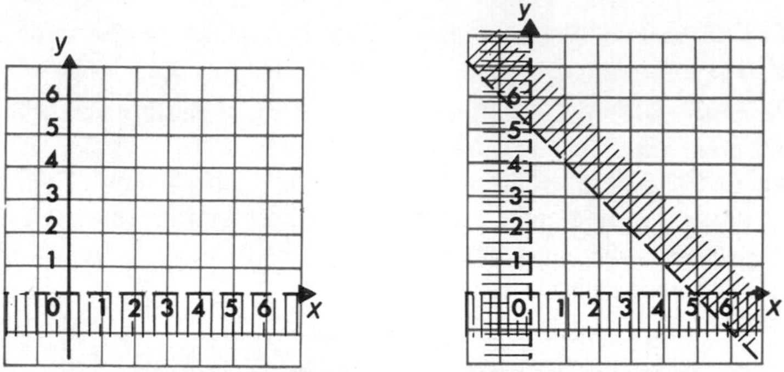

FIG. 7

The set of pairs of coordinates of these points is called the solution set of the *system* of inequations.

Exercise 1

Indicate on a coordinate plane, using rectangular axes with equal scales, the points whose coordinates satisfy all the inequations of the following systems. Comment on the shapes of the sets of points which indicate these solution sets; x and y are variables on the set of real numbers.

1 $x > 0$ *and* $y > 0$ *and* $x < 3$ *and* $y < 2$.

2 $y \geqslant 0$ *and* $y \leqslant x$ *and* $y < 5-x$.

3 $y > x$ *and* $y < 5$ *and* $x > 2$.

4 $x > 2$ *and* $x \leqslant 4$.

5 $-2 \leqslant y \leqslant 2$ *and* $-3 < x < 1$.

6 $x < 0$ *and* $y < 0$ *and* $x+y > -5$.

7 $y > x$ *and* $y > -x$ *and* $y < 4$.

8 $y < 2x$ *and* $y \leqslant 4-\frac{1}{2}x$ *and* $y > 0$.

9 Repeat question 1 using axes which are not at right angles.

10 Repeat question 5 using different scales on the two axes.

11 Repeat question 7 using axes which are not at right angles and scales which are not the same on each axis.

12 Copy Figure 6*a* on page 108 of the Geometry section. Insert a set of rectangular axes and use these to describe each of the L-shapes by the union of two systems of inequations.

13 Repeat question 12 for other letters and shapes. Compare results with your neighbour.

2 Intersection of solution sets—equations

In the last Section we showed the solution sets of systems of linear inequations. Now we are going to do the same with systems of linear equations.

Example 1.—Show the solution set of each of the equations $y = 5-x$, $y = x+1$. Hence give the solution set of the system of equations $y = 5-x$ *and* $y = x+1$.

Figure 8 indicates the solution sets of the two equations. Note that two points are sufficient to define the position of a line, and that often the points which can be found most readily are the points where the

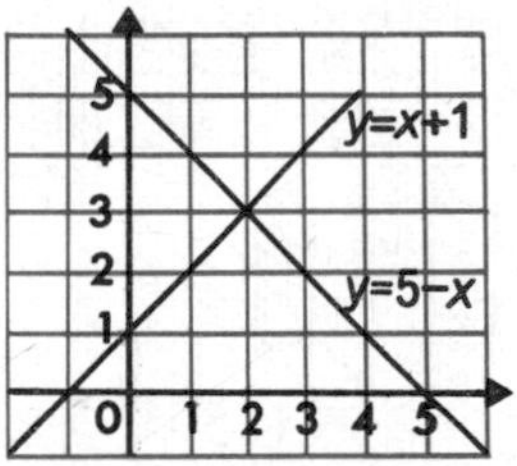

FIG. 8

line crosses the x- and y-axes. Thus for the line $y = 5-x$, when $x = 0$, $y = 5$; and when $y = 0$, $x = 5$. So the line passes through the points (0, 5) and (5, 0).

The pair of coordinates of the one point where the two lines meet is a member of the solution set of the system $y = 5-x$ and $y = x+1$. Evidently it is the only member; thus the solution set of the two equations is $\{(2, 3)\}$.

Example 2.—Show the solution set of the system of equations $y = 3$ *and* $y = x-1$.

See Figure 9. The only point common to the two lines is (4, 3); so (4, 3) is the only number pair satisfying both equations. The solution set is $\{(4, 3)\}$.

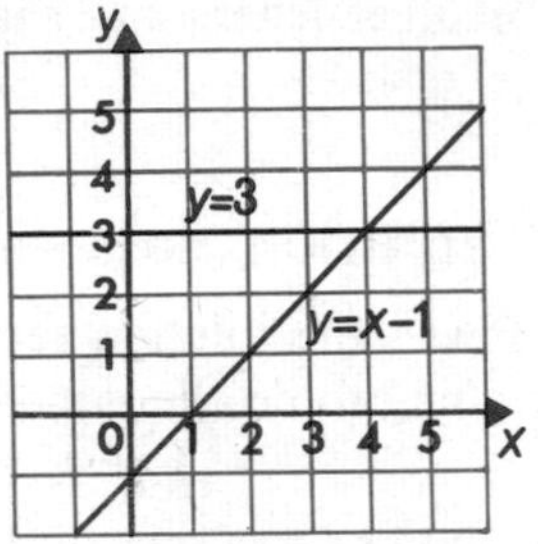

FIG. 9

Example 3.—Show the solution set of the system of equations $y = x+2$ *and* $y = x+1$.

See Figure 10. Evidently these two lines do not intersect. There is no point whose coordinates satisfy *both* equations. The solution set of the system of equations is $\emptyset$.

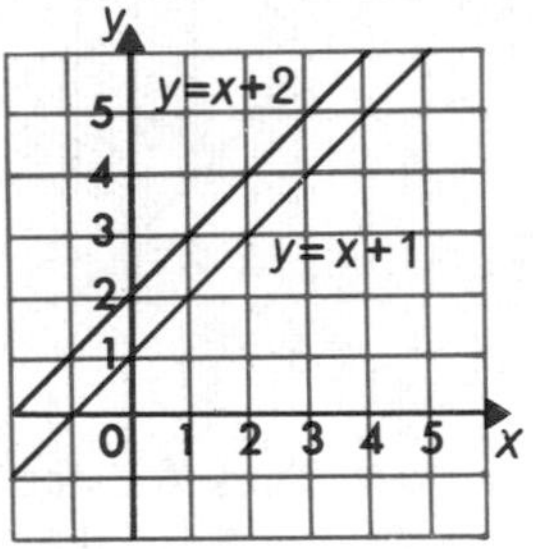

FIG. 10

Example 4.—Show the solution set of the system of equations $y = x$ *and* $x+y = 5$ *and* $x = 4$.

See Figure 11. Evidently there is no point which lies on all three lines, i.e. there is no point whose coordinates satisfy all three equations. The solution set is $\emptyset$.

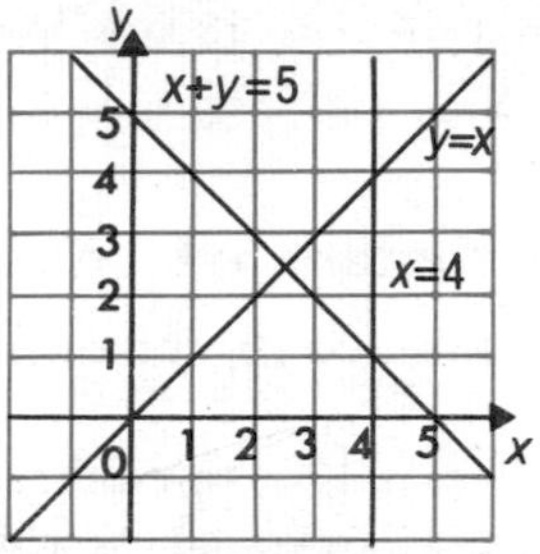

FIG. 11

Systems of equations whose solution set is empty (e.g. Examples 3 and 4) are sometimes said to be *inconsistent*.

Exercise 2

(Use $\frac{1}{2}$-cm squared paper for questions 1–10, and 2-mm squared paper for questions 11–20.)

For each equation indicate the set of points whose coordinates belong to the solution set of the equation. Then show clearly the intersection of these sets. Finally write down the solution set of the system in the form of a set of ordered pairs.

The variables are on the set of real numbers.

1 $y = 6-x$ *and* $y = x$.
2 $x+y = 7$ *and* $y = 3$.
3 $x+y+6 = 0$ *and* $x = -3$.
4 $x-2y = 3$ *and* $x+y = 0$.
5 $y = 4$ *and* $x = 3$.
6 $y = x+2$ *and* $y = 4-x$.
7 $y = 2x-2$ *and* $y = 3-\frac{1}{2}x$.
8 $3x+4y = 25$ *and* $4x-3y = 0$.
9 $y = 3x+4$ *and* $y = 3x+5$.
10 $y = x$ *and* $y = 2x$ *and* $x+y = 8$.

In questions 11–20 give solution sets to a degree of approximation which is reasonable from your graph. It is customary to omit '*and*' when it is clear that we are interested in the number pairs which turn both equations into true statements.

11 $3x+2y = 6, \quad y = x+4$.
12 $y = x-2, \quad 5y-2x = 0$.
13 $2x+y+2 = 0, \quad y = x+2$.
14 $y = 6x-6, \quad y = 2x$.
15 $x+3y = 3, \quad x+y = 0$.
16 $y = x-4, \quad y+3x+2 = 0$.

17 $x+y+4 = 0, \quad 2y = x-4.$

18 $x+7y = 0, \quad 7x-y = 0.$

19 $3x+y = 5, \quad 3x+y = 6.$

20 $x = 2, \quad y = 3, \quad x+y = 4.$

3 Solution of a system of equations

The sum of two whole numbers is 10, and their difference is 2. Can you guess the numbers?

The sum of two numbers is 120; three times one of the numbers is equal to five times the other. Can you guess what the numbers are now? There are systematic ways of finding out the answer to this problem and to harder ones.

Suppose we let a denote the larger number and b the smaller number. Then $a+b = 120$ and $3a = 5b$. In other words (a, b) belongs to the solution set of the system of equations $x+y = 120$ and $3x = 5y$. By drawing the graphs of the equations $x+y = 120$ and $3x = 5y$, we could find the solution set of the system. This method is time-consuming and is not very accurate, so in this Section we study other ways of obtaining the solution set.

We have to find ordered pairs which belong to the solution sets of both equations; in set language, $(a, b) \in S$ *and* $(a, b) \in T$, so that $(a, b) \in S \cap T$.

We are now going to find the solution sets of such systems by using operations of the number systems. The advantages of these methods are:

(*a*) for approximate results the degree of approximation is not limited by inaccuracies of drawing;

(*b*) the methods can be extended to systems of three equations in three variables, four in four, or a hundred in a hundred;

(*c*) they can be used on computers and a method equivalent to Method 1 is in fact used daily to solve systems of equations in large numbers of variables.

Preliminary Exercise

1 On a coordinate plane draw the graphs of the two equations $x+y-6 = 0$ and $2x-y = 0$. Then draw the graphs of

$$p(x+y-6)+q(2x-y) = 0$$

for each of the following cases, using the same axes:

(i) $p = 1, q = 0$ (ii) $p = 0, q = 1$ (iii) $p = -1, q = 1$
(iv) $p = 1, q = 1$ (v) $p = 1, q = -2$ (vi) $p = 2, q = -1$

Compare with your neighbour to make sure you get these right.

2 (i) Notice that all the lines you have drawn pass through the same point. Thus, you may choose whichever two you prefer, and they will provide you with a system of equations with the same solution set as the original pair, i.e. an *equivalent system*. Which pair gives the point of intersection most easily?

(ii) By obtaining this pair, the solution set is at once evident. Write down the solution set of $x+y-6 = 0$, $2x-y = 0$.

Method 1. The method of elimination by linear combination

Example 1.—Solve $\left.\begin{aligned} 3x+4y-7 &= 0 \\ 4x-3y-1 &= 0 \end{aligned}\right\}$

Consider the equation,

$$p(3x+4y-7)+q(4x-3y-1) = 0 \quad \ldots\ldots\ldots\ldots \text{(i)}$$

If we can choose p and q so that the coefficient of y is zero, the solution set of the resulting equation will be shown by a line parallel to the y-axis. The coefficient of y in equation (i) is $4p - 3q$. Some choices of p and q which make $4p-3q = 0$ are

$p = 3, q = 4;\ p = -3, q = -4;\ p = 6, q = 8;\ p = \frac{1}{4}, q = \frac{1}{3};\ldots$

Many other suitable ordered pairs (p, q) can be found. Write out some other suitable choices for p and q.

Taking $p = 3, q = 4$, equation (i) is equivalent to

$$9x+12y-21+16x-12y-4 = 0$$
$$\Leftrightarrow \qquad 25x = 25$$
$$\Leftrightarrow \qquad x = 1$$

Thus the x-coordinate of the common point of the two lines is 1 (see Figure 12).

By choosing p and q so that the coefficient of x is zero, we could now obtain an equation involving only y. Do this, noting that the coefficient of x is $3p+4q$.

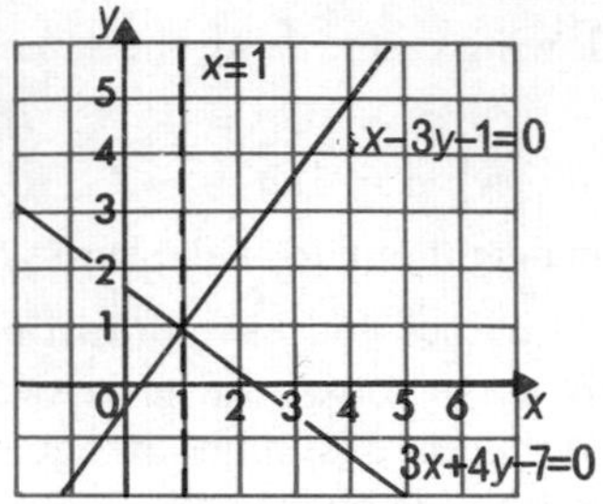

FIG. 12

It is shorter, however, to use one of the original equations. Replacing x by 1 in the equation $3x+4y-7 = 0$, we get

$$
\begin{aligned}
& 3+4y-7 = 0 \\
\Leftrightarrow \quad & 4y = 7-3 \\
\Leftrightarrow \quad & 4y = 4 \\
\Leftrightarrow \quad & y = 1
\end{aligned}
$$

The solution set of the two given equations is $\{(1, 1)\}$.

Example 2.—Solve $\left.\begin{aligned} 4x-5y &= 22 \\ 7x+3y &= 15 \end{aligned}\right\}$ i.e. $\left.\begin{aligned} 4x-5y-22 &= 0 \\ 7x+3y-15 &= 0 \end{aligned}\right\}$

Consider the equation,

$$p(4x-5y-22)+q(7x+3y-15) = 0$$

Choose p and q so that the coefficient of x (or y) is zero.
The coefficient of x is $4p+7q$.
Choosing $p = 7$ and $q = -4$,

$$
\begin{aligned}
& 7(4x-5y-22)-4(7x+3y-15) = 0 \\
\Leftrightarrow \quad & 28x-35y-154-28x-12y+60 = 0 \\
\Leftrightarrow \quad & -47y = 154-60 \\
\Leftrightarrow \quad & -47y = 94 \\
\Leftrightarrow \quad & y = -2
\end{aligned}
$$

Thus, the y-coordinate of the common point of the two lines is -2 (see Figure 13).

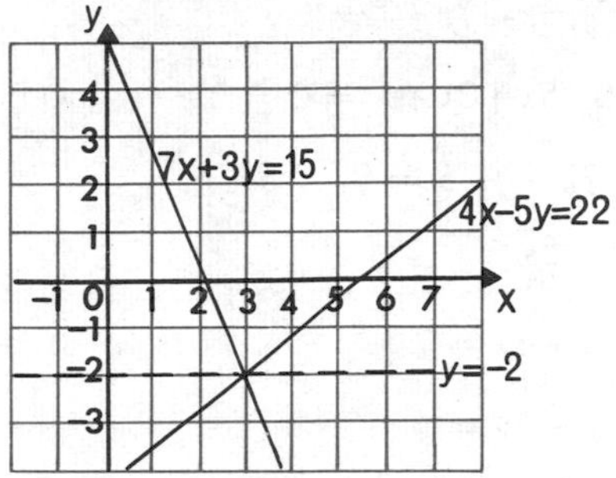

FIG. 13

Replacing y by -2 in $7x+3y = 15$, we get

$$7x-6 = 15$$
$$\Leftrightarrow \quad 7x = 15+6$$
$$\Leftrightarrow \quad 7x = 21$$
$$\Leftrightarrow \quad x = 3$$

The solution set is $\{(3, -2)\}$.

Exercise 3

If each of the following equations is true for all values of p and q, find the replacements for x and for y in questions 1–6.

1 $p(x-y+2)+q(2x+y-2) = 0$
2 $p(x+y-5)+q(2x+y-7) = 0$
3 $p(x+2y+4)+q(3x-y-9) = 0$
4 $p(2x+y-3)+q(4x-3y+4) = 0$
5 $p(3x+2y-2)+q(9x-4y-1) = 0$
6 $p(4x+6y-11)+q(17x-5y-1) = 0$

Solve the systems of equations 7–20:

7 $x+y-8 = 0$, $x-y-2 = 0$
8 $x-y+2 = 0$, $2x+y-2 = 0$
9 $x-y+1 = 0$, $x+y-5 = 0$
10 $2x+3y-2 = 0$, $x-y-1 = 0$

11 $2x-7y+3 = 0$, $3x-7y+1 = 0$

12 $7x+4y-1 = 0$, $5x+2y+1 = 0$

13 $x+y+1 = 0$, $2x-y-5 = 0$

14 $2x-3y = 0$, $2x-y-5 = 0$

15 $2x-3y = 0$, $6x+6y = 7$

16 $4x-3y = 3$, $4x-3y = 5$

17 $\left.\begin{aligned} 5x+y &= 5 \\ 17x-y &= -5 \end{aligned}\right\}$

18 $\left.\begin{aligned} 2x+3y &= 8 \\ 3x-3y &= 12 \end{aligned}\right\}$

19 $\left.\begin{aligned} y-x &= 6 \\ 2x-y &= 1 \end{aligned}\right\}$

20 $\left.\begin{aligned} 3x-y &= 1 \\ x-2y &= -8 \end{aligned}\right\}$

Method 2. The method of elimination by substitution

If the coefficient of either variable in one of the equations is unity, this method is usually shorter than Method 1.

Example 1.—Solve $y = 2x-1$ *and* $3x-2y = 5$.

If (a, b) is a member of the solution set of this system, then it is true that

$$b = 2a-1 \quad \text{and} \quad 3a-2b = 5$$

From this it is easily seen to be true that

$$3a-2(2a-1) = 5$$

In other words, every member of the solution set of the system also satisfies the equation

$$3x-2(2x-1) = 5$$

and so an equivalent system can be formed by taking this equation with the other two.

But this equation when simplified gives $x = -3$, and then the first equation gives $y = 2(-3)-1 = -7$.

The solution set is $\{(-3, -7)\}$.

Example 2.—Solve $x = y-1$, $2x-3y = 1$.
The working may be set down as follows:

Substituting for x in the second equation, we get

$$2(y-1)-3y = 1$$
$$\Leftrightarrow\ 2y-2-3y = 1$$
$$\Leftrightarrow\ -y = 1+2$$
$$\Leftrightarrow\ y = -3$$

From the first equation, $x = -3 - 1$

$$\Leftrightarrow x = -4$$

The solution set is $\{(-4, -3)\}$.

Exercise 4

Solve these equations by the method of substitution:

1 $y = 7$, $x+3 = y$

2 $x = 3y$, $4x-5y = 14$

3 $y = 3x$, $5x-2y = 7$

4 $x+3y = 8$, $x = y+4$

5 $2y+x = 20$, $y = x-5$

6 $y = 2x-1$, $3y-2x = 5$

7 $y = 2x-2$, $4y-5x = 1$

8 $x = 2y+9$, $x+5y = -5$

9 $x = 2y+3$, $5x-2y = -1$

10 $x = 2y-6$, $3x+3y = 9$

11 $y+2x = 0$, $4x+y = 3$

12 $2x+y = 0$, $7x+5y = 1$

13 $2y = x-2$, $3y-5x = 4$

14 $2x-y+10 = 0$, $5y = 2-2x$

15 $6x-y = 1$, $3y-4x = 4$

16 $x-2y+1 = 0$, $2x+3y = 7$

4 Systems of equations with fractions

When one or both equations contain fractions the best way to proceed is to form equivalent equations without fractions, and then to solve the system of equations as before. The example illustrates the method.

Example.—Solve $x-y = -1,\ \frac{x}{2} - \frac{y-3}{5} = 1.$

$$\begin{aligned}
&\frac{x}{2} - \frac{y-3}{5} &&= 1 \\
\Leftrightarrow\ &10\left\{\frac{x}{2} - \frac{y-3}{5}\right\} &&= 10 \quad \text{(The LCM of 2 and 5 is 10.)} \\
\Leftrightarrow\ &5x-2(y-3) &&= 10 \\
\Leftrightarrow\ &5x-2y+6 &&= 10 \\
\Leftrightarrow\ &5x-2y-4 &&= 0
\end{aligned}$$

In $p(x-y+1)+q(5x-2y-4) = 0$ put $p = 2, q = -1$.

$$\begin{aligned}
&2x-2y+2-5x+2y+4 = 0 \\
\Leftrightarrow\ &\qquad -3x+6 = 0 \\
\Leftrightarrow\ &\qquad x = 2
\end{aligned}$$

From the first equation

$$\begin{aligned}
&2-y = -1 \\
\Leftrightarrow\ &-y = -3 \\
\Leftrightarrow\ &y = 3
\end{aligned}$$

The solution set is $\{(2, 3)\}$.

Exercise 5

Solve:

1 $x-y = 0,\ \frac{x}{2}+\frac{y}{3} = 5$

2 $x+y = 6,\ \frac{x}{2}-\frac{y}{4} = 0$

3 $\frac{x}{5}+y = 1,\ x-y = 5$

4 $x-y = 0,\ \frac{x}{4}-\frac{y-1}{3} = 0$

5 $x+y = 2,\ \frac{2x}{3}+y = 1$

6 $2x+4y = 1,\ \frac{x+y}{3}-\frac{x-y}{4} = -1$

7 $x+\frac{2y}{9} = 9,\ \frac{x}{5}-\frac{y}{6} = -2$

8 $\frac{x+1}{3}+y = 8,\ x-\frac{y+1}{3} = -4$

9 $\frac{2x+y}{3} = 5,\ \frac{3x-y}{5} = 1$

10 $\frac{x-1}{2}+\frac{y+1}{5} = 4\frac{1}{5},\ \frac{x+y}{3} = y-1$

11 $0{\cdot}5x-0{\cdot}7y = 2$, $1{\cdot}8x-2{\cdot}2y = 8{\cdot}8$

12 $1{\cdot}2x-0{\cdot}8y = 0{\cdot}4$, $y = 0{\cdot}3-0{\cdot}1x$

5 Some applications

Here we have to analyse a problem and construct a mathematical model in the form of a system of equations. We then have to interpret the solution set of this system in relation to the problem.

Example.—The perimeter of a rectangle is 75 cm, and the length is 13 cm more than the breadth. Find the length and breadth.

Let x cm denote the length, and let y cm denote the breadth.
Then $2x+2y = 75$ *and* $x-y = 13$.
So $p(2x+2y-75)+q(x-y-13) = 0$.
Take $p = 1, q = 2$.

$$2x+2y-75+2x-2y-26 = 0$$
$$\Leftrightarrow \quad 4x = 101$$
$$\Leftrightarrow \quad x = 25\tfrac{1}{4}$$

Replacing x by $25\frac{1}{4}$ in the second equation,

$$25\tfrac{1}{4}-y = 13$$
$$\Leftrightarrow 25\tfrac{1}{4}-13 = y$$
$$\Leftrightarrow \quad y = 12\tfrac{1}{4}$$

The length of the rectangle is $25\frac{1}{4}$ cm, and the breadth is $12\frac{1}{4}$ cm.

Exercise 6

In each of the questions 1–8 form a system of equations and use them to solve the problems:

1 The sum of two whole numbers is 112 and their difference is 36. Find the numbers.

2 The sum of two rational numbers is 63 and their difference is 12. Find the numbers.

3 Two angles are complementary. One is 57° larger than the other. Find the sizes of the angles.

4 Two angles are supplementary. One is 68° larger than the other. Find the sizes of the angles.

5 The sum of the length and breadth of a rectangle is 84 cm. The length is 18 cm more than the breadth. Calculate the length and breadth.

6 The perimeter of a rectangle is 68 cm. The length is 27 cm more than the breadth. Find the length and breadth.

7 Six records of one make and 4 of another cost £3·40. Three of the first type and 10 of the second cost £4·90. Find the price of each type of record.

8 Twelve expensive flower bulbs and 8 cheap ones cost £3·80. Nine of the expensive ones and 4 of the cheap ones cost £2·65. Find the price of each kind of bulb.

9 When a wire of length L inches is stretched by a weight W lbf, L and W are related by the equation $L = a+bW$, where a and b represent certain numbers.
When the weight is 4 lbf, the length of the wire is 18 inches; when the weight is 14 lbf, the length is 23 inches.
Find a and b. Hence calculate (i) the length of the wire when the weight is 15 lbf, and (ii) the weight when the length is 20 inches.

10 The speed V feet per second of a train t seconds after the brakes are applied is given by $V = at+b$, where a and b represent certain numbers.
When $t = 0$, $V = 40$; when $t = 8$, $V = 30$.
Find a and b, and hence calculate (i) V when $t = 10$, (ii) t when $V = 24$.

11 In a machine a load W lbf is raised by an effort of P lbf, where $W = a+bP$, a and b representing numbers.
$P = 3$ when $W = 17$; $P = 6$ when $W = 35$. Find a and b. Hence find what load could be raised by an effort of 10 lbf.

12 Two machines, A and B, produce items at the constant rate of 50 and 40 items per hour respectively. An order for 1,000 items is to be completed.

(*a*) If the total number of machine hours of operation used is exactly 24, show that to fill the order there is one and only one way of assigning a number of hours of operation to each machine.

(*b*) If it costs £3 an hour to operate machine A and £2 an hour to operate machine B, what is the total cost of production satisfying the specifications in part (*a*)?

(*c*) If the total number of machine hours of operation used is to be *at most* 24 hours, the entire order for 1,000 items could be handled by machine A. Find the cost of production under such a scheme and compare it with that of the production plan in (*a*).

CHAPTER 4 Formulae

1 Introduction

In this course we have already constructed and used various formulae. Do you recognize the following?

$A = lb$, $A = l^2$, $A = \frac{1}{2}bh$, $A = \pi r^2$, $P = 2(l+b)$, $C = 2\pi r$, $V = lbh$, $V = \pi r^2 h$, $C = \frac{5}{9}(F-32)$.

In this chapter we study formulae more closely and consider various ways in which they are used in mathematics and science.

2 Constructing and using a formula

(i) Bus routes

Figure 1 shows bus routes between three towns. How many routes are there from Ayton to Beeton? For each of these routes, how many routes are there from Beeton to Seaton? So how many routes could you possibly take from Ayton to Seaton?

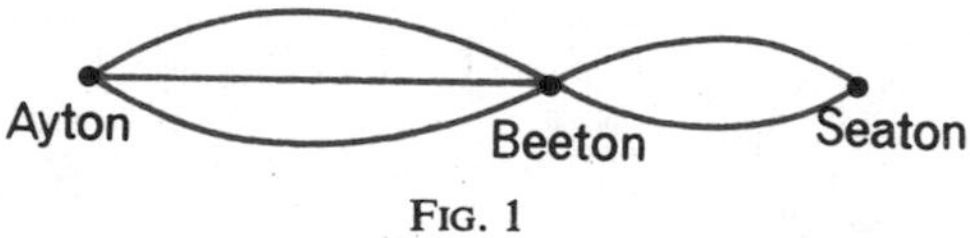

FIG. 1

If there were m routes from Ayton to Beeton and n routes from Beeton to Seaton, we could argue like this:

There are m routes from Ayton to Beeton; whichever of these we take, we have the choice of n routes from Beeton to Seaton. Then if R denotes the number of routes possible from Ayton to Seaton we have the formula

$$R = m \times n$$

If there were p routes from Seaton to a fourth town, Deeton, what would be the formula for the number (R') of different routes from Ayton to Deeton?

The important thing about a formula is that, once established, it can be used in any calculation concerning the situation to which it refers.

For example, if there were 5 routes from Ayton to Beeton and 4 from Beeton to Seaton, then $m = 5$, $n = 4$, and $R = m \times n$

$$= 5 \times 4$$
$$= 20$$

so there would be 20 routes from Ayton to Seaton.

Use the formula $R' = mnp$ to find the number of routes from Ayton to Deeton, given that there are 4 from Ayton to Beeton, 3 from Beeton to Seaton, 2 from Seaton to Deeton.

(ii) The area of a metal plate

Figure 2 represents a metal plate in the shape of a rectangle and an isosceles triangle with the dimensions shown.

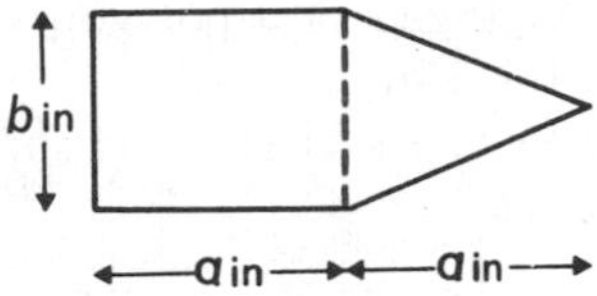

FIG. 2

Denote the area of the whole plate by A in², the area of the rectangle by R in², and of the triangle by T in².

$$A = R+T$$
$$R = ab$$
$$T = \tfrac{1}{2}ab$$
$$\text{So } A = ab+\tfrac{1}{2}ab$$
$$= \tfrac{3}{2}ab$$

When $a = 10$ and $b = 7$, $A = \frac{3}{2} \times 10 \times 7 = 105$.
What is the area when $a = 8$ and $b = 5$?

(iii) The sum of the angles of a polygon

A polygon can be divided into triangles as indicated in Figure 3. What is the sum of the angles of a triangle in degrees and in right angles?

FIG. 3

Copy and complete this table:

Number of sides	4	5	6	7	8	10	20	n
Number of triangles	2	3						
Sum of angles of polygon in right angles	4							

Suppose the sum of the angles of a polygon with n sides is S right angles; give the formula for S in terms of n.

For a polygon with 100 sides, what is the sum of the angles (i) in right angles, (ii) in degrees?

Exercise 1

1 If a rectangle is x cm long and y cm broad, give a formula for its perimeter P cm. Calculate P when $x = 9\frac{1}{2}$ and $y = 5\frac{1}{2}$.

2 A square has each side of length x metres and its perimeter is P metres. Write down a formula for P, and calculate P when $x = 6$.

3 A triangle has each side of length m cm and its perimeter is P cm. Find a formula for P, and hence calculate (i) P when $m = 16$, (ii) m when $P = 24$.

4 A plane flies x miles north, then y miles east. The total distance it flies is d miles. Write down a formula for d. Find d if $x = 525$ and $y = 289$.

5 In Figure 4, P cm is the perimeter; write down a formula for P in terms of x, y, and z.

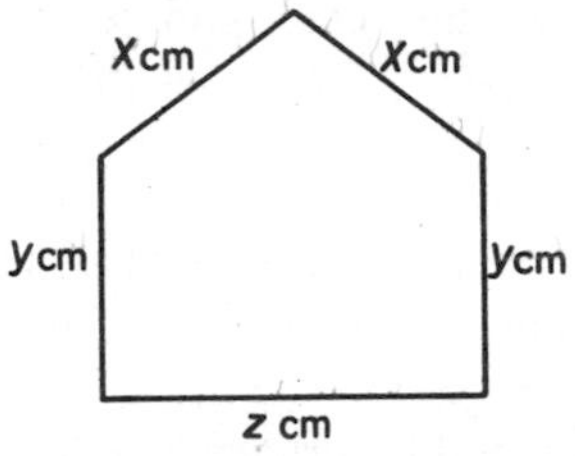

FIG. 4

(i) Find P when $x = 35$, $y = 15$, $z = 55$.
(ii) Find z when $P = 64$, $x = 12$, $y = 10$.

6 An aircraft weighs t tonf when loaded. It uses up f tons of fuel per hour. If W tonf is the weight of the aircraft after h hours flying, write down a formula for W. Hence calculate W when $t = 12$, $f = \frac{1}{4}$, and $h = 3$.

7 The two sets of equally spaced parallel lines in Figure 5 represent a network of roads in a town. The distances between adjacent junctions are x metres and y metres as shown.

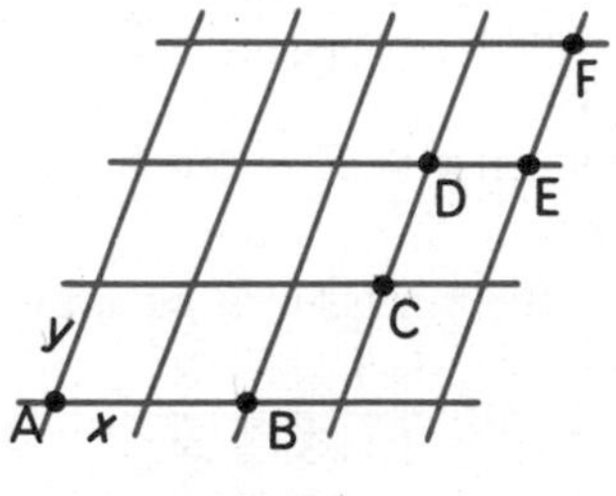

FIG. 5

If the shortest distance by road from A to B is denoted by b metres, from A to C by c metres, from A to D by d metres, and so on, we could write a formula for the distance from A to C: $c = 3x+y$.

Write down formulae for the distances (i) from A to B (ii) from A to D (iii) from A to E (iv) from A to F.
Calculate each of these distances when $x = 75$ and $y = 50$.

8 In this question you have to obtain a formula for the greatest number of diagonals that can be drawn from one chosen vertex in a polygon. Refer back to Figure 3 and copy and complete this table:

Number of sides	4	5	6	7	8	10	20	n
Number of diagonals	1	2						

If the greatest number of diagonals that can be drawn from any chosen vertex in a polygon with n sides is d, give a formula for d in terms of n.

How many diagonals can be drawn in a polygon with 100 sides?

9 Figure 6 represents a metal plate in the form of a square of side $2x$ cm and a semicircle. Write down formulae for (i) the perimeter P cm of the plate (ii) the area A cm^2 of the plate.

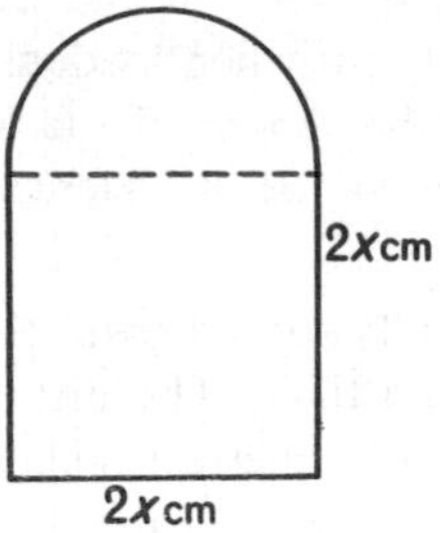

FIG. 6

Calculate P and A when $x = 10{\cdot}0$ and $3{\cdot}14$ is taken as an approximation for π.

10 Find a formula for the nth term of each of these sequences:

(i) $1, \frac{1}{4}, \frac{1}{9}, \frac{1}{16}, \ldots,$ (ii) $\frac{1}{2 \times 3}, \frac{2}{3 \times 4}, \frac{3}{4 \times 5}, \ldots$

Use your formula to give the 20th term of each sequence.

11 $A = \{a\}$. List the subsets of A. (Do not forget the empty set.) How many are there?

$B = \{a, b\}$. List the subsets of B. How many are there?

$C = \{a, b, c\}$. List the subsets of C. How many are there?

Can you guess the number of subsets of $D = \{a, b, c, d\}$?

Can you suggest a formula for the number of subsets there are for a set containing n elements?

12 We indicate the number of elements in a set P by $n(P)$.
Draw a Venn diagram, with the number of elements entered, to show $n(P) = 12$, $n(Q) = 10$, $n(P \cap Q) = 4$. What is $n(P \cup Q)$? Can you give a formula for $n(P \cup Q)$ in terms of $n(P)$, $n(Q)$, and $n(P \cap Q)$?

13 Repeat question 12 for $n(X) = 12$, $n(Y) = 14$, $n(X \cap Y) = 5$.

14 Construct a network of bus routes between various towns, and work out formulae for the number of routes possible between different towns.

3 Looking at equations

In algebra so far we have studied equations in one variable of the following kinds:

$2x = 8,\quad x+2 = 9,\quad \dfrac{x}{100} = 10$ ...... in Book 1.

$2x+4 = -9,\quad 4(1-2x) = 12-7x$ ...... in Book 2.

$\dfrac{x}{3}+\dfrac{1}{4} = 0,\quad \dfrac{x}{2}+\dfrac{5}{4}-x+1 = 3$ ...... in Book 3.

You will remember that all of these could be solved by adding to each side, and multiplying each side by, appropriate inverses. In this Section we shall assume that all variables are on the set of real numbers.

Revision Examples

1.
$$
\begin{aligned}
& 6x+12 = -9 \\
\Leftrightarrow\ & 6x+12-12 = -9-12 \\
\Leftrightarrow\ & 6x = -21 \\
\Leftrightarrow\ & \frac{1}{6}\cdot 6x = \frac{1}{6}(-21) \\
\Leftrightarrow\ & x = \frac{-21}{6} \\
\Leftrightarrow\ & x = \frac{-7}{3}
\end{aligned}
$$

2.
$$
\begin{aligned}
& \frac{3x}{100} = 10 \\
\Leftrightarrow\ & 100 \times \frac{3x}{100} = 100 \times 10 \\
\Leftrightarrow\ & 3x = 1{,}000 \\
\Leftrightarrow\ & \frac{1}{3}\cdot 3x = \frac{1}{3}\cdot 1{,}000 \\
\Leftrightarrow\ & x = \frac{1{,}000}{3}
\end{aligned}
$$

Where there were fractions, we multiplied each side by the LCM of the denominators of the fractions; where there were brackets, we used the distributive law.

Revision Examples

3. $\frac{x}{3}+\frac{1}{4} = -1$

(*Note.*—LCM is 12.)

$\Leftrightarrow 12(\frac{1}{3}x+\frac{1}{4}) = -1 \times 12$

$\Leftrightarrow 4x+3 = -12$

$\Leftrightarrow 4x = -15$

$\Leftrightarrow x = -3\frac{3}{4}$

4. $4(1-2x) = 12-7x$

$\Leftrightarrow 4-8x = 12-7x$

$\Leftrightarrow -8x+7x = 12-4$

$\Leftrightarrow -x = 8$

$\Leftrightarrow x = -8$

Before studying formulae further, you must be able to carry out all the above processes competently.

Exercise 2 (for revision)

Solve the following equations, where x is a variable on the set of real numbers. You may omit some of the steps in the working.

1 $3x = 8$

2 $x-10 = -7$

3 $\frac{1}{12}x = 6$

4 $2x+1 = -7$

5 $\frac{2}{3}x = 8$

6 $2(x+1) = 15$

7 $\frac{1}{2}x+\frac{1}{3} = 1$

8 $\frac{1}{3}x-\frac{1}{4} = 0$

9 $\frac{1}{2}x = 1+\frac{1}{5}x$

10 $3x+2 = 0$

11 $3(2x-1) = 10x$

12 $5(x+1) = 2(1-x)$

13 $\frac{3}{4}x+\frac{1}{2} = 1$

14 $\frac{1}{5}(x+1) = 7$

15 $5x-9 = -12$

16 $\frac{2}{3}(x+1)-1 = 0$

17 $5 = \frac{1}{6}x-\frac{1}{3}x$

18 $8(1-3x) = 5(4x+6)$

19 $2-x = x-2$

20 $1-\frac{1}{2}(1-x) = 0$

21 $\frac{1}{2}(x+5)-\frac{1}{4}(x-1) = 3$

4 Literal equations

An equation involves a variable and numerals. An equation in which letters take the place of numerals is called a *literal equation.* The solution set will of course be expressed in terms of these letters. It can be assumed in what follows that only those replacements may be made which do not at any stage indicate a division by zero—which is meaningless. Thus, if we write b/a we understand that a cannot be replaced by zero. Again in the fraction $1/(p-q)$, we assume that p and q may not both be replaced by the same number.

Example 1.—Solve for x, $ax+b = c$	*Compare*
$ax+b = c$	$2x+3 = 4$
$\Leftrightarrow ax+b-b = c-b$ ......(A)	$\Leftrightarrow 2x+3-3 = 4-3$
$\Leftrightarrow ax = c-b$	$\Leftrightarrow 2x = 1$
$\Leftrightarrow \frac{1}{a} \times ax = \frac{1}{a} \times (c-b)$ ......(B)	$\Leftrightarrow \frac{1}{2} \times 2x = \frac{1}{2} \times 1$
$\Leftrightarrow x = \frac{c-b}{a}$	$\Leftrightarrow x = \frac{1}{2}$

Example 2.—Solve for x, $\frac{px}{q} = r$	*Compare*
$\frac{px}{q} = r$	$\frac{5x}{6} = 7$
$\Leftrightarrow q \times \frac{px}{q} = q \times r$ ......(C)	$\Leftrightarrow 6 \times \frac{5x}{6} = 6 \times 7$
$\Leftrightarrow px = qr$	$\Leftrightarrow 5x = 42$
$\Leftrightarrow \frac{1}{p} \times px = \frac{1}{p} \times qr$ ......(D)	$\Leftrightarrow \frac{1}{5} \times 5x = \frac{1}{5} \times 42$
$\Leftrightarrow x = \frac{qr}{p}$	$\Leftrightarrow x = \frac{42}{5}$

Note.—(i) *We usually remove fractions first, and then isolate the term or terms containing x on one side of the equation.*

(ii) *In the above examples, lines (A), (B), (C), (D) need not be written down when proficiency has been attained.*

Example 3.—Solve for x, $\frac{x}{l} = \frac{m}{n}$

$$\frac{x}{l} = \frac{m}{n}$$

$$\Leftrightarrow l \times \frac{x}{l} = l \times \frac{m}{n}$$

$$\Leftrightarrow \quad x = \frac{lm}{n}$$

Note.—(i) *Equations of this form occur very frequently, for example in the geometry of similar figures. It is very helpful to be able to write down the solution immediately.*

(ii) *It should be noted that the numerical solution of an equation of this form is given very quickly on a slide-rule. If m on the C scale is placed opposite n on the D scale, then x will be found on the C scale opposite l on the D scale.*

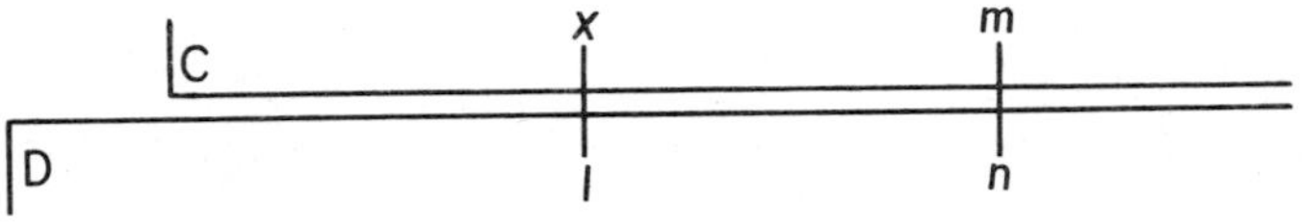

FIG. 7

$$\frac{x}{l} = \frac{m}{n}$$

Exercise 3

Solve for x, carefully setting out each step:

1 $x+a = 5$

2 $x+a = b$

3 $x-a = 4$

4 $x-p = q$

5 $2x = c$

6 $px = 7$

7 $ax = b$

8 $\frac{x}{4} = p$

9 $\frac{x}{h} = 10$

10 $\frac{x}{m} = n$ 11 $\frac{x}{a} = \frac{b}{c}$ 12 $2x+4 = p$

13 $2x+a = 1$ 14 $ax+3 = b$ 15 $px+q = r$

16 $\frac{3x}{4} = h$ 17 $\frac{ax}{5} = b$ 18 $\frac{cx}{p} = q$

19 $(a+b)x = c$ 20 $\frac{x}{r+1} = q$ 21 $d = e+2x$

22 $k = mx+n$ 23 $a+x = b-x$ 24 $2x-a = x-b$

25 $\frac{1}{3}(x+1) = 7$ 26 $\frac{x}{a}+1 = b$ 27 $\frac{x}{k}-m = n$

28 $\frac{1}{3}(x+4) = 1$ 29 $\frac{x+a}{b} = 1$ 30 $\frac{x+a}{b} = c$

31 $\frac{px-q}{r} = s$ 32 $5(x-2) = 20$ 33 $a(x+b) = c$

34 $p(qx+r) = s$ 35 $\frac{x}{a}-b = 2$ 36 $b+a(x-c) = d$

37 $\frac{x}{a}+\frac{y}{b} = 1$ 38 $a(x-b) = cx$ 39 $\frac{x}{a}+\frac{x}{b} = 1$

40 $\frac{x}{p}-\frac{x}{q} = r$ 41 $\frac{x}{a}-b = \frac{x}{c}$ 42 $a(x-b) = b(x+a)$

5 Changing the subject of a formula

Example 1.—Here is a simple formula by which a distance which is known in kilometres can be expressed approximately in miles.

If k kilometres is the same distance as m miles, then $m = \frac{5}{8}k$ approximately.

Using the formula,
if $k = 16$, $m = \frac{5}{8} \times 16 = 10$; so 16 kilometres = 10 miles, approximately;
if $k = 23$, $m = \frac{5}{8} \times 23 = 14\frac{3}{8}$; so 23 kilometres = $14\frac{3}{8}$ miles, approximately.

Suppose we now wish to find the equivalent of 3 miles in kilometres. We have $m = \frac{5}{8}k$ and $m = 3$

$$\Leftrightarrow \quad 3 = \tfrac{5}{8}k$$
$$\Leftrightarrow 24 = 5k$$
$$\Leftrightarrow \quad k = \frac{24}{5} = 4\tfrac{4}{5}$$

i.e. 3 miles is equivalent to about $4\frac{4}{5}$ kilometres.

If the formula has to be used in this way several times, it is more convenient to *change the subject* of the formula from m to k as follows:

$$m = \tfrac{5}{8}k$$
$$\Leftrightarrow 8m = 5k$$
$$\Leftrightarrow \quad k = \tfrac{8}{5}m$$

Then if $m = 12$, $k = \frac{8}{5} \times 12 = 19\frac{1}{5}$; so 12 miles = $19\frac{1}{5}$ km, approximately.

Example 2.—We have seen that the equation of a straight line can be written $y = mx+c$. To make c the subject:

$$y = mx+c$$
$$\Leftrightarrow y-mx = c$$
$$\Leftrightarrow \quad c = y-mx$$

To make m the subject:

$$y = mx+c$$
$$\Leftrightarrow \quad y-c = mx$$
$$\Leftrightarrow \quad m = \frac{y-c}{x} \quad \text{assuming } x \text{ is not zero.}$$

Example 3.—If the hypotenuse and sides of a right-angled triangle measure a, b, c units respectively, then by Pythagoras' theorem $a^2 = b^2+c^2$.

We can make b the subject of this formula as follows:

$$a^2 = b^2+c^2$$
$$\Leftrightarrow a^2-c^2 = b^2$$
$$\Rightarrow \quad b = \sqrt{(a^2-c^2)} \quad \text{(since } b \textit{ must} \text{ be positive)}$$

Note.—If P and Q are sentences, $P \Leftrightarrow Q$ *means that P is equivalent to Q, i.e. if P is true, then Q is true; and if Q is true, then P is true.*

$P \Rightarrow Q$ (P 'implies' Q) means only that if P is true, then Q is true.

For example: If $x = 3$, then $x^2 = 9$, i.e. $x = 3 \Rightarrow x^2 = 9$.

But if $x^2 = 9$, then $x = 3$ or -3, and it is not correct to write $x^2 = 9 \Rightarrow x = 3$, so we *cannot* write

$$x^2 = 9 \Leftrightarrow x = 3$$

Exercise 4

1 If p pints of water weigh w lbf, then $w = \frac{5}{4}p$ approximately. Find the approximate weight of (i) 12 pints (ii) 20 pints of water.
Use the same formula to find how many pints of water weigh (iii) 10 lbf (iv) 14 lbf.
Now change the subject to p and use this formula to find how many pints of water weigh (v) 8 lbf (vi) 9 lbf.

2 If M mph is the same speed as F ft/s, $F = \frac{22}{15} M$.
(*a*) Express in ft/s a speed of (i) 45 mph (ii) 1,200 mph.
(*b*) Change the subject to M and express in mph a speed of (i) 33 ft/s (ii) 1,100 ft/s.

3 The area, A square metres, of a rectangle of breadth b metres and length l metres is given by $A = lb$.
Change the subject to l. Calculate l when $A = 60$ and $b = 8$.

4 The average speed v mph of a train travelling s miles in t hours is given by $v = \dfrac{s}{t}$.

Change the subject to (i) s (ii) t.

5 In an electric circuit, if the voltage is V volts and the resistance is R ohms, then a current of I amperes will flow, where $I = \dfrac{V}{R}$.

Make R the subject, and calculate the resistance when the voltage is 240 volts and the current is 5 amperes.

6 If the length of the circumference of a circle of radius r cm is C cm, then $C = 2\pi r$. Change the subject to r. Calculate r when $C = 165$, taking $\frac{22}{7}$ as an approximation for π.

7 The area, A square metres, of a triangle having base b metres and height h metres is given by $A = \frac{1}{2}bh$.
Change the subject to h, and then calculate the height of a triangle having an area of 20 square metres and a base 8 metres long.

8 The perimeter, p feet, of a rectangle of length a feet and breadth b feet is given by $p = 2(a+b)$.
Change the subject to b, and hence calculate the breadth of a rectangle with perimeter 22 feet and length 7 feet.

9 The sum of the angles of an n-sided polygon is R right angles, where $R = 2n-4$.
Change the subject to n, and find how many sides a polygon has if its angle-sum is 10 right angles.
Can a polygon have an angle sum of 15 right angles?

10 The illumination, I units, of a lamp of candle-power C units at a distance d units is given by $I = \dfrac{C}{d^2}$.

Change the subject to (i) C (ii) d

11 From the statement of Pythagoras' theorem, $a^2 = b^2+c^2$, make c the subject. Hence calculate c when $a = 12$ and $b = 8$.

12 Write down the formula for the area, A square metres, of a square with side of length x metres.
Make x the subject of the formula, and hence calculate x when $A = 89{\cdot}6$.

13 The area, A square feet, of a circle of radius r feet is given by the formula $A = \pi r^2$.
Make r the subject of the formula, and calculate r when $A = 154$ and $\frac{22}{7}$ is taken as an approximation for π.

14 The volume of a cylinder, V cm^3, is given by $V = \pi r^2 h$, where r is the radius in cm, and h is the height in cm.

(i) Make h the subject.
(ii) Make r the subject. Calculate r when $V = 33$, $h = 14$, $\pi = \frac{22}{7}$ approximately.

6 Harder examples

Example 1.—A formula for the approximate length L units of a circular arc is $L = \frac{1}{3}(8h-c)$, where c units is the length of the chord of the arc and h units is the length of the chord of half the arc.

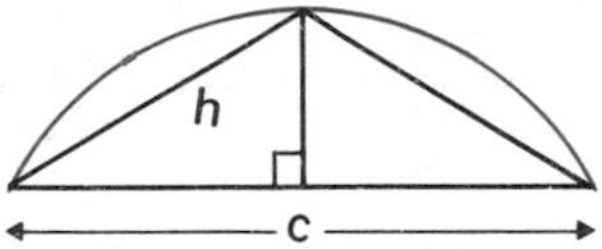

FIG. 8

Transform the formula (i.e. change the subject) to give h in terms of L and c.

$$L = \tfrac{1}{3}(8h-c)$$
$$\Leftrightarrow \quad 3L = 8h-c$$
$$\Leftrightarrow \quad 3L+c = 8h$$
$$\Leftrightarrow \quad h = \tfrac{1}{8}(3L+c)$$

Exercise 5

1 The relation between a temperature $F°$ Fahrenheit and $C°$ Centigrade is given by $C = \frac{5}{9}(F-32)$.

(*a*) Use this formula to give the Centigrade equivalents of (i) 98° F (ii) 212°F (iii) 65°F (iv) 0°F

(*b*) Change the subject of the formula to F, and hence find the Fahrenheit equivalent of (i) 100°C (ii) 27°C (iii) 0°C (iv) −40°C

2 The profit p per cent on a sale is given by $p = \dfrac{100(s-c)}{c}$, where s and c are the selling price and cost price respectively.

(i) Express s in terms of p and c.
(ii) Express c in terms of p and s.

3 The sum of a series like $4+7+10+13+\dots+22$ is given by the formula $S = \frac{1}{2}n(a+l)$, where S is the sum, n the number of terms that are added, a is the first term and l is the last term.

(i) Verify that the formula is correct for the series given.
(ii) Find S when $a = 12$, $l = 72$, $n = 31$.
(iii) Make l the subject of the formula. Hence find the last term in a series of 20 terms whose first term is 8 and whose sum is 250.

4 The area of a cylinder closed at both ends is given by $A = 2\pi r(r+h)$. Transform the formula to give h in terms of A and r.

5 Make m the subject of $\frac{a}{m} = \frac{m}{b}$ (m, a, and b represent positive numbers).

6 The following formulae are used in dynamics. Transform the formula in each case to the variable named:

(i) $v = u+ft; f$ (ii) $s = ut+\frac{1}{2}ft^2; u$

(iii) $s = \frac{u+v}{2}t; t$ (iv) $v^2 = u^2+2fs; s$

(v) $s = ut+\frac{1}{2}ft^2; f$ (vi) $v^2 = u^2+2fs; u$

7 The sum of a series like $32+16+8+4+\dots$ to an 'infinite number of terms' is given by the formula $S = \frac{a}{1-r}$, where S is the sum, a the first term, and r the ratio of any term to the preceding term.

(i) Use the formula to find the sum of the given series.
(ii) By adding the terms find the sum of 4 terms; also of 5 terms, 6, 7, 8, 9, and 10 terms.
(iii) Make r the subject of the formula. Hence calculate r when $S = 121\frac{1}{2}$, and $a = 81$.

8 A formula for an electric current is $I = \frac{nE}{R+nr}$. Make n the subject of this formula.
Find n when $I = 1{\cdot}2$, $R = 3{\cdot}0$, $r = 0{\cdot}5$, $E = 1{\cdot}5$.

Revision Exercises

Revision Exercise on Chapter 1

Further Sets

1 State whether each of the following is a well-defined set. If it is, say whether it is a finite, infinite, or empty set.

(*a*) Members of the staff of your school.
(*b*) Pupils in your school who are more than 21 years old.
(*c*) Even numbers.
(*d*) Geometrical figures which are symmetrical about one line.
(*e*) Prime numbers between 48 and 52.
(*f*) The bees in a hive.

2 List the set of printed capital letters of the alphabet which are not altered when they are turned upside down. List the sets which are not altered when they are turned over sideways. List the intersection of these two sets.

3 List the following sets, using dots when necessary:

(*a*) All natural numbers with two digits.
(*b*) All negative integers greater than -25.
(*c*) All numbers which have no prime factor other than 2.
(*d*) All numbers of the form $3n+2$, where $n \in N$.

4 In this question the universal set is the set of all triangles.

$A = \{\text{isosceles triangles}\}$
$B = \{\text{equilateral triangles}\}$
$C = \{\text{right-angled triangles}\}$
$D = \{\text{triangles all of whose angles are equal}\}$

(*a*) State which of the following statements are true, and which are false: $A \subset B$; $A = C$; $B = D$; $C \subset D$; $A \subset D$.

(*b*) If $a \in A$ is $a \in B$? If $d \in B$ is $d \in A$? If $b \in B$ is $b \in C$? If $c \in A$ *and* $c \in C$ give the sizes of the angles of c. If $f \in D$ what can you say about the sides of f?

5 In this question a special notation is used. The natural numbers up to and including 32 are each in turn divided by 4.
$\bar{2}$ is the set of such numbers which give a remainder 2 on division by 4, and similarly for $\bar{0}$, $\bar{1}$, $\bar{3}$.
List the sets $\bar{0}$, $\bar{1}$, $\bar{2}$, $\bar{3}$.

6 Which of the following are equal sets and which are subsets of others in the question?

P = {letters of the word MAD}
Q = {prime factors of 30}
R = {letters of the word MADMAN}
S = {prime factors of 90}
T = {letters of the word MADAM}
V = {prime numbers less than 10}

7 Write formulae using n, where $n \in N$, for each of the following:
(*a*) Even numbers. (*b*) Odd numbers. (*c*) Multiples of 4.
(*d*) Numbers which are 3 more than multiples of 5.
(*e*) Numbers which are 2 less than multiples of 10.
(*f*) Numbers which are 1 more than the squares of the natural numbers.
(*g*) Numbers which are 3 more than the cubes of the natural numbers.

8 In this question $E = \{1, 2, 3, 4, 5, 6, 7, 8, 9\}$ $B = \{2, 4, 6, 8\}$
$C = \{3, 6, 9\}$ $D = \{2, 3, 5, 7\}$

List and draw graphs of the sets given by:
(*a*) $\{x : x > 5, x \in E\}$ (*b*) $\{x : x \leqslant 6, x \in B\}$
(*c*) $\{x : 2 < x < 7, x \in E\}$ (*d*) $\{x : 2 \leqslant x \leqslant 7, x \in B\}$
(*e*) $\{x : 2x+1 = 9, x \in E\}$ (*f*) $\{x : 3x-5 = 13, x \in D\}$
(*g*) $\{(x, y) : x = 2y, x \in E, y \in E\}$
(*h*) $\{(x, y) : x+y = 9, x \in B, y \in D\}$
(*i*) $\{(x, y) : x+y = 9, x \in E, y \in E\}$

9 In this question the universal set is taken to be

$$E = \{a, b, c, d, e, f, g, h, k\}$$

and subsets are:

$A = \{a, b, c, e, g\}$ $B = \{a, c, f, g\}$ $C = \{b, d, f, h\}$
$D = \{c, f, k\}$ $F = \{b, d, e, f, h, k\}$ $K = \{b, e, h\}$

Write down the following sets:

(i) $A \cap E$ (ii) $A \cup E$ (iii) $B \cup D$
(iv) $K \cap F$ (v) $F \cap K$ (vi) $A \cup F'$
(vii) $A' \cap F$ (viii) $B' \cap F'$ (ix) $(B \cup C) \cup K$
(x) $B \cup (C \cap K)$ (xi) $(A \cap C) \cap F$ (xii) $A \cap (C \cap F)$
(xiii) $A \cap A'$ (xiv) $A \cup A'$ (xv) $A \cup D$
(xvi) $A' \cap D'$ (xvii) $(A \cup D)'$ (xviii) $C \cap F$
(xix) $C' \cup F'$ (xx) $(C \cap F)'$ (xxi) $B \cup (C \cap D)$
(xxii) $(B \cup C) \cap (B \cup D)$ (xxiii) $D \cap (B \cup K)$
(xxiv) $(D \cap B) \cup (D \cap K)$

10 Draw Venn diagrams to illustrate parts (i), (iii), (vi), and (viii) of question 9.

11 Answers to certain of the parts of question 9 are the same. In each case draw Venn diagrams to illustrate these equal answers and try to deduce probable rules from these Venn diagrams. For each rule you discover, make up another example from the given sets.

12 The universal set in this question is the set E consisting of all points in the shaded portions of Figure 1. Draw a diagram to show by shading each of the following sets:

(i) A' (ii) C' (iii) $A \cup D$
(iv) $A \cup C$ (v) $A' \cap C'$ (vi) $(A \cup D)'$
(vii) $C \cap D$ (viii) $A' \cup D'$ (ix) $A \cup B \cup D$
(x) $C' \cap D'$ (xi) $C \cap B'$ (xii) $(A \cap B) \cup D$

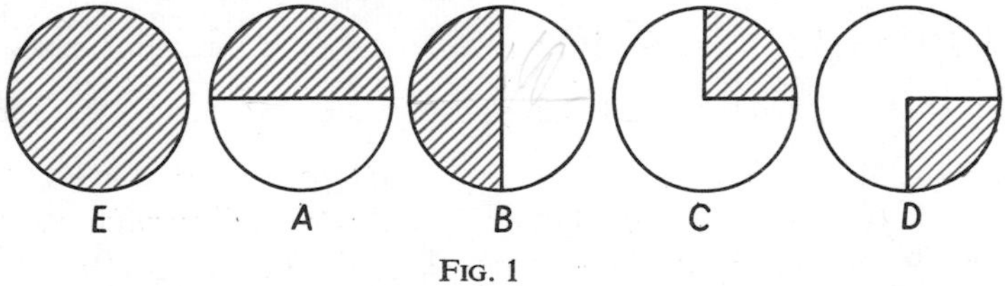

FIG. 1

If you shade $A \cup B$ you will see that this gives you D', so $A \cup B = D'$. Find the simplest way of expressing each of the following, using different colours where necessary.

(*a*) $C \cup D$ (*b*) $A' \cap B'$ (*c*) $C' \cup B$
(*d*) $C \cap D$ (*e*) $(A \cup B) \cap (C \cup D)$
(*f*) $(A' \cup B')' \cup C$ (*g*) $(C' \cup D')' \cap A$

13 In Figure 2, a is the set of points on the perimeter of a square, and c is the set of points on the circumference of a circle. Now if

$$p = a \cap c$$

you can see that $p = \{P, Q\}$, and $n(p) = 2$.

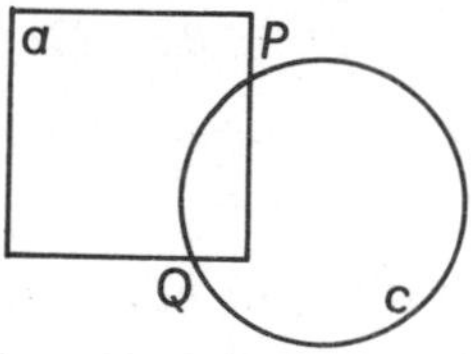

FIG. 2

Draw diagrams to show each of the following and list the set p (letter your diagrams) in each case:

(i) $n(p) = 0$ (ii) $n(p) = 1$ (iii) $n(p) = 3$
(iv) $n(p) = 4$ (v) $n(p) = 8$ (vi) $n(p) = 6$

14 Draw a diagram showing intersecting sets A and B. Shade set A in red and set B in blue. Explain how the diagram gives the formula

$$n(A \cup B) = n(A) + n(B) - n(A \cap B)$$

Draw diagrams to show how this formula holds:

(*a*) when $A \cap B = \emptyset$ (*b*) when $A \subset B$ (*c*) when $B \subset A$

15 P, Q, S, T, G, H, A, and B are sets.

(i) If $n(P) = 76$, $n(Q) = 24$ and $n(P \cap Q) = 10$, find $n(P \cup Q)$.
(ii) If $n(S) = 83$, $n(T) = 17$ and S and T are disjoint, find $n(S \cup T)$.
(iii) If $n(G) = 57$, $n(H) = 69$ and $G \subset H$, find $n(G \cup H)$.
(iv) If $n(A) = 192$, $n(B) = 76$ and $B \subset A$, find $n(A \cup B)$.

16 In this question, the universal set $E = \{a, b\}$. List *all* the subsets of E. How many are there? Two of the subsets are $\{a\}$ and $\{b\}$; call these A and B. The others are $\emptyset$ and E.

Copy and complete the following tables of union and intersection:

$\cup$	$\emptyset$	A	B	E
$\emptyset$				
A				
B				
E				

$\cap$	$\emptyset$	A	B	E
$\emptyset$				
A				
B				
E				

In what ways do these tables of union and intersection of sets resemble the tables you have drawn up for addition and multiplication of numbers?

17 To cater for the school party all of the 115 pupils brought at least one of these: sandwiches, cakes, or lemonade. 70 brought lemonade and 54 brought sandwiches. 19 brought lemonade and cakes only, and 22 brought lemonade and sandwiches only. 24 brought lemonade only, and 15 brought sandwiches only. How many brought cakes only?

Revision Exercise on Chapter 2

Linear Equations and Inequations in Two Variables

1 Telephone hire is £5·50 for a year and each local call costs 1p for the first six minutes. Using £c for the cost, and n for the number of local calls, per year, write an open sentence and draw its graph. Assume the telephone is used for local calls of less than six minutes only.

2 Draw the graphs of these equations where x and $y \in R$:
(i) $y = 2x-1$ (ii) $2x-y = 1$ (iii) $2x-y-1 = 0$

3 Make a table of pairs of replacements from W which make the open sentence $2x+y = 5$ a true sentence.

4 Make a table of pairs of replacements from Z which satisfy the equation $x+2y = 5$.

5 Draw the graph of $2x+4y = 5$ for $x, y \in R$. Do pairs of replacements from Z exist which satisfy this equation?

6 On a Cartesian diagram mark each of the points of the set

$$\{(x, y) : x < 5, y < 5, x, y \in W\}$$

according to the following procedure: Replace x and y in $x+y-5$ by the coordinates of the point, and if the result is positive write a +, if negative a −, if zero, a 0. Which part of the plane belongs to the solution set of $y > 5-x$?

7 Divide the coordinate plane into two half-planes by the line $y = x-1$. Label them $y > x-1$ and $y < x-1$. Check by considering the origin.

8 On one diagram show the solution set of each of the following ($x, y, \in R$):

(i) $x+y \geqslant 4$ (ii) $x-y \leqslant -4$ (iii) $x+y \leqslant -4$ (iv) $x-y \geqslant 4$

9 On one diagram show the solution set of each of the following ($x, y \in R$):

(i) $2x+y \geqslant 6$ (ii) $2x-y \leqslant -6$ (iii) $2x+y \leqslant -6$ (iv) $2x-y \geqslant 6$

10 On one diagram show the solution set of each of the following, using different colours for each ($x, y \in Z$):

(i) $x > 1$ (ii) $y > 1$ (iii) $x < -1$ (iv) $y < -1$

Revision Exercise on Chapter 3

Systems of Linear Equations and Inequations in Two Variables

1 Indicate on a coordinate plane, using rectangular axes with equal scales, the points whose coordinates satisfy all the inequations of each of the following systems:

(i) $x \geqslant 0,\ y \geqslant 0,\ x \leqslant 4,\ x+y \leqslant 6$
(ii) $y \geqslant 0,\ 3x+y \geqslant 7,\ 4x-3y \geqslant 0$
(iii) $x+y < 3,\ y > x-4,\ y \geqslant -2x$
(iv) $y > x+6,\ y-x < 2$

2 Obtain graphically the solution of the following system of equations:

$x-y+2 = 0, \quad 2x+y-2 = 0, \quad 3x-y+2 = 0$

3 The shaded region in each of the following graphs shows the solution set of an inequation. Write down an appropriate inequation for each case.

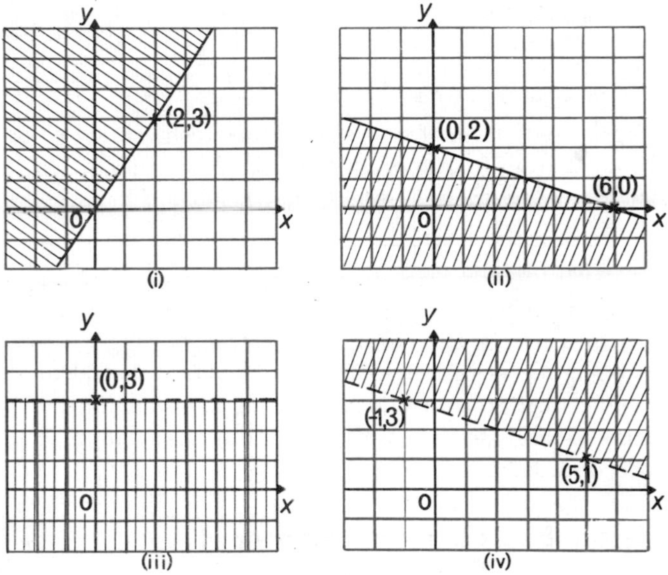

FIG. 3

4 On $\frac{1}{2}$-cm squared paper, plot the points A(2, 7), B(–2, 2) and C(2, 2). These points are the verticles of triangle ABC. Find a system of inequations whose solution set is shown by the interior of triangle ABC.

5 (i) If $y-x = 10$ and $y \leqslant 15$, what can you say about x?
(ii) If $x-y = 10$ and $x \geqslant 4$, what can you say about y?

6 Sketch the graphs of (i) $y = \frac{1}{2}x-3$, (ii) $x = y$, and (iii) $x+y = 6$. Indicate the region for which $y > \frac{1}{2}x-3$ and $x > y$ and $x+y < 6$.

7 Solve the following systems of equations:

(i) $\left.\begin{aligned} 2x+5y-14 &= 0 \\ 3x-2y+17 &= 0 \end{aligned}\right\}$ (ii) $\left.\begin{aligned} y &= 5-3x \\ 3x+4y+16 &= 0 \end{aligned}\right\}$

(iii) $\left.\begin{aligned} 3x &= 4y \\ \tfrac{1}{2}x+\tfrac{1}{3}y &= 1 \end{aligned}\right\}$ (iv) $\left.\begin{aligned} \frac{2x}{3}-\frac{y}{5} &= \frac{1}{15} \\ \tfrac{1}{4}x+\tfrac{1}{3}y &= \tfrac{5}{4} \end{aligned}\right\}$

8 The formula for finding the area of a circular ring is

$$A = \tfrac{22}{7}(R+r)(R-r)$$

If $A = 44$ and $R+r = 7$, find r.

9 Marks which range from 24 to 88 are to be scaled so as to range from 20 to 100. An original mark x becomes a scaled mark y where $y = ax+b$ and a and b are constants. Find a and b.

(i) What is the scaled mark for an original mark of 60?
(ii) What original mark gives the same scaled mark?

10 An engineering firm has a machine X which turns out 30 components per hour and has installed a new machine Y which turns out 40 components of the same kind per hour. If 600 of these components were produced on a particular day when the total number of hours of machine operation was 18, how many hours were X and Y each operated?

Revision Exercise on Chapter 4

Formulae

1 Solve for x:

(i) $a+bx = c$ (ii) $(p+q)x = r$ (iii) $\frac{ax}{b} = \frac{b}{a}$

(iv) $x-a = b-x$ (v) $cx = \frac{1}{a}+\frac{1}{b}$ (vi) $\frac{x}{a+b}-c = d$

(vii) $ax+b = c+x$ (viii) $\frac{x}{ab} = \frac{1}{bc}+\frac{1}{ca}$ (ix) $\frac{1}{x} = a$

(x) $\frac{1}{x} = \frac{1}{a}+\frac{1}{b}$ (xi) $1-\frac{1-x}{a} = b$ (xii) $a(x+b) = b(x+a)$

2 Find a formula for the nth term of each of these sequences:

(i) 0, 1, 2, 3, . . .

(ii) 2, 5, 10, 17, 26, 37, . . .

(iii) $\frac{1}{2}, \frac{1}{6}, \frac{1}{12}, \frac{1}{20}, \frac{1}{30}, \ldots$

Use your formulae to give the 12th term of each sequence.

3 Find a formula for $n(P \cap Q)$ in terms of $n(P)$, $n(Q)$ and $n(P \cup Q)$.

4 Make (i) l and (ii) n the subject of the formula $d = \dfrac{l-a}{n-1}$ and find a when $d = 3$, $n = 22$, and $l = 70$.

5 Make (i) S and (ii) l the subject of the formula $r = \dfrac{S-a}{S-l}$.

6 Use the relation 1 inch = 2·540 cm to express 3 feet in cm. From this relation obtain a suitable relation to express cm in feet.

7 Given that 50 litres = 11 gallons, obtain a relation to express gallons in terms of litres.

8 If the lengths of the parallel sides of a trapezium are a feet and b feet and if the distance between them is d feet, then the area A square feet of the figure is given by the formula $A = \frac{1}{2}(a+b)d$. Change the subject of this formula to d, and calculate the distance between the parallel sides of a trapezium having an area of 26 square feet and parallel sides of lengths 11 feet 6 inches and 4 feet 9 inches.

9 The volume V cm^3 of a cone is given by the formula $V = \frac{1}{3}\pi r^2 h$ where r cm is the radius of the base and h cm is the height.

(i) Make h the subject.

(ii) Make r the subject. Calculate r when $V = 200$ and $h = 8$.

10 The surface S cm^2 of a sphere of radius r cm is given by $S = 4\pi r^2$. Make r the subject and calculate r when $S = 10$.

11 The square of the number $n+\frac{1}{2}$ can be calculated using the formula $(n+\frac{1}{2})^2 = n(n+1)+\frac{1}{4}$.

Use this formula to calculate mentally

$(4\frac{1}{2})^2$; $(11\frac{1}{2})^2$; $(3{\cdot}5)^2$; $(9{\cdot}5)^2$; 75^2; 55^2

12 The square of the number $n+\frac{1}{4}$ can be calculated using the formula $(n+\frac{1}{4})^2 = n^2+\frac{1}{2}n+\frac{1}{16}$.

Use this formula to calculate mentally

$(2\frac{1}{4})^2$; $(6\frac{1}{4})^2$;

$(4{\cdot}25)^2$; $(3{\cdot}25)^2$ [Note $\frac{1}{16} = 0{\cdot}0625$]

625^2; 1225^2

General Revision Exercises (Books 1-4)

General Revision Exercise 1

Sets and Mathematical Sentences

1 State whether each of the following is true or false:

(i) $23 \in \{\text{prime factors of } 506\}$
(ii) $\{a, b, c, d\} = \{c, a, d, c, b, a\}$
(iii) $\emptyset = \{0\}$
(iv) If $A \cap B = A$, then $B \subset A$

2 (*a*) List the members of $\{x : x \text{ is a positive even integer}, x < 15\}$.
(*b*) Write $\{3, 6, 9, 12, 15\}$ in set-builder notation.
(*c*) List all the subsets of $\{p, q, r, s\}$.

3 Write out the following sets in full.
(*a*) $A = \{\text{prime factors of } 210\}$,
(*b*) $B = \{\text{odd numbers less than } 11\}$,
(*c*) $C = \{\text{common factors of 24 and 60}\}$.
If the universal set $E = \{1, 2, 3, \ldots, 12\}$, draw a Venn diagram to represent these sets.
Write down the sets $B \cap C$, $A \cap C$ and $A \cap B \cap C$.
If X is a set such that $X \cap B = \emptyset$ and $X \subset A$, find X if it is not empty.

4 x is a variable on $\{1, 2, 3\}$ and y is a variable on $\{4, 5\}$.
(i) Write down the set of all possible values of $x+y$.
(ii) What is the greatest possible value of $2x+3y$?
(iii) What is the least possible value of $y-x$?

5 (*a*) From the Venn diagrams, complete the statements (i), (ii), (iii) in Figure 1.
(*b*) Draw a Venn diagram to represent the following sets:
$E = \{\text{all pupils in school A}\}$,
$C = \{\text{all pupils under 17 years of age}\}$,
$B = \{\text{all pupils under 13 years of age}\}$.
Shade in the area which represents pupils between 13 and 17 years of age.

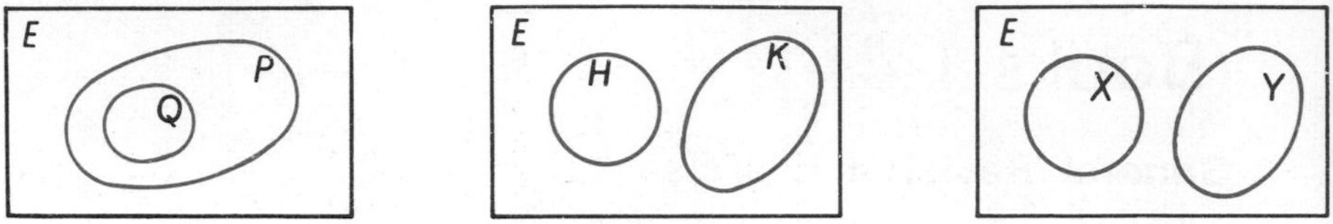

(i) $P \cap Q =$ (ii) $H \cap K =$ (iii) $X \cap E =$

FIG. 1

6 In a certain village, A = {people who like to play golf}, B = {people who like to play cricket}, C = {people who like to play football}. Describe, in words, the sets represented by the shaded areas.

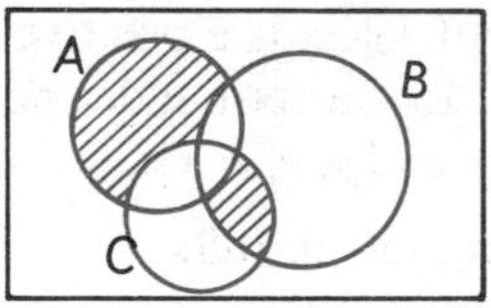

FIG. 2

7 $A = \{0, 1, 2, 5, 7, 9\}$, $B = \{2, 3, 4, 5\}$, and $C = \{3, 5, 8, 9\}$. List the sets:

(*a*) $B \cup C$ (*b*) $A \cap B$ (*c*) $A \cap C$ (*d*) $A \cap (B \cup C)$
(*e*) $(A \cap B) \cup (A \cap C)$

What law is illustrated by the answers to (*d*) and (*e*)?

8 P is the solution set of $5x-2 > 3(x+4)$, and Q is the solution set of $4x+3 < 7x-9$, where $x \in N$. List $P \cap Q$.

9 A survey was made of the TV programmes watched by people living in a street. Each family had only one TV set and the following figures were obtained:

114 people were questioned
62 people watched S.T.V.
70 people watched B.B.C.
26 people watched both S.T.V. and B.B.C.

Draw a Venn diagram to illustrate the survey.
How many people did not watch television?

10 There are 120 pupils in a Form III who take one or other or all of Mathematics, French, and Science. All the Science pupils take Mathematics. 108 take Mathematics, 106 take French, and 92 take Science. 88 take French and Science. Draw a Venn diagram to illustrate these statements, and find:

(i) how many take Mathematics but not French or Science;

(ii) how many take Mathematics and French but not Science.

11 $E = \{1, 2, 3, 4, 5, 6, 7, 8\}$, $A = \{1, 3, 5, 7\}$, $B = \{2, 4, 6, 8\}$, $C = \{3, 6\}$, and $D = \{3\}$.

Say whether each of the following statements is true or false:

(i) $A' = B$ (ii) $A \cup C = (B \cap D)'$ (iii) $(A \cap B) \cap C = C$

(iv) As replacements for X, four different sets satisfy $X \cup \{1, 2\} = \{1, 2\}$.

12 Given that $E = \{1, 2, 3, 4, 5, 6, 7, 8\}$, $A = \{1, 2, 3, 4\}$, and $B = \{2, 3, 4, 6, 7\}$, find

(i) A' (ii) $A \cap B'$ (iii) $A' \cap B'$ (iv) $(A \cup B)'$

Make a statement about your results in (iii) and (iv).

13 A and B are two sets.

Make shaded Venn diagrams to illustrate

(i) $A \cap B'$ and $A' \cap B$ (ii) $(A \cup B)'$ (iii) $A' \cap B'$ (iv) $(A \cap B)'$

(v) $A' \cup B'$

What do you notice about (ii) and (iii) and also (iv) and (v)?

14 The universal set is the set of real numbers.

$A = \{(x, y) : y = x+3\}$, $B = \{(x, y) : y \geqslant x+3\}$ and $C = \{(x, y) : 3 \leqslant y \leqslant 6\}$.

(i) Sketch the graph of A.

(ii) Show the graph of B by using vertical shading.

(iii) Indicate by horizontal shading the region representing C.

(iv) Identify the set $B \cap C$.

(v) Identify the set $A \cap C$.

General Revision Exercise 2

The Associative, Commutative, and Distributive Laws

1 Write in shortest form:

(i) $k+k+k$ (ii) $k \times k \times k$ (iii) $9 \times a \times 5$
(iv) $6 \times a \times 4 \times b$ (v) $3a^2 \times 12a$ (vi) $1{\cdot}5 \times a^2 \times b^3 \times 4$

2 Simplify the following:

(i) $-3+7+3$ (ii) $5-7-8$ (iii) $-1+3-9$
(iv) $-2a-3a$ (v) $-2a \times (-3a)$ (vi) $(-a)^3$
(vii) $-7m+20m-8m$ (viii) $-3p^2 \times (-4q^2)$
(ix) $-49a^3 \div 7a$ (x) $-18m^3n \div (-3m^2n^3)$
(xi) $35x^3 \div (-7x^2)$ (xii) $(-4a)^2+(4a)^2$
(xiii) $\sqrt{(25p^4)}$ (xiv) $9x^2y-8y+7x^2y-4y$
(xv) $-2a(3a-4b)$

3 Simplify:

(i) $3(5-2x)+2(7+x)-4(1-x)$ (ii) $\frac{1}{2}(x+3)-\frac{1}{3}(x-2)$
(iii) $10x-(-6x)+(-2x)$ (iv) $2x(x-3)-4x(x+1)$
(v) $\frac{1}{2}(2a+3)-\frac{1}{3}(3a-2)$ (vi) $\frac{1}{2}\cdot\frac{2}{3}\cdot\frac{3}{4}\cdots\frac{n}{(n+1)}$

4 If $a = 5+\sqrt{2}$ and $b = 5-\sqrt{2}$, find in their simplest forms the values of (i) $a+b$ (ii) $a-b$

5 Using short methods, calculate each of the following:

(i) $(13 \times 49)+(13 \times 51)$ (ii) $(7 \times 129)-(29 \times 7)$
(iii) 199×147 (iv) $\dfrac{(14 \times 11)+(14 \times 27)}{76}$

6 (*a*) Find the sum of $2a-3b$, $3b-4c$, and $4c-2a$.
(*b*) Subtract $5x-3y+7z$ from $7x+3y-5z$.
(*c*) If $A = 2p-5q$ and $B = 5p-2q$, find simple expressions for
(i) $A+B$ (ii) $A-B$

7 In each of the following state whether answer A, B, or C is correct:

	A	B	C
(i) If $xy = 0$, then	x must be zero	y must be zero	Either x or y must be zero
(ii) If a, b, c are integers, which answer must be false?	$(ab)c = a(bc)$	$a+b = b+a$	$a-b = b-a$
(iii) $12-(x-5)$ is equal to	$7-x$	$17+x$	$17-x$
(iv) If $a = b+5$ and $b = c-4$ then	$a < c$	$a > c$	$a = c$

8 If $A = 3(x+2y)$ and $B = 2(2x-3y)$ which of the following are correct?

(i) $A+B = 7x$ (ii) $A-B = 12y-x$
(iii) $B > A \Rightarrow x > y$ (iv) $2A-B = 0 \Rightarrow x : y = -1 : 3$

9 (*a*) Simplify $(x-2)-(x-3)$
(*b*) Is it true that $-(a-b) = (-a)+(-b)$?
(*c*) Simplify the following:
(i) $6+(-4)$ (ii) $-6+(-4)$ (iii) $6 \times (-4)$ (iv) $-6 \div (-4)$

10 Study the following series of six terms:

(*a*) $2+3+5+8+13+21 = 52$
(*b*) $1+7+8+15+23+38 = 92$

Note that the sums are 4×13 and 4×23.

(i) Choose any two positive whole numbers and form a series in the same way as the above. Verify that the sum of the six terms is *four* times the second last term.
(ii) Prove that this rule is always true for any two whole numbers a and b.

11 An operation $*$ on the set of integers is defined by
$a * b = ab+2(a+b)$, e.g. $2 * 3 = (2 \times 3)+2(2+3) = 6 + 10 = 16$.
Find the values of:

(i) $1 * 2$ (ii) $2 * 1$ (iii) $4 * 5$
(iv) $(1 * 2) * 3$ (v) $1 * (2 * 3)$ (vi) $-3 * 4$
(vii) $4 * (-3)$ (viii) $-4 * (-5)$ (ix) $(-4 * 3) * (-5)$

Is $a * (b * c) = (a * b) * c$ for *all* numbers?
What is the name of the above law?

12 Simplify:

(i) $\frac{3x}{5}+\frac{x}{5}$ (ii) $\frac{a}{4}-\frac{a}{3}$ (iii) $\frac{2x}{3}-\frac{3x}{5}$

(iv) $\frac{3a}{2}+\frac{4b}{3}$ (v) $\frac{2x}{3}-\frac{y}{5}+\frac{1}{2}$ (vi) $\frac{4}{3p}+\frac{3}{4p}$

(vii) $\frac{3}{x}-\frac{4}{y}$ (viii) $\frac{5}{4a}+\frac{3}{5b}$

General Revision Exercise 3

Evaluations

1 If $a = 3$, $b = 2$, and $c = 1$, find the values of:

(i) $2a+3b+4c$ (ii) $4a-3b+c$
(iii) $4(a+2b+3c)$ (iv) $a^2+b^2+c^2$
(v) $3a^2-2b^2+5c$ (vi) $a(b+c)+b(b-c)$

2 Find the value of each of the following when $x = 4$, $y = -3$, and $z = 2$:

(i) x^2-y^2 (ii) $x(y^2-z)$ (iii) $\frac{1}{4}(2x+3y)$
(iv) $\frac{1}{2}(3x-2z)$ (v) $\frac{1}{3}(-2y-z)$ (vi) $\frac{1}{2}(x^2+y^2)$
(vii) $\frac{1}{2}(y^2-z^2)$ (viii) $\frac{1}{4}(4x^2+3yz)$

3 If x is a variable on $\{1, 2\}$ and y is a variable on $\{4, 5\}$,

(i) write down the set of all possible values of $x+y$;
(ii) what is the greatest possible value of $2x+3y$?
(iii) what is the least possible value of $y-x$?

4 Using the formula $f = \frac{v-u}{t}$, calculate f when $u = -18$, $v = 54$, and $t = 5$.

5 (*a*) If $(3\frac{3}{4})^2-(2\frac{1}{4})^2 = n^2$, find n.
(*b*) The parabola $y = ax^2+b$ cuts the y-axis at the point $(0, -4)$ and also passes through the point $(3, 5)$. Find a and b.

6 (*a*) Calculate the value of a^2-3 where $a = 2\frac{1}{2}$.
(*b*) If $21^2-16^2 = 5k$, find k.
(*c*) Express $5{\cdot}5 \times 10^7 \times 4 \times 10^{-3}$ in standard form.

7 (i) Evaluate $\dfrac{2 \times 10^3 \times 9 \times 10^4}{6 \times 10^7}$

(ii) In this question $p * q$ means 'add three times p to q'. State which of the following is true (T) and which is false (F).

(*a*) $6 * 4 = 4 * 6$ (*b*) $3 * 2 = 4 * (-1)$

(*c*) $(2 * 1) * 1 = 22$ (*d*) $\frac{1}{3}p * q = \frac{1}{3}q * p$

8 State whether each of the following open sentences is true or false when the variables are replaced by the numbers given:

(i) $3a^2 - 1 = 2$, when $a = -1$

(ii) $x^2 + 3x + 4 = 0$, when $x = -2$

(iii) $\dfrac{a+b}{a-b} = 0$, when $a = -2$ and $b = 2$

(iv) $x^2 - xy + y^2 = 37$ when $x = 4$ and $y = -3$.

9 (*a*) If $s = ut + \frac{1}{2}ft^2$, find s when $u = 48$, $t = \frac{3}{4}$, and $f = -32$.

(*b*) In the formula $s = \frac{1}{2}(u+v)t$, find v when $s = 180$, $u = 21$, and $t = 10$.

10 Show that $2{,}345 = (2 \times 10^3) + (3 \times 10^2) + (4 \times 10) + 5$

$= 2t^3 + 3t^2 + 4t + 5$

where t is written for 10.

(*a*) Write in a similar manner, using t for 10,

273 6,842 8,051

(*b*) What numbers are represented by the following expressions?

$3t^2 + 4$ $5t^3 + 2t^2 + 7$ $8t^3 - 4t^2 + 5t - 3$

11 (*a*) Evaluate $\dfrac{\sqrt{(a^2 - b^2)}}{c}$ exactly when $a = 3{\cdot}9$, $b = 3{\cdot}6$, and $c = 4{\cdot}5$.

(*b*) If the nth term of a sequence is $2n^2 - n + 1$, write out the first four terms.

By examining the difference between successive terms, can you write down the next two terms without using the formula?

12 Here is a multiplication called matrix multiplication:

$$(2 \quad 4 \quad 5) \times \begin{pmatrix} 3 \\ 1 \\ 6 \end{pmatrix} = (2\times 3) + (4\times 1) + (5\times 6) = 40$$

Work out the following in the same way:

(i) $(3 \quad -2 \quad 7) \times \begin{pmatrix} -1 \\ 3 \\ 4 \end{pmatrix}$ (ii) $(3 \quad -1 \quad -2) \times \begin{pmatrix} a \\ 2a \\ 3a \end{pmatrix}$

General Revision Exercise 4

Equations and Inequations

1 x is a variable on the set of real numbers. Find the solution set of each of the following equations:

(i) $3x-7 = 26$ (ii) $\frac{5x}{4} = 22$

(iii) $3x-5 = 7x+23$ (iv) $\frac{1}{2}x-5 = 6-\frac{3}{5}x$

(v) $3(2x+7) = 2(5x-3)$ (vi) $\frac{1}{5}(x-4) = \frac{1}{3}(2x-1)$

2 If x is a variable on Z, which of the following are true and which are false?

(i) $x = 14 \Rightarrow x^2 = 196$ (ii) $x^2 = 196 \Rightarrow x = 14$

(iii) $x = 14 \Leftrightarrow x^2 = 196$ (iv) $5x+6 = 1 \Rightarrow x = -1$

(v) $x = -1 \Rightarrow 5x+6 = 1$ (vi) $5x+6 = 1 \Leftrightarrow x = -1$

3 (i) If x and y are variables on the set $\{1, 2, 3, 5\}$, what values of x and y make $x+2y = 8$ a true statement?

(ii) Does $x = 3$ satisfy the equation $3x-5 = \frac{1}{2}(2x+1)$?

4 The universal set is the set of whole numbers. Find the solution sets of the following:

(i) $a+6 > 7$ (ii) $2y-3 > 4$

(iii) $2p-4+3p > 3$ (iv) $5 < 3x < 44-x$

(v) $9+x > 2x > x+3$ (vi) $3y+7 < 1$

5 In a certain number system $\Box$, $\triangle$, and $\odot$ are the only number symbols. The operation of addition is defined by the table shown.

$+$	$\odot$	$\Box$	$\triangle$
$\odot$	$\odot$	$\Box$	$\triangle$
$\Box$	$\Box$	$\triangle$	$\odot$
$\triangle$	$\triangle$	$\odot$	$\Box$

(i) Is addition a commutative operation? Give a reason for your answer.

(ii) What is the identity element?

(iii) Solve the following equations:

(*a*) $x+\Box = \odot$ (*b*) $x-\Box = \triangle$ (*c*) $\triangle - x = \Box$ (*d*) $\Box - x = \odot$

6 (*a*) If x is a variable on the set of natural numbers, solve

(i) $3x-7 = 8$ (ii) $4 = 19-5x$ (iii) $7+2x = 10$

(*b*) If x is a variable on the set of rational numbers, solve

(i) $7+2x = 10$ (ii) $x+2x+3x = 15$ (iii) $\frac{7}{3}x = 21$

7 a and b are variables on the set $\{1, 2, 3, 4\}$ and $a * b$ is the remainder obtained when a and b are multiplied together and divided by 5, e.g. $3 * 4 = 2$.
Copy and complete the table.

$*$	1	2	3	4
1				
2		4		
3				2
4		3		

(*a*) Is $*$ a commutative operation? Why?
(*b*) Is $(2 * 3) * 4 = 2 * (3 * 4)$?
(*c*) Use your table to find the solution set for

(i) $3 * x = 2$ (ii) $y * 2 = 4$

8 x is a variable on the set of real numbers. Find the solution sets of the following:

(i) $\frac{1}{2}x-\frac{1}{3}x = 5$ (ii) $\frac{2}{3}x+\frac{5}{6}x+2 = 20$
(iii) $5x+7 \geqslant 2x-11$ (iv) $\frac{3}{2}x-2 < 2x+\frac{1}{4}$

9 The universal set is the set of real numbers. Solve each of the following inequations and find the intersection of the solution sets of each pair. Illustrate graphically.

(i) $2x+3 \leqslant 9$ and $3x-2 \geqslant 1$
(ii) $3x+4 \geqslant 16-3x$ and $x-\frac{1}{3} > \frac{1}{6}x-2$
(iii) $2x+5 \leqslant 7$ and $\frac{1}{2}(3x+1) > x+1$

10 The variables are on the set of real numbers. Find the solution sets of the following:

(i) $\frac{1}{2}(x-2)+\frac{1}{3}(x-1) = 2$ (ii) $\frac{1}{4}(x+3)-\frac{1}{3}(2x-3) = 2\frac{1}{6}$

(iii) $\frac{1}{2}x-\frac{1}{3}(x-4) > \frac{1}{6}(5x-7)$ (iv) $16-\frac{1}{3}x \leqslant 2x-5$

(v) $0{\cdot}6(1-0{\cdot}8x) = 0{\cdot}5-0{\cdot}4(2-1{\cdot}8x)$

11 Represent on a number line the solution set of each of the following where $x \in R$:

(i) $-2(-x) = -6$ (ii) $-2 \leqslant x+1 \leqslant 3$ (iii) $5x^2+1 = 21$

12 If the universe is the set of real numbers, say whether each statement is true (T) or false (F):

(i) The solution set of $x+3 = 3$ is $\emptyset$.

(ii) If $x > 3$ and $x+y > 7$, then $y > 4$.

(iii) $x(x-2) = 1 \Rightarrow x = 1$ or $x = 3$.

13 Solve (i) $\left.\begin{aligned} 2x+3y &= 5 \\ \tfrac{1}{5}(2x-1)-\tfrac{1}{3}y &= -2 \end{aligned}\right\}$ (ii) $\left.\begin{aligned} 3x-2y &= 14 \\ 2x+5y-3 &= 0 \end{aligned}\right\}$

(iii) $\left.\begin{aligned} 2x-3y &= 6 \\ 3x+2y &= 6 \end{aligned}\right\}$

General Revision Exercise 5
Formulae and Problems

1 A rectangle is $(2x-5)$ cm long and 3 cm broad.

(i) If its perimeter is 22 cm, find x.

(ii) If its area is 60 cm^2, find x.

2 ABCD is a square. AB = 10 cm. PQRS is a rectangle with PQ = 8 cm and PS = 6 cm (Figure 3).

(i) If the area of the circle is x cm^2, write down two inequations in x.

(ii) Deduce that $1{\cdot}92 < \pi < 4$.

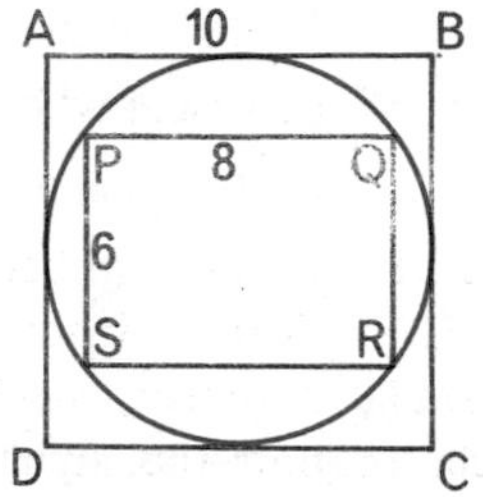

FIG. 3

3 A man's living expenses are £x per day, where x lies between 1 and 2, and he started a week with £15. If he had £y left at the end of the week, write down two inequations involving y.

4 (i) Write down a formula in terms of x for the total area A in^2 of the cross.

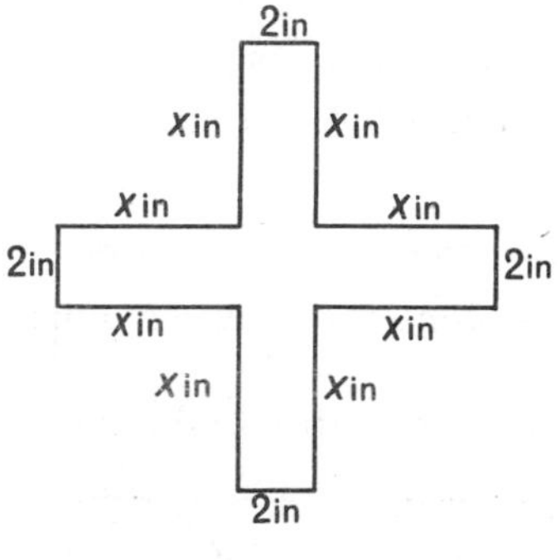

FIG. 4

(ii) Copy and complete the table

x	1	2	3	4	5
A					

(iii) Draw a graph to show the relation between A and x, where x is a variable on the set of positive real numbers.

5 Write down the next whole number larger than n, assuming that n is a whole number.

(i) To find S, the sum of the first n whole numbers, i.e.

$$1+2+3+\ldots+n$$

multiply n by the next whole number larger than n and divide the answer by 2. Express these instructions as a formula. Test to see if your formula is correct when $n = 1, 2, 5$.

(ii) Use your formula to find the sum of the first 1,000 whole numbers.

6 Write each of the following in the form of an inequation:

(i) The average of a and b is less than 49.

(ii) When 5 is subtracted from twice x, the result is greater than 2.

(iii) The square of the sum of y and 3 is less than or equal to 42.

7 A cylinder of diameter d units just fits into a cube of edge d units. Find a formula which gives the difference D cubic units between the volume of the cube and the volume of the cylinder.

8 The sides of a triangle are $9n$, $12n$, and $15n$ units of length. Show that the triangle is right-angled. Find the length of the sides when $n = 10$.

9 (i) The sum of two consecutive numbers is 113. Find them.

(ii) The sum of two consecutive even numbers is 190. What are the numbers?

(iii) The sum of two consecutive odd numbers is 1,728. Find them.

FIG. 5

10 The rectangle and the circle shown in Figure 5 are equal in area and they are between the same parallels.
Find a relation between x and r.

11 Figure 6 shows a bowl of depth d cm, which is part of a hollow sphere of radius r cm. The volume, V cm^3, of the bowl is given by the formula $V = \frac{1}{3}\pi d^2(3r - d)$.

(i) Make r the subject of the formula.

(ii) Evaluate r when $V = 17\frac{1}{3}\pi$ and $d = 2$ and hence calculate the radius of the circular top of the bowl.

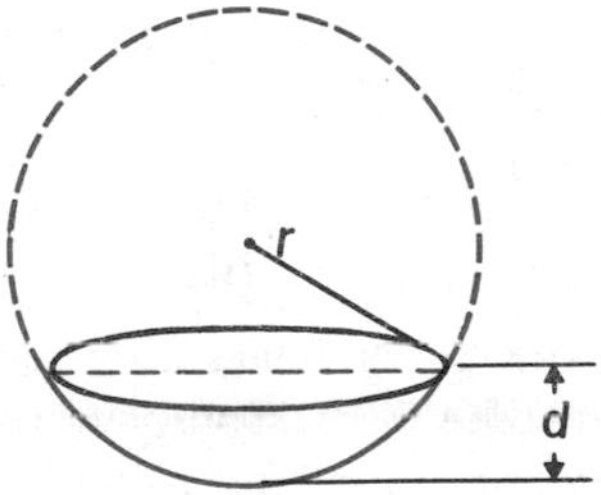

FIG. 6

12 The formula for the total surface area of a cylinder is $A = 2\pi r(r+h)$. Change the subject of the formula to h, then calculate h when $A = 154$ and $r = 3\frac{1}{2}$, taking $\frac{22}{7}$ as an approximation for π.

13 A school has £150 to spend on slide rules and calculating machines. Slide rules cost £1·25 each and machines cost £45 each. How many of each can be purchased? Illustrate your answer by a sketch.

14 If an electrical circuit has two resistors connected as shown in Figure 7 then the total resistance R in the circuit is related to the

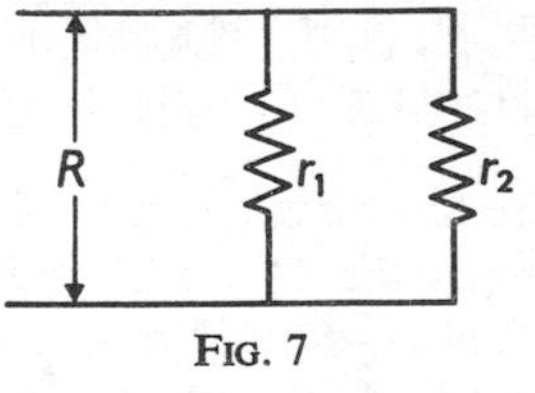

FIG. 7

resistances r_1 and r_2 by the formula $\frac{1}{R} = \frac{1}{r_1} + \frac{1}{r_2}$. Solve for R in terms of r_1 and r_2 and hence calculate R when $r_1 = 30$ and $r_2 = 45$.

15 A train travels x miles at m_1 miles per hour and then y miles at m_2 miles per hour. Find as a single fraction (i) the time taken in hours, and (ii) the average speed for the whole journey.

General Revision Exercise 6
Relations, Mappings, and Graphs

1 If $F = \{\frac{1}{2}, \frac{3}{4}, \frac{5}{8}, \frac{7}{16}\}$, illustrate the relation 'is less than' on the set F by means of an 'arrow' diagram.

2 (*a*) $A = \{(x, y) : y = x+3\}$.

(i) If $(5, y) \in A$, what is y? (ii) If $(x, -5) \in A$, what is x?

(*b*) On $\frac{1}{2}$-cm squared paper, mark the points A(6, 8), B(−6, 6), C(−9, −5) and D(8, −7). Complete the quadrilateral ABCD. By shading the appropriate part of the quadrilateral, show the set of points (x, y) such that (x, y) lies inside the quadrilateral and $x < -2$.

3 $A = \{2, 3, 6, 8, 9\}$. Show by means of a 'balloon' diagram the relation on A defined by the open sentence x divides y.

(i) This relation is $\{(x, y) : x \in A, y \in A$ and x divides $y\}$. Write the relation as a set of ordered pairs.

(ii) Write out in full $\{(x, y) : x \in A, y \in A$ and x is a multiple of $y\}$.

4 In this question, say whether each statement is true or false:

$A = \{1, 5, 9\}, \quad B = \{a, b, c, d\}$.

(i) If $R = \{(1, a), (5, c), (9, a)\}$, R is a mapping of A into B.

(ii) $\{(1, a), (5, b), (9, c), (1, d)\}$ is another mapping.

(iii) There are 64 mappings of A into B.

5 A, B, C, D, and E are five Sixth Form pupils. A and B study Maths, A, C, and D study Science, B and E study History, A, D, and E study German and E also studies French. Arrange the set of pupils and the set of subjects in a list and show the relation 'studies' from the set of pupils to the set of subjects.

(i) Who is studying both Maths and History?

(ii) Who is studying Science but not Maths?

(iii) Who is studying only one subject?
(iv) Who is studying German but not History?

6 $S = \{1, 2, 3, 4, 5\}$.

	1	2	3	4	5
1	(1,1)	(1,2)			
2					
3					
4					
5					

(i) Find the set of all ordered pairs (x, y) such that $x \in S$ and $y \in S$ by completing the table shown.
(ii) Hence show that a pair of numbers whose sum is even can be chosen in 13 ways.
(iii) What is the probability that the sum is 6?
(iv) What is the probability that the sum is 6 or more?

7 (i) Show, using an 'arrow' diagram, the relation 'is less than or equal to' from the set of numbers $A = \{1, 2, 3\}$ into the set of numbers $B = \{1, 3, 5\}$.
(ii) Explain why this relation is not a mapping.
(iii) List all the ordered pairs of the inverse of the relation given in (i), i.e. the relation 'is greater than or equal to'.

8 (i) Make a mapping diagram in the form of a table for the mapping $x \rightarrow -4+1\frac{1}{2}x$, x a variable on set $S = \{0, 2, 3, 4, 5, 6\}$.
(ii) Draw a graph of the mapping, using scale $\frac{1}{2}$ inch to 1 unit.
(iii) If x is a variable on the set T of non-negative real numbers, how is the graph of $x \rightarrow -4+1\frac{1}{2}x$ obtained from (ii)?
(iv) Give a set definition of the region above the graph of (iii).

9 If x and y are variables on the set of real numbers, indicate on a sketch graph the set of points whose coordinates satisfy

$$x > 0 \quad \text{and} \quad x-2 < y < x+2$$

10 (i) Which of the lines in Figure 8 has equation $y = x+1$?
(ii) What are the coordinates of (*a*) C (*b*) E?
(iii) Give a set definition of the region
(*a*) to the right of PQ,
(*b*) which is shaded.

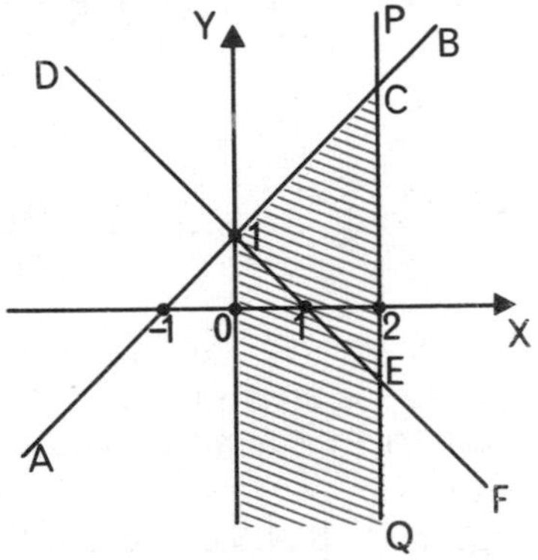

FIG. 8

11 In this question, x and y are variables on the set of real numbers.
(i) Draw the graphs of $A = \{(x, y) : y > x\}$ and $B = \{(x, y) : y > 2-x\}$
(ii) Shade the region which represents $A \cap B$.

12 (i) Make a mapping diagram in the form of a table for the mapping $x \to x^2-4$, x a variable on the set

$$A = \{-3, -2, -1, 0, 1, 2, 3\}.$$

(ii) Draw a graph of the mapping, using a scale of 1 cm to 1 unit.
(iii) Deduce the graph of the mapping $x \to x^2-4$, where x is a variable on R.

Geometry

CHAPTER 1 Specification of Triangles

1 General discussion

1 (*a*) If you wanted to draw a square, and you knew that the length of one side was to be 3 inches, could you draw it?

(*b*) Could you draw it if, instead, you were told that one diagonal was to be 4 inches long?

2 If the teacher wanted every pupil to make a 'Meccano' rhombus of the same shape and size, and said that each side was to be 3 inches long, would you expect all the rhombuses to be congruent? What other information do you think you should be given? (There are several good answers.)

In this Section we are going to examine just what information you must be given in order to be able to construct a required triangle.

3 Suppose the teacher has a cardboard triangle ABC. You are to consider how to make an accurate drawing of it. You can ask the teacher for the length of any side you like, and the size of any angle you like; but you can ask for only one piece of information at a time, and you are to stop asking when you have enough information to finish the drawing satisfactorily.

Sometimes the teacher may be awkward and refuse to give you what you want, perhaps offering you something else. Take it if it will do, refuse it if it will not.

The object is to decide *how much* information is necessary; and whether, for example, if three items suffice, any three items will do.

This question is often important in practice: for example a map-maker wants to get an accurate map without the expense of making unnecessary measurements; an engineer building a structure involving triangles must specify clearly the shape and size of the triangles; a draughtsman in his drawings must include enough information about lengths and angles to enable the fitter to make the component the drawing depicts, and since every straight-sided shape can be built up from triangles, if we master the art of 'specifying' the data required for a triangle, we shall be able to cope with all other figures.

Some of the questions you will have discussed, in connection with the cardboard triangle, are:

(*a*) Can you succeed without including at least one *side* in your set?
(*b*) If you know all three sides, do you need any information about angles?
(*c*) If you know two of the angles, do you need to ask for the size of the third?
(*d*) If you know the lengths of two sides, and ask for the size of an angle, does it matter which angle you ask for?
(*e*) If you know the length of one side, and the angle at one end of it, and the teacher says you are to ask for the length of another side, does it matter which side you ask for? Does it always matter?
(*f*) If you are trying to manage with one side and two angles, does it matter which two angles you choose?

We now look at some of the possibilities, in turn, from a different point of view. It is not necessary to work all three of the Sections 2, 3, and 4 before going on to the drawing exercises of Section 6.

2 One side, two angles

1 Here in Figure 1 is a novel type of coordinate system which you can copy and complete or trace.

A and B are two fixed points. Lines are drawn outwards from A and B at 10° intervals from 0° to 180°, going round anti-clockwise from A and clockwise from B.

Draw a careful diagram. Take A and B near the middle of a page, 3 inches apart. Draw the lines from A with a sharp pencil and those from B with a fine pen or coloured pencil. Extend each line to the edge of the

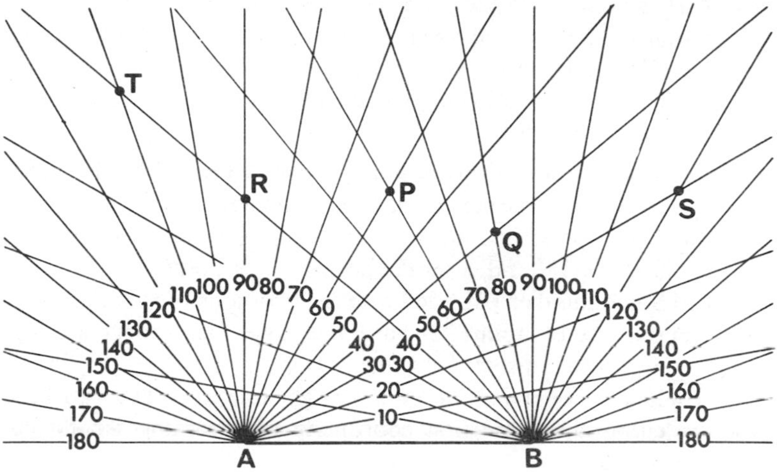

FIG. 1

page, and label each line you draw with the appropriate number: 0, 10, 20, . . . 180.

The ordered number pair [20, 50] refers to the point of intersection of the line from A marked 20, and the line from B marked 50. We use square brackets to remind ourselves that these are not the 'usual' coordinates.

(*a*) State the 'coordinates' of each of the points P, Q, R, S, T.

(*b*) Make up (or obtain from a neighbour) a list of coordinate pairs in which each number is a multiple of ten not exceeding 180. Try to find the corresponding points. Some of the points will be easily found on the page. For some coordinate pairs, the point will be 'off the page'; for some (e.g. [90, 120], [120, 150], etc.) there will be no possible corresponding point.

(*c*) If there is a point corresponding to [a, b], what can we say about a and b? If there is no point corresponding to [p, q], what can we say about p and q?

(*d*) Mark on your page, as accurately as you can, the points [26, 52], [26, 102], [106, 52]. Why would you expect to be able to mark some points more accurately than others?

(*e*) Mark a point at random on the page (but not a point of intersection of lines already drawn). Estimate its coordinates; then give its coordinates as accurately as you possibly can.

(*f*) Think about the following statements; then state whether each one is true or false:

(i) The position of every point above AB could be described by means of a pair of these coordinates.

(ii) Every possible number pair $[x, y]$ when $0 < x < 180$ and $0 < y < 180$ indicates the position of a point.

(iii) Some number pairs indicate the positions of two points.

(iv) If a set of points all have the same first coordinate, the points lie on a straight line.

(v) If a set of points lie on a straight line, they must all have either the same first coordinate or the same second coordinate.

(vi) All the points of the set $\{[x, y]: x = y \neq 0\}$ lie on a certain straight line.

(vii) If the points A and B had been a different distance apart, it would have made no difference to the coordinates of the points on the page.

2 Suppose we want to draw a triangle, using AB as base, and with angles of 70° and 50° at the ends of the base. One possible position of the third vertex P is [70, 50]. State the coordinates of a second possible position Q (on the same side of AB).

If we had a tile in the shape of triangle PAB, could it be moved to occupy exactly the position of triangle QAB (or QBA)? Would you have to turn the tile over or not?

Note.—If we know the length of one side of a triangle, and the size of the angles at the ends of this side, then the triangle is completely specified or determined. All triangles with these measurements will be congruent.

3 Three sides

1 Figure 2 shows another kind of coordinate system for indicating position on the plane of the paper.

Mark two points, Y and Z, 5 cm apart near the middle of the page

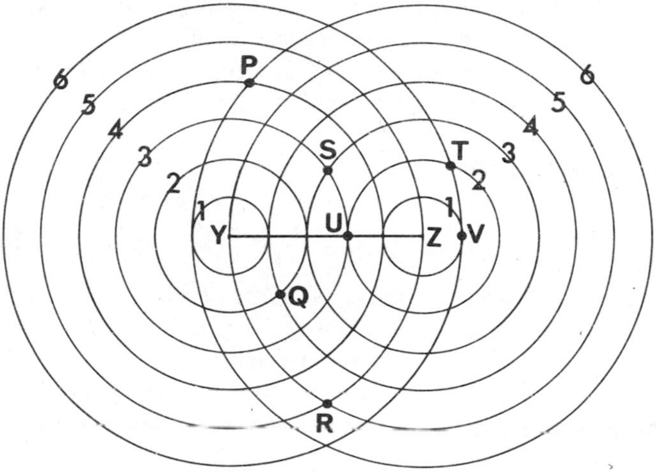

FIG. 2

using pencil. Draw circles with centre Y and radii 1 cm, 2 cm, . . . 6 cm. Label each with the appropriate number 1, 2, . . . 6. Do the same for a set of circles, centre Z, using a fine pen or coloured pencil.

This time the ordered number pair [5, 3] refers to a point on the 5-cm circle round Y and on the 3-cm circle round Z. How many points [5, 3] are there?

A quadrilateral has as its vertices these two points, and the points Y and Z, what kind of quadrilateral is it?

If we want to distinguish between the two points [5, 3], we shall write $[5, 3]_a$ and $[5, 3]_b$, where *a* and *b* indicate 'above' and 'below' the line YZ.

What can you say about the points $[4, 3]_a$ and $[4, 3]_b$; and about $[2, 6]_a$ and $[2, 6]_b$? Write down some more couples of coordinate pairs which are related to one another in the same way.

2 (*a*) State the coordinates of each of the points P, Q, R, S, T, U, V, Y (Figure 2).

(*b*) Make up (or obtain from a neighbour) a list of coordinate pairs in which each number is a natural number. Try to find the corresponding points. Some of the points will be easily found;

for some coordinate pairs, the point will be 'off the page'; for some, there will be no possible corresponding point.

(*c*) Remember that the length of YZ is 5 cm. Check that if $p+q = 5$ or $p+5 = q$, there is just one point $[p, q]$. State another possible relation between p and q for such a point. Where are all such points to be found?

(*d*) Check that if $p+q < 5$, there is no point $[p, q]$. State two other inequations involving p, q, and 5, each of which would ensure that there is no point $[p, q]$.

(*e*) Choose a number of points of intersection of circles in your diagram. For each such point $[r, s]$ verify that $r+s > 5$ and $r+5 > s$, and state a third true inequation.

(*f*) Mark on your page, as accurately as possible, points [5·3, 2·1] and [4·6, 3·3].

(*g*) Mark a point at random on the page (but not a point of intersection of the circles drawn). Estimate its coordinates; then give its coordinates as accurately as possible.

(*h*) Mark the two points whose coordinates are [6, 4]; call them A and B. What kind of figure is YAZB? What can you say about the triangles AYZ and BYZ?

Mark also the two points whose coordinates are [4, 6]; call them C and D. If you made a tracing of the whole diagram, and turned it over and put it down with the positions of Y and Z interchanged, where would you find the tracing-paper triangles CYZ and DYZ? What can you say about the four triangles AYZ, BYZ, CYZ, DYZ?

Make a list of all the angles in these triangles that are equal to one another.

Notes

(i) *The sum of the lengths of any two sides of a triangle is greater than the length of the third side.* (*This is called* '*the triangle inequality*'.)

(ii) *If two triangles are drawn such that the sides of one are equal to the sides of the other, the triangles are congruent.* (*Equal angles will be found opposite equal sides.*)

4 Two sides and included angle

1 Still more coordinates! See Figure 3.

Mark L and M near the middle of the page, 5·5 cm apart. With centre L, and radii 1, 2, 3, . . . 6 cm, draw a series of circles. Label them 1, 2, 3, . . . 6 as before.

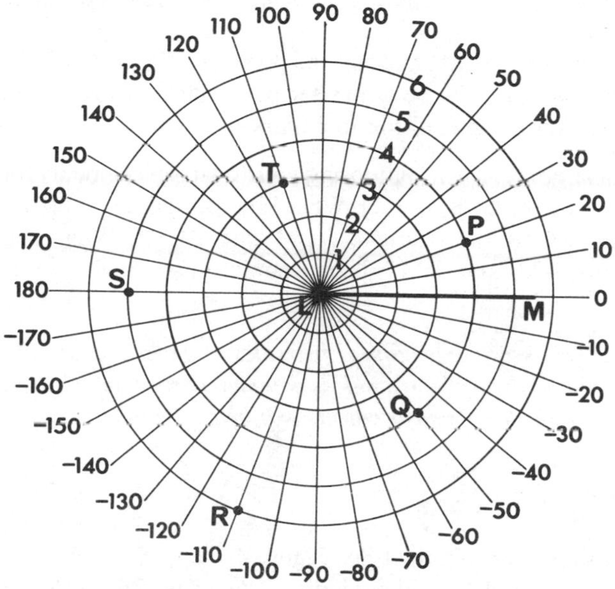

FIG. 3

Draw from L a series of straight lines to the edge of the page at 10° intervals like those from A in Figure 1. Label them 0, 10, 20, . . . 180.

Draw from L another series of straight lines, starting with one at 10° to LM but below LM; then at 20°, 30°, etc. Label them −10, −20, −30, . . . −180.

One line carries two labels: we shall call it 180.

The ordered number pair [5, 50] refers to the point of intersection of the circle marked 5 and the line marked 50. (You may remember doing some exercises with Polar Coordinates in Book 2.) State the coordinates of the points P, Q, R, S, T, M.

2 If you were told about a point [*a*, *b*] for which $-180 < b \leqslant 180$, would you be able to mark (or imagine) the position of this point for every possible replacement for *a* and *b*?

(First choose a certain replacement for *a*, say $a = 5$, and think of a variety of replacements for *b*. Then take some other replacements for *a*.)

Would there be any coordinate pairs [*a*, *b*] which would refer to two different positions?

If you were to mark, at random, the position of a point on the plane of the paper, would there be a number pair which corresponded to it? Would there ever be several number pairs?

3 Mark some point A[*h*, *k*], choosing your own replacements for *h* and *k*. Mark also the point B[*h*, −*k*]. What kind of figure is ALBM? What can you say about the triangles ALM and BLM? What about the line-segments AM and BM? Name some equal angles in the two triangles.

Note.—If we know the lengths of two sides of a triangle, and the size of the angle between them, the triangle is completely specified or determined. All triangles with these measurements will be congruent.

5 Ambiguous case

1 One last set of coordinates! See Figure 4.

Mark points L and M in the middle of the page, 5 cm apart. From L draw lines as in Figure 1, labelling them from 0 to 180 and 0 to −180. This time draw circles with centre M and radii 0, 1, 2, . . . 6 cm. Label them accordingly.

The ordered number pair [6, 40] this time refers to a point of intersection of the circle round M marked 6 and the line from L marked 40. State the coordinates of the points P, Q, R, S, T, U, M in Figure 4.

2 Will it be possible to find a point in the plane of the paper whose position cannot be described by means of coordinates in this way?

3 How many points can you find with coordinates [6, 40]? How many

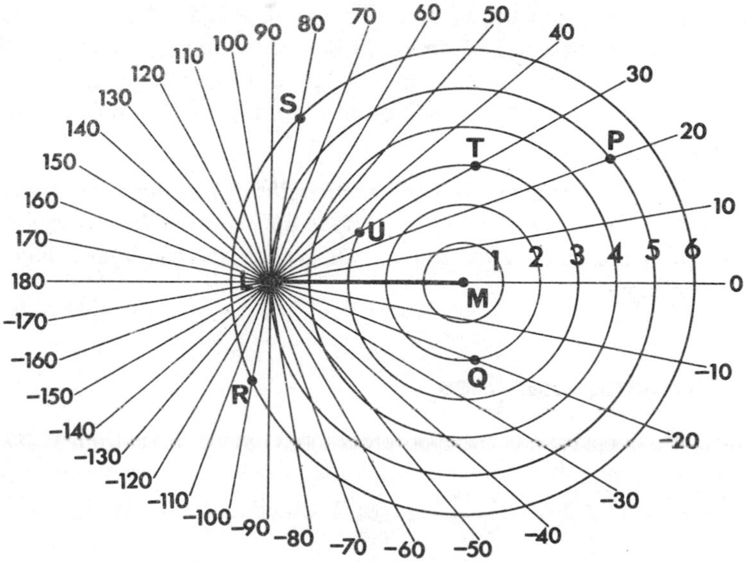

FIG. 4

with coordinates [5, 40], [4, 40], [3, 40], [2, 40]? How large must the first coordinate be to ensure that [x, 40] refers to just one point?

4 How large must the first coordinate be to ensure that each of the following coordinate pairs refers to just one point? (i) [p, 60] (ii) [q, 20] (iii) [r, 110].

5 Does [r, 110] indicate a point for all possible values of r? What about $r = 5$? What can you say about r if [r, 110] indicates a point of the plane? What can you say about s if [s, 90] indicates a point of the plane?

6 Does [t, 30] indicate a point or points of the plane if $t = 1$? Is this true if $t = 2$, $t = 3$, $t = 4$? Try to estimate from your diagram the least value of t such that [t, 30] indicates a point of the plane. (Use compasses if you like.)

7 (*a*) Call the points indicated by [4, 50] A_1, and A_2. Name two triangles which have one side of length 5 cm, one 4 cm, and one angle of 50°. Are these triangles congruent?

(*b*) In the figure of (*a*), what kind of triangle is MA_1A_2? Why must either triangle A_1LM or A_2LM be obtuse-angled? Why must the other be acute-angled? If you cut out triangles congruent to A_1LM and A_2LM, could you fit them together to make another isosceles triangle?

Note.—If for a triangle we know the lengths of two sides, and the size of an angle not *between them, we may be able to draw two triangles of quite different shapes. The data do not always specify or determine a unique triangle.*

6 Drawing exercises

Before you begin each of these problems, you have two decisions to take. (*a*) Is it possible to draw one (or more than one) triangle using the given information (the 'data')? (*b*) If so, how should you set about it—what should you draw first, what next, etc.?

The first thing to do is to draw a rough sketch, and mark on it the length of each side and the size of each angle that is known. 'Rough' does not mean 'untidy'. The sketch should not be too small. It should give you a fairly good idea of what the finished drawing will look like; for example, an angle of 128° should certainly look 'obtuse' in the sketch.

While you are drawing the sketch, you will be thinking about the next stage. For example, if you find that you have been given two sides and the angle between them, you know it will be possible to draw just one triangle. In this case it will not matter whether you draw first an angle of the required size, or a line segment of one or other of the required lengths. If you are given the lengths of three sides, you will need a pair of compasses. But you will need to check that the greatest of the three lengths is not too great in relation to the others!

1 Each of the following sets of data is to be considered as an attempt to 'specify' a triangle ABC.

For each, draw a rough sketch, and decide whether it would be possible to draw such a triangle; and if so, whether all the triangles that might be drawn would be congruent; or whether there could be two possible shapes; or whether there is no limit to the number of different shapes or sizes that could be obtained. (All the lengths are in centimetres, all the angles in degrees. The last three (x, xi, xii) are rather hard.)

	BC	CA	AB	CAB	ABC	BCA	Number of possibilities
(i)				50	60	70	
(ii)	6·0			60	70	80	
(iii)	6·0				70	80	
(iv)	6·0			60	70		
(v)	6·0	6·5	7·0				
(vi)	6·0	6·5	20·5				
(vii)	6·0	6·5	7·0		150		
(viii)	6·0		7·0		150		
(ix)	6·0		7·0		40		
(x)	6·0		7·0	40			
(xi)	6·0		7·0			40	
(xii)	6·0		7·0	140			

2 Make accurate drawings of some of the triangles specified in question 1. (The teacher may tell you which parts of the question to do.) Measure the remaining sides and angles of each triangle you draw.

3 From a ship sailing due east a rock is sighted 43° north of east. After the ship sails 3·5 km the rock is sighted 35° north of west. Can

you make an exact drawing of this situation in your exercise book? If you wish to find the distances of the ship from the rock in the two given positions, what must you do? Find from your diagram how far the ship was from the rock when it passed nearest to it.

4 Three towns A, B, C are situated as follows: B is 10 miles due north of A; C is $7\frac{1}{2}$ miles from B and 5 miles from A. You are to make a scale drawing showing the positions of the three towns. What else will you need to be told before you can even make a reliable rough sketch?

If C is over to your left as you travel from B to A, make a good drawing and complete the following sentence:

'From A the bearing of C is . . . degrees . . . of north;
from B the bearing of C is . . . degrees . . . of south.'

5 Two straight roads cross at an angle of 60°. Starting from the intersection, one car travels along one road at 45 feet per second and another travels along the other road at 60 feet per second. Find from a scale drawing how far apart they are after 10 seconds. Read the question again carefully and find another correct answer besides the one you have found. Try to rephrase the question so that there is only one correct answer.

6 The base BC of a quadrilateral ABCD measures 5·0 cm. Angle ABC measures 78° and angle DCB measures 85°. BA measures 4·2 cm and DC 3·6 cm. Draw the quadrilateral. What is the sum of its angles?

7 In a quadrilateral PQRS, PQ measures 4·4 cm, QR 4·0 cm, RS 2·8 cm, SP 3·6 cm. The diagonal QS measures 4·8 cm. Draw the quadrilateral. What is the sum of its angles?

Summary

A triangle is uniquely specified by giving:

(i) one side and two angles
(ii) three sides
(iii) two sides and the 'included' angle.

A triangle is not necessarily uniquely specified if two sides and the non-included angle are given.

The triangle inequality. The sum of the lengths of two sides is greater than the length of the third side.

CHAPTER 2 Similar Figures

1 Scale drawings and scale models

Figure 1 illustrates some of the ways in which people use 'scale drawings' to convey on paper information about the shapes and sizes of things that interest them. In cases in which precise information is wanted, the diagrams are not mere pictures, but are two-dimensional drawings, drawn accurately to scale.

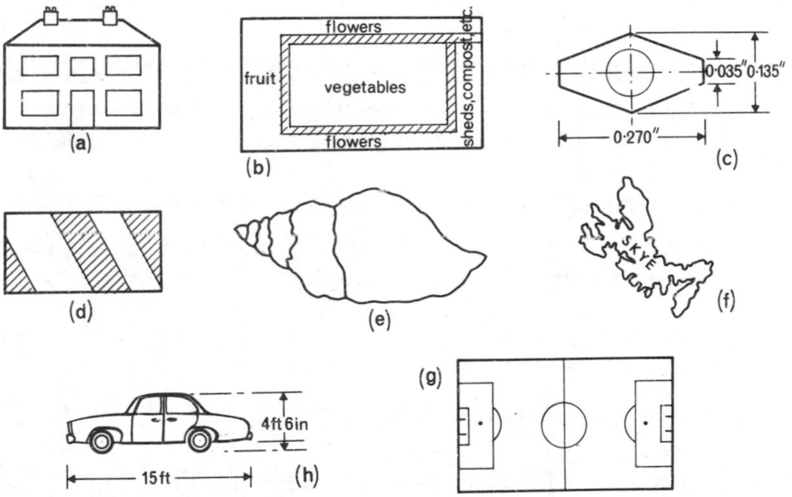

FIG. 1

1 In Figure 1*a*, which shows the 'front elevation' of a house on a scale of '$\frac{1}{16}$ inch represents 3 feet', use your ruler to find the length of the house frontage, the height to the eaves, and the length of the roof ridge.

2 Figure 1*b* represents the plan of a rectangular garden. What fraction of the total area is under vegetables? If the scale is '1 inch represents 20

yards', what area is under vegetables, and what is the length of the diagonal of the garden?

3 Figure 1*e* is a drawing of a whelk, with its linear dimensions reduced to $\frac{3}{4}$ life size. What is the true length of the whelk, from end to end?

4 Figure 1*g* shows the plan of a football pitch. Suppose the plan of a pitch is in the form of a rectangle measuring 8·0 inches by 6·0 inches.

(i) If you know that the length of a pitch must be between 100 and 130 yards, what can you say about the breadth of the pitch to which the plan refers?

(ii) The penalty spot is 12 yards from the goal line. If this distance on the plan is 0·90 inch, what is the distance, on the plan, from the penalty spot to one of the nearer corner flags? And what will this distance be on the actual pitch?

* * * * * * *

Worked Example.—In a photograph of the front of a house, the height of the door is 1·25 inches and the height of the house is 4·75 inches. The actual height of the door is 7 feet 6 inches. Calculate the height of the house.

Let the height of the house be h feet. We can proceed in two ways.

(i) Compare 'height of house' with 'height of door' in the actual house, and again in the photograph.

This gives $$\frac{h}{7\frac{1}{2}} = \frac{4{\cdot}75}{1{\cdot}25} \qquad \text{(A)}$$

$$\Leftrightarrow \frac{h}{7\frac{1}{2}} = \frac{19}{5} \text{ leading to } h = 28\tfrac{1}{2}.$$

(ii) Compare the height of the actual house with the height of the house in the photograph; and similarly for the height of the door.

This gives $$\frac{12h}{4{\cdot}75} = \frac{12 \times 7\frac{1}{2}}{1{\cdot}25} \qquad \text{(B)}$$

$$\Leftrightarrow \frac{h}{4{\cdot}75} = \frac{7\frac{1}{2}}{1{\cdot}25} \text{ and again } h = 28\tfrac{1}{2}.$$

The height of the house is about $28\frac{1}{2}$ feet.

Notice that at line (A) we stated that the ratio of the two interesting heights, both in the real house and in the photograph, was 19 : 5; and at line (B) we stated that the ratio of a length in the real house to the corresponding length in the photograph was $12 \times 7\frac{1}{2} : 1{\cdot}25 = 72 : 1$. In problems like this, we can choose to compare *different* lengths in the *same* figure, or *corresponding* lengths in the *different* figures.

The proportion can be set out as follows:

	Actual	In photograph
Height of house	*h* feet	4·75 inches
Height of door	$7\frac{1}{2}$ feet	1·25 inches

$$\text{Then } \frac{h}{7\frac{1}{2}} = \frac{4{\cdot}75}{1{\cdot}25} \quad \text{and also} \quad \frac{h}{4{\cdot}75} = \frac{7\frac{1}{2}}{1{\cdot}25}$$

Note.—Examples of this kind give good practice in the use of the slide rule, which may also be used to solve the problems involving similar triangles and equal ratios to be found in Section 4.

* * * * * * *

5 A light aircraft has an overall length of 40 feet and a wing span of 50 feet. A scale model is to be made with a wing span of $7\frac{1}{2}$ inches. Calculate the overall length of the model using each of the two methods described above.

6 The motor-car of Figure 1*h* has overall length 15 feet and overall height $4\frac{1}{2}$ feet. A scale model of the car is $3\frac{3}{4}$ inches long. Calculate the height of the scale model.

Find also the 'reduction ratio', i.e. the ratio in which all dimensions are reduced.

If the distance between front and back axles is 9 feet and the track width is 4 feet, find the corresponding dimensions for the model. If the overall width of the model is $1\frac{1}{4}$ inches, what is the width of the car?

2 Similar figures

In Section 1 we took it for granted that a scale drawing (or model) had the same *shape* as the original, but was of a different size; each length measured in the drawing would be the corresponding original length, increased or reduced in a certain ratio.

We now look more closely at the idea of 'same shape'.

1 Which, if any, of the following could be regarded as being of 'the same shape' as a football pitch measuring 100 yards by 60 yards?

(*a*) A square 8 metres by 8 metres.
(*b*) A rectangle 5 inches by 3 inches.
(*c*) A parallelogram with sides of 10 cm and 6 cm and one angle 85°.

2 Which, if any, of the following could be regarded as being of 'the same shape' as a boxing 'ring' 5 yards square?

(*a*) A carpet measuring 6 yards by 6 yards.
(*b*) A page of your textbook.
(*c*) A square field of side 280 metres.
(*d*) One of the smallest squares on a sheet of graph paper.
(*e*) The shape formed by bolting together in pairs, at their ends, four 3-inch 'Meccano' strips.

Note.—In geometry we use the word 'similar' with a special meaning. We want to restrict its use to the kind of resemblance between figures which is illustrated by a photograph of an object and an enlargement of the same photograph.

As far as *figures with straight sides* are concerned, we shall say they *are similar if*

(i) *pairs of corresponding sides are in the same ratio*, and
(ii) *corresponding angles are equal.*

3 In Figure 2, which of the quadrilaterals (*b*), (*c*), (*d*), (*e*) might be, and which cannot be, similar to (*a*)? (You will have to reach a clear idea about the meaning of the phrases 'corresponding sides' and 'corresponding angles'.)

4 A rectangular photographic mount measures 20 cm by 30 cm. A photograph placed centrally on the mount leaves a uniform margin 2·5 cm all round. Is the rectangle of the photograph *similar* to the rectangle of the mount?

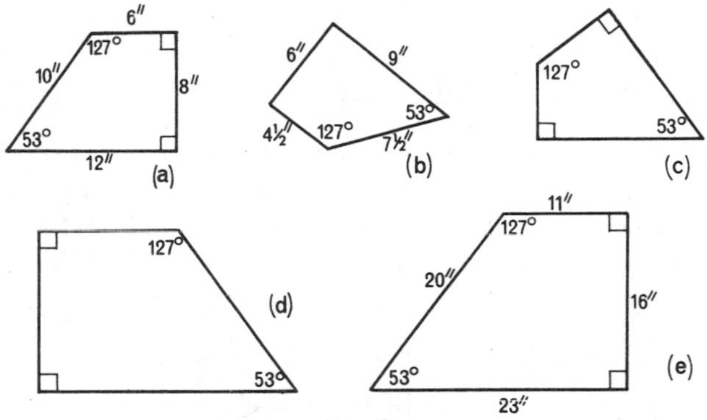

FIG. 2

5 A photograph is mounted on a card which is 20 cm wide and 30 cm tall, so as to leave a margin 3 cm wide at the top and at each side. If the photograph is *similar* to the mount, what width of margin will be left at the foot of the mount?

6 In a football pitch, certain dimensions are fixed by law, e.g. the centre circle is 10 yards in diameter, the penalty area extends to 18 yards from the goal line, the goals are 8 yards wide.

Two pitches are fully marked out; one measures 120 yards by 80 yards, the other 105 yards by 70 yards.

(i) Are the rectangular playing areas similar?

(ii) Are the figures consisting of all the marking lines similar?

7 (*a*) ABC and DEF are two equilateral triangles. Must they be regarded as similar?

(*b*) What about two regular hexagons?

8 Figure 1*d* represents a pattern for a rug. If in the scale drawing the bands of colour make angles of 62° with the edges, what angles will they make in the actual rug?

9 In the car illustrated in Figure 1*h* the steering column is set at 68° to the vertical. What will be the size of the corresponding angle in the scale model?

3 Enlarging and reducing

1 Figure 3 illustrates an embroidery stitch known as 'wave stitch filling'. Copy it on squared paper, some members of the class using half-centimetre squares and others 2-mm squares. There will then be in the room, diagrams of the pattern in three different sizes. Will they all be 'similar'?

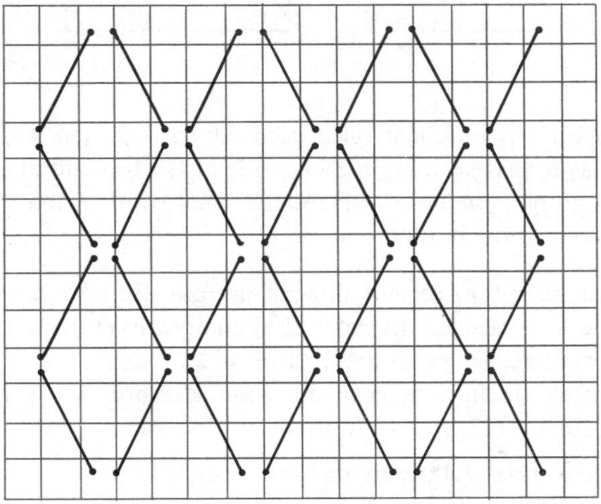

FIG. 3

2 Figure 4 bears some resemblance to a face in profile. Copy it on half-centimetre squared paper, inserting an eye and an ear in reasonable positions. On the same sheet of paper make a drawing which is similar to your first one, and magnified either two-fold or three-fold.

Draw it again half-size.

3 Figure 5*a* is a crude 'full face' drawing. In Figure 5*b* all 'widths' have been doubled, 'heights' remaining unchanged. Copy and complete 5*b*. Copy and complete 5*c* and 5*d*, which are variations on the same drawing.

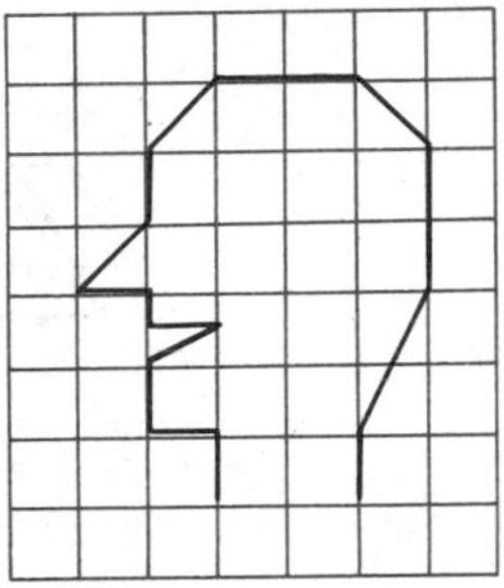

FIG. 4

Make a fifth drawing in some ways like and in some ways unlike each of the first four. Are any of your five drawings similar?

Relate what you see on your squared paper to what you sometimes see on the television screen.

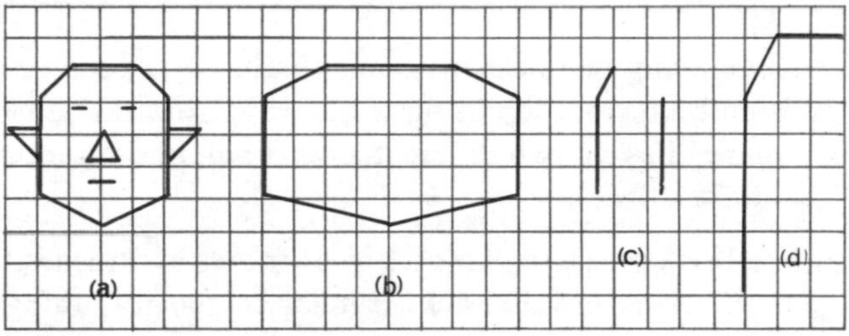

FIG. 5

4 Draw a shape on squared paper using straight or curved lines or both.

Make a drawing which is similar to the original, enlarged or reduced in some ratio you choose.

5 The square grid drawn in red in Figure 6*a* may be regarded as a net, like a fishing net or the net of hessian used in rug-making. Such a net can be pulled out of shape, as in Figure 6*b*, to give a grid of rhombuses; the sides of the rhombuses are equal in length to the sides of the square.

The two L shapes shaded in (*a*) are intended to be 'similar'. The second one has been drawn incorrectly; how would you correct it? They appear distorted in (*b*).

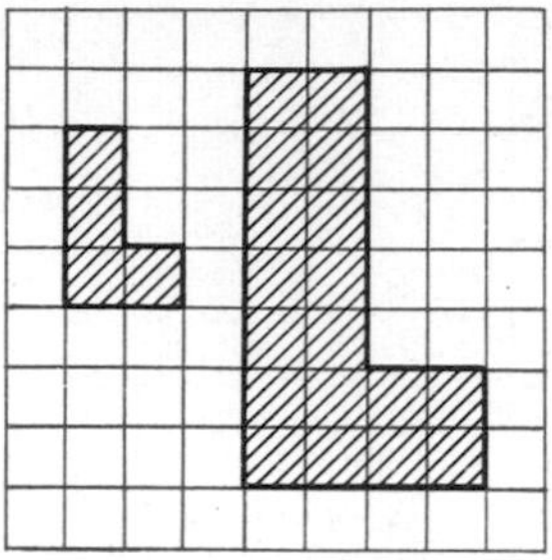

FIG. 6*a*

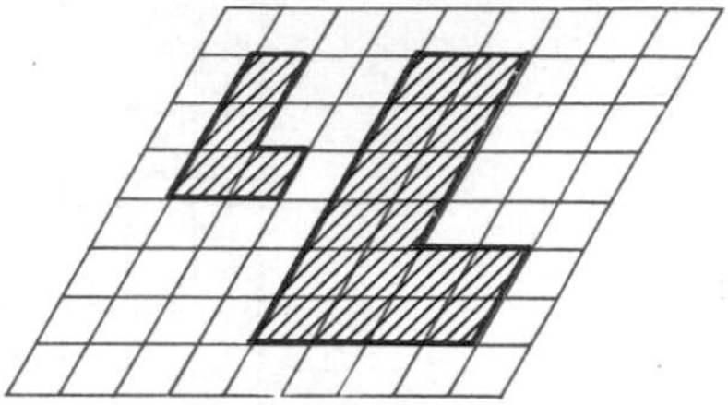

FIG. 6*b*

Of the four L shapes, including the corrected one:

(i) which have corresponding angles equal?
(ii) which have corresponding sides in proportion (or equal)?
(iii) which are similar?

Find the ratios of corresponding sides, perimeters, and areas of the two Ls in (*b*).

It is worth noticing that both in (*a*) and (*b*) the two Ls can be regarded as having been built up, each in the same way, from the same number (four) of square 'tiles' of two different sizes (in *a*), and rhombus tiles of two different sizes (in *b*).

6 A standard brick measures 9 inches by $4\frac{1}{2}$ inches by 3 inches. A child's building set contains model bricks, similar to the real thing, and $1\frac{1}{2}$ inches long. What are the other dimensions?

Find the ratios of:

(i) the total lengths of the edges of the two bricks;
(ii) the total surface areas of the two bricks;
(iii) the volumes of the two bricks.
(iv) Repeat for two similar bricks whose dimensions are a, b, c units and $2a$, $2b$, $2c$ units respectively.
(v) Repeat, with dimensions a, b, c and ma, mb, and mc units.

7 A pyramid on a square base measuring 12 metres by 12 metres is 8 metres high. The triangular faces are isosceles.

(i) Check that the altitude of each isosceles triangle is 10 metres and that the slant edges of the pyramid measure about 11·5 metres.

(ii) By means of a scale drawing find the angles of the isosceles triangles. (Later you will learn how to do this without making an accurate drawing.)

(iii) What makes you think that the angles in the real pyramid are the same size as those in your drawing? (We shall look into this further in the next Section.)

4 Similar triangles

1 Figure 7 shows a 'tiling' of scalene triangles. Two of the sets of parallel lines are identified by numerals and letters, so that each point of intersection can be identified by an ordered pair like *e*5, *g*3, etc.

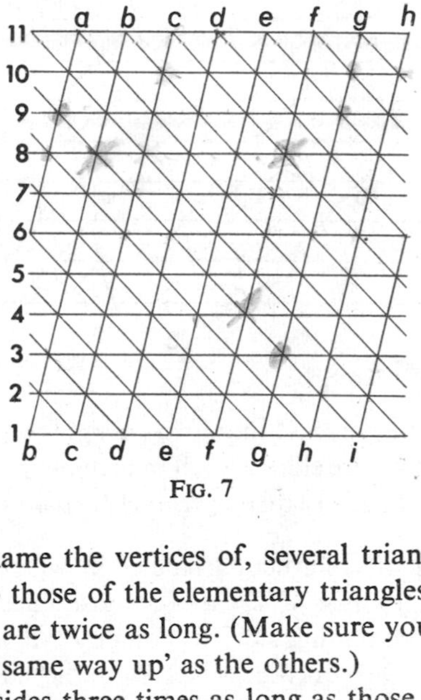

FIG. 7

(i) Find, and name the vertices of, several triangles whose angles are equal to those of the elementary triangles of the tiling and whose sides are twice as long. (Make sure you find some which are not 'the same way up' as the others.)

(ii) Repeat for sides three times as long as those of the elementary triangles.

(iii) Repeat for sides five times as long.

(iv) Name two triangles which are equiangular to one another, and whose side lengths are in the ratio 2 : 3.

(v) Repeat for the ratio 5:2.

(vi) Repeat for the ratio 3:1.

Note.—The triangular tiling contains numerous triangles that are similar to one another.

2 Figure 8 shows a number of hexagons that are equiangular to one another ('corresponding' angles being equal). Are any of these hexagons similar, i.e. are their corresponding sides in proportion?

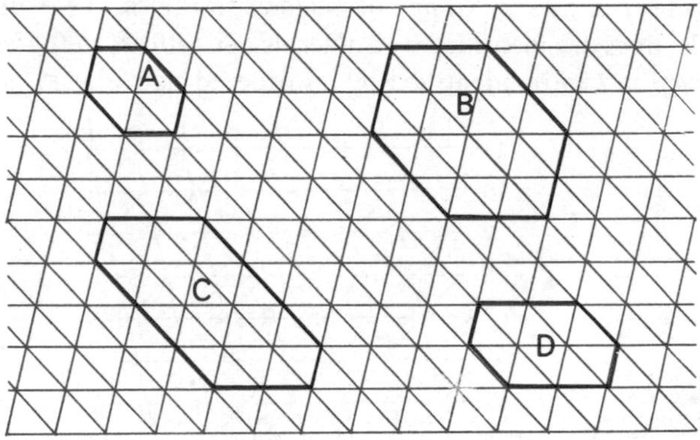

FIG. 8

See if you can find, in the tiling, two *triangles* which are equiangular to one another and whose sides are *not* in proportion. Could a triangular tiling be drawn in which two such triangles *could* be found?

3 Imagine a tiling of congruent triangles in which there is a triangle PQR, and another triangle XYZ each of whose sides is the same fraction (say $\frac{5}{3}$) of the corresponding side of triangle PQR.

Suppose we set out to draw a triangle with the side lengths of triangle PQR increased in the ratio 5:3. Can we say anything about the sizes of its angles? We argue as follows:

We know that the triangle we would get would have its sides equal to those of triangle XYZ. Now we found in Chapter 1 that a triangle is completely determined by the lengths of its sides. So the triangle we draw cannot be other than congruent to the triangle XYZ, and so it must be equiangular to triangle PQR.

Note.—For us to be able to assert that two figures are similar, we must be able to assert that (i) *they are equiangular to one another* (*corresponding angles being equal*) *and* (ii) *their corresponding sides are in proportion.*

But *triangles are very special figures.* We have seen in questions 2 and 3 that

if *two triangles are equiangular to one another*
it follows that *corresponding sides are in proportion; and*
if *two triangles have corresponding sides in proportion,*
it follows that *they are equiangular to one another* (*corresponding angles being equal*).

If in triangles ABC and XYZ we know that angle A = angle X, angle B = angle Y, and angle C = angle Z, *it follows that*

$$\frac{BC}{YZ} = \frac{CA}{ZX} = \frac{AB}{XY}$$

i.e. the ratios of the lengths of corresponding sides are equal.

If in triangles ABC and XYZ we know that $\frac{BC}{YZ} = \frac{CA}{ZX} = \frac{AB}{XY}$, *it follows that* angle A = angle X, angle B = angle Y, angle C = angle Z.

Note.—Question 2, *and question* 5 *of Section* 3, *stress the fact that it is* only *in the case of triangles that* one *of the conditions for similarity entails the other.*

4 Examine the pairs of triangles shown in Figure 9 on page 112. State whether each diagram contains enough information to enable you to say whether the triangles are similar or not. If the triangles are similar, state the sizes of any unmarked sides or angles.

5 Triangles whose side lengths are 7, 24, and 25 inches and 20, 21, and 29 centimetres are known to be right-angled. Are they equiangular to one another? Which of the following side lengths specify triangles which are similar to one or other of the given triangles?

(*a*) $10\frac{1}{2}$, 36, $37\frac{1}{2}$ feet
(*b*) 40, 42, 59 units
(*c*) 5, $5\frac{1}{4}$, $7\frac{1}{4}$ inches
(*d*) 77, 264, 285 centimetres

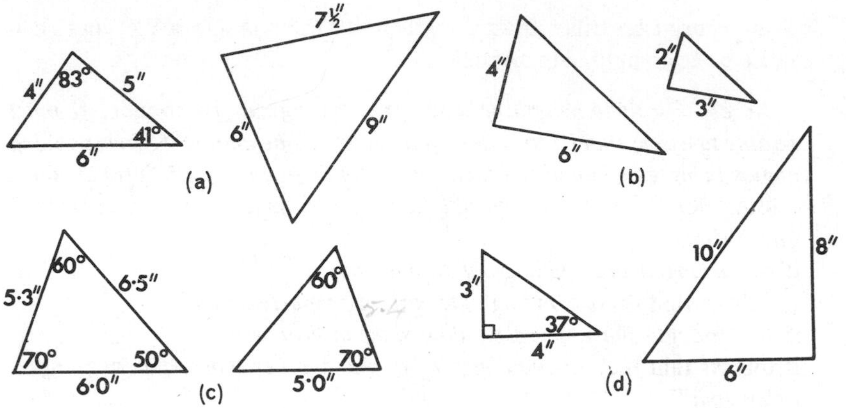

FIG. 9

6 Figure 10 shows a side view of a camp stool. Prove that the triangles are equiangular to one another. How far apart are the feet of the stool?

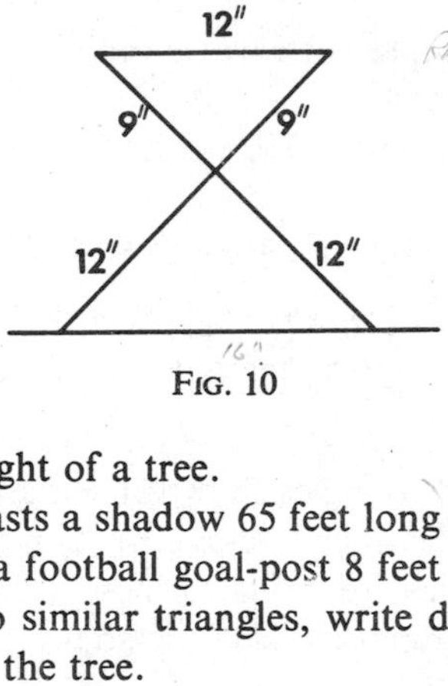

FIG. 10

7 How to find the height of a tree.

A tree h feet high casts a shadow 65 feet long on horizontal ground, and at the same time a football goal-post 8 feet tall casts a shadow 10 feet long. Identify two similar triangles, write down two equal ratios, and find the height of the tree.

8 A rugby goal-post casts a shadow 32 feet long. The part of the post below the crossbar, which is 10 feet above the ground, casts a shadow 24 feet long. Calculate the height of the post, correct to the nearest six inches.

(*Note.—In the situation described, the shadow of the crossbar would usually be* less *than* 24 *feet from the goal-line. Can you account for this?*)

9 (i) The ratio of corresponding lengths in two similar figures is 4:5. Two corresponding line segments differ in length by 2 centimetres, what are their lengths?

(*Hint.*—Suppose the lengths are x and $x+2$ centimetres, then $x/(x+2) = 4/5$. Now obtain an equivalent equation, *either* by multiplying both sides by $5(x+2)$ *or* by using the fact that $a/b = c/d \Leftrightarrow ad = bc$.)

(ii) Repeat (i) using y and $y-2$ as measures of the two lengths.

10 The height of one tree is three-fifths of the height of another. The shadow of the second tree is 25 feet longer than that of the first. Calculate the lengths of the two shadows.

11 Figure 11*a* is an important type of diagram. We can calculate all the unknown lengths.

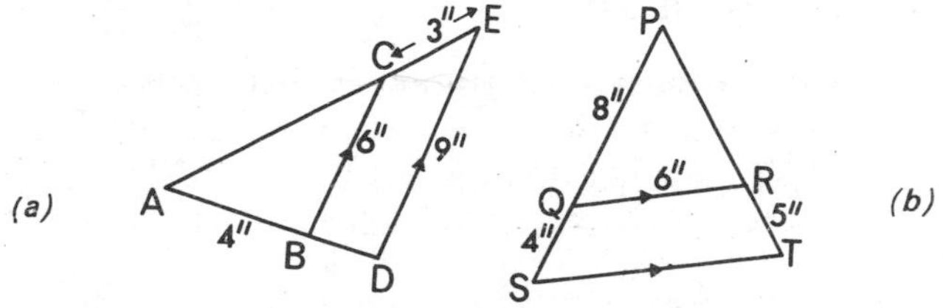

FIG. 11

(i) Prove that the triangles ABC and ADE are equiangular to one another.

(ii) What is the value of the ratio AB/AD? Hence calculate the lengths of AD and BD.

(iii) Denote the length of AC by x inches. Write down another ratio, involving x, which is equal to AB/AD. Hence find the lengths of AC and AE.

12 In Figure 11*b* calculate the lengths of ST and PR.

13 Figure 12 shows a ladder leaning against a wall, with its foot 10 feet from the foot of the wall. The ladder just touches the corner of a shed 10 feet high and 6 feet wide built out from the wall. How far up the wall does the ladder reach? (The figure contains *three* similar triangles.

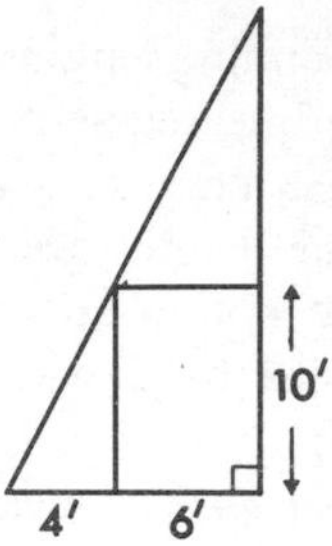

FIG. 12

Introduce a symbol for the length of an unknown vertical segment, and write down some equal ratios.)

5 Gradient of a line

1 Figure 13 shows a tiling of congruent parallelograms. Check that the parallelograms ABCD, HIJK and PQRS are similar; also the triangles ADE, HKL, PST; also the triangles BEF, ILM, QTU; also the triangles CDF, JKM, RSU; also the triangles DEF, KLM, STU.

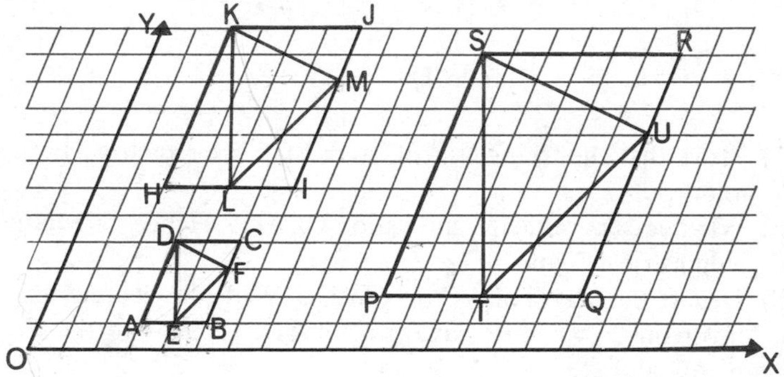

FIG. 13

Check also that DE, KL, and ST are parallel; also EF, LM, TU; also FD, MK, US.

2 If we are interested in talking about the directions of the lines DE, EF, FD, etc., we can do this in more than one way. We can, for example,

indicate them by telling what angles the lines make with the two axes; or we can do it in terms of 'components' in the direction of the two axes. Thus, the direction of DE could be indicated either by '1 left, 3 up' or '1 right, 3 down', i.e. by

$$\begin{pmatrix} -1 \\ +3 \end{pmatrix} \text{ or } \begin{pmatrix} +1 \\ -3 \end{pmatrix}$$

Write down both versions of the number pairs which could be used to indicate the directions of the other line segments in the figure, including segments like AE and BF.

3 (i) Write down, from your answer to question 2, a set of number pairs which indicate the direction of all the segments which are parallel to DE.
(ii) Repeat for segments parallel to EF.
(iii) Repeat for segments parallel to FD.
(iv) Repeat for segments parallel to AE.
(v) Repeat for segments parallel to BF.

Note.—All the segments parallel to DE have one direction. To specify the direction we use the ratio $\dfrac{y\text{-component}}{x\text{-component}}$, *where these are the components of any one of the parallel segments. We call this ratio the 'gradient ratio' of the direction.*

Thus the gradient ratio of DE and of all lines parallel to DE is -3.

4 Write down the gradient ratio of each of the following segments: EF; TU; MK; FD; AC; PR; IK; QS; AB; AE; DC; PQ; IL.

Note.—In question 4 no segments parallel to OY were listed, because no value can be given to their 'gradient ratio'; symbols like $\dfrac{4}{0}$ *or* $\dfrac{-3}{0}$ *have no meaning.*

5 Look back over questions 2–4 and see if you can say what feature of a line corresponds to a *positive* gradient ratio. What does a negative gradient ratio indicate?

6 In Figure 14 the segments AB and A′B′ are parallel; also DE and D′E′. The 'components' of these segments parallel to the axes are dotted.

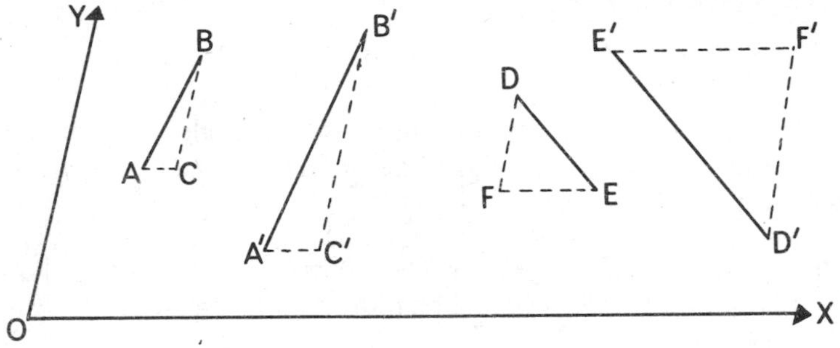

FIG. 14

(i) Name the pairs of equal angles in triangles ABC, A′B′C′.

Hence write down two other ratios equal to $\frac{AB}{A'B'}$.

Write down also another ratio equal to $\frac{CB}{AC}$.

(ii) Name the pairs of equal angles in triangles DEF, D′E′F′.

Write down two other ratios equal to $\frac{DE}{D'E'}$.

Write down also another ratio equal to $\frac{FD}{EF}$.

Note.—In question 6, the ratio $\frac{CB}{AC}$ *gives the magnitude of the gradient ratio of every line parallel to AB. It is a positive ratio.*

Similarly $\frac{FD}{EF}$ *gives the magnitude of the gradient ratio of every line parallel to ED. This ratio is negative.*

In most cases we use axes at right angles. In these cases 'gradient ratio' is determined in exactly the same way as before. Triangles drawn like those in Figure 14 would then be right-angled.

For the rest of the Section use axes perpendicular to one another if you like.

7 For perpendicular axes state again the relation between the *direction* of a line and the *sign* of its gradient ratio.

8 Plot, with reasonable accuracy, the following pairs of points, and find the gradient ratio of the straight line through each pair (if possible):

(i) (5, 3), (6, 7) (iii) (5, −3), (6, 7) (v) (−5, −3), (−10, −3)
(ii) (5, 3), (6, 0) (iv) (−5, 3), (−6, 0) (vi) (5, 3), (5, −4).

9 (i) Draw a line through the origin whose gradient ratio is +2. Write down an equation which is true for the coordinates (x, y) of every point on this line.
(ii) Write down the coordinates of a number of points whose coordinates satisfy the equation $y = 3x$. Calculate the gradient ratio of the line segments joining several pairs of these points.

10 (i) Draw a line through the origin whose gradient ratio is $-\frac{1}{2}$. Write down an equation which is true for the coordinates (x, y) of every point on this line.
(ii) Write down the coordinates of a number of points whose coordinates satisfy the equation $y = -2x$. Calculate the gradient ratio of the line segments joining several pairs of these points.

11 (i) Check that the line joining A(0, 2) to (1, 5) has gradient +3. Work out what the y-coordinates of the following points will have to be if the line joining A to each point is to have gradient +3:

(2,), (5,), (20,), (−4,)

Write down an equation which is true for the coordinates (x, y) of every point on the line through (0, 2) of gradient +3.
(ii) Write down the coordinates of a number of points whose coordinates satisfy the equation $y = \frac{1}{2}x + 4$. Calculate the gradient of the line segments joining several pairs of these points.

12 (i) Check that the line joining A(0, 3) to (−10, 7) has gradient $-\frac{2}{5}$. Work out what the y-coordinates of the following points will

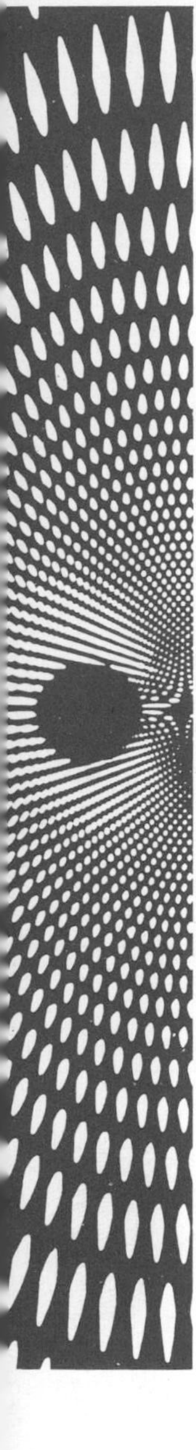

have to be, if the line joining A to each point is to have gradient $-\frac{2}{5}$:

$$(20,\quad),\ (15,\quad),\ (10,\quad),\ (5,\ ),\ (-5,\quad)$$

Write down an equation which is true for the coordinates (x, y) of every point on the line through $(0, 3)$ of gradient $-\frac{2}{5}$.

(ii) Write down the coordinates of a number of points whose coordinates satisfy the equation $y = -x+3$. Calculate the gradient of the line segments joining several pairs of these points.

Note.—The coordinates of every point on a straight line which is not parallel to the y-axis satisfies an equation of the form $y = mx+c$, where m is the gradient ratio of every segment of the line, and $(0, c)$ is the point where the line meets the y-axis; and all points whose coordinates satisfy one equation of this form are collinear (in line).

13 Write down the equations of the lines through the origin with gradients stated. Indicate all the lines on the same diagram, and label each with its equation.

(i) $+4$ (ii) $+\frac{2}{3}$ (iii) $+\frac{3}{2}$ (iv) -4 (v) $-\frac{2}{3}$ (vi) $-\frac{3}{2}$ (vii) 0

14 Write down the equations of the lines through the point $(0, 4)$ with the gradients given in question 13. Sketch and label the lines.

15 Write down the equations of the lines of gradient (*a*) $+2$ (*b*) -1 which pass through the following points. Sketch and label the lines.

(i) $(0, 4)$ (ii) $(0, 0)$ (iii) $(0, 1)$ (iv) $(0, -4)$

16 For each of the lines whose equations are given here, state its gradient and the coordinates of the point where it cuts the y-axis.

(i) $y = 2x+5$	(ii) $y = -x+3$	(iii) $y = -2x-4$
(iv) $y = \frac{3}{4}x-3$	(v) $y-x = 2$	(vi) $y-4 = 3x$
(vii) $2x+y = 5$	(viii) $5x-y+7 = 0$	(ix) $2y = x+6$

Summary

The ratio of the lengths of corresponding lines in two similar figures is equal to the ratio of the lengths of corresponding sides.

See also notes on pages 111, 115 and 118.

CHAPTER 3 Circle I: Rotational and Bilateral Symmetry

1 Rotational symmetry

1 Figure 1 shows a simplified drawing of a bicycle wheel with equal and equally spaced spokes ('radii') radiating from the hub ('centre') O to the rim ('circumference').

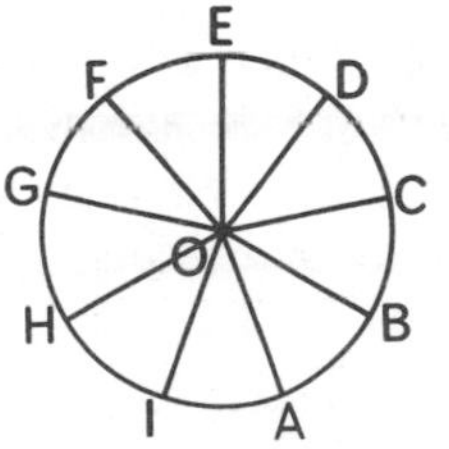

FIG. 1

Imagine a tracing of the diagram superposed on it, and rotated about the point O. Discuss what happens to the tracings of the spokes, and to the tracing of the rim.

2 Now imagine Figure 1 without the spokes, leaving the centre and circumference only, and the corresponding tracing. Discuss the rotation as in question 1.

Note.—Every point on the circumference is equidistant from the centre. During rotation about the centre every point on the traced circumference remains on the original circumference.

3 Suppose the tracing of Figure 1 is rotated over the figure, as in question 1. Describe the locus of a point on one of the spokes.

Notice that the tracing of Figure 1 could be brought into a new position of coincidence with the original by rotating it through angles of

40°, 80°, 120°, . . . 320°; so it can be 'placed on itself', without turning it over, in *nine* different ways. (If the rotation goes beyond 360°, we get the same positions over again.) Because of this the figure is said to have *cyclic symmetry of order* 9. ('Cyclic' is from a Greek word meaning 'circle'.)

Now think of a circle. Through how many different angles (smaller than 360°) can you rotate a tracing about the centre so as to bring it into coincidence with the circle? Is there any limit to the number?

We say the circle has *cyclic* or *rotational symmetry* of infinite order. The circle is 'conserved' by every rotation about its centre.

The word 'circle' is used with two different meanings. Sometimes it refers to the circumference, and sometimes it refers to the circumference together with the disc-like region it encloses. For example we say that a penny and a hoop are both circular and each can be thought of as a circle. When it matters, we shall have to make the distinction clear. For example if we are speaking of the intersection of (i.e. the set of points common to) a circle and an infinite straight line, we have to allow for Figure 2*a* and also for Figure 2*b*. See question 4.

4 (*a*) What is the intersection of the circle and infinite line indicated in Figure 2*a*?

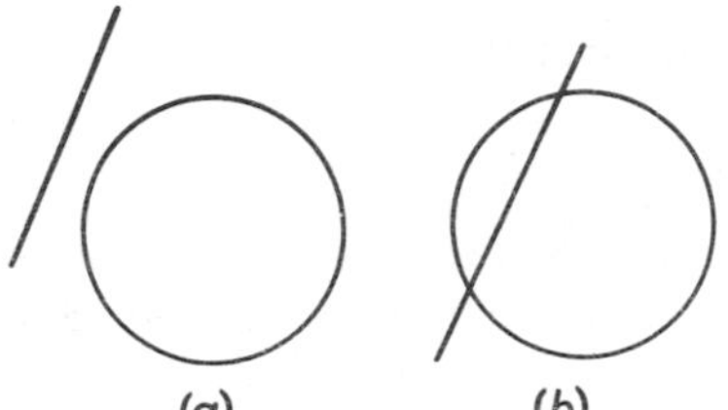

(*a*) (*b*)

FIG. 2

(*b*) We cannot answer the corresponding question for Figure 2*b* until we know whether 'circle' here means 'circumference' or disc. How many points of intersection are there in these two cases?

(*c*) There is a third possibility not illustrated in Figure 2. Supply the corresponding diagram, and discuss the 'intersection' in this case.

5 When we speak of the area of a circle, which meaning of the word *circle* must we have in mind?

6 What does *diametrically opposite* mean?

Supply the missing words in the following sentence:

'A . . . of a circle is a straight-line segment which joins two points on the . . . and passes through the . . . . Its length is double that of the . . . .'

Chords

7 Mark any two points on the circumference of a circle. For all such pairs of points, the straight-line segment which joins them is a 'chord' of the circle.

Is every diameter a chord? Is every chord a diameter?

Which (if any) of the following is true?

(i) The set of chords is a subset of the set of diameters.

(ii) The set of diameters is a subset of the set of chords.

8 Draw three circles with centres A, B, C.

(i) In the first draw a chord PQ equal in length to the radius. Describe the triangle APQ.

(ii) In the second, draw a chord RS shorter than the radius. Describe the triangle BRS.

(iii) In the third, draw a chord TU longer than the radius. Describe the triangle CTU. Is it obtuse-angled? Must it be obtuse-angled?

(iv) Is it possible to draw in a circle a chord which is longer than a diameter? (In a circle with centre O, draw any chord HK, and use the triangle inequality in triangle OHK.)

9 (*a*) Imagine a circular wheel, in which the hub is not at the centre. Try to describe how a bicycle would behave if it had such a front wheel.

(*b*) It will help to explain the behaviour of this bicycle if we look at Figure 3. O is the centre and H is the hub of the wheel.

What names do we give to the lines AB and CD?

Which point of the circumference is nearest to H and which is farthest from H? Are you absolutely sure?

(*c*) To be quite sure of our answers in (*b*), we must be sure that $HC > HA$ and $HD < HB$. Let us look at HC and HA in a circle of radius 13 inches in which OH is 2 inches in length.

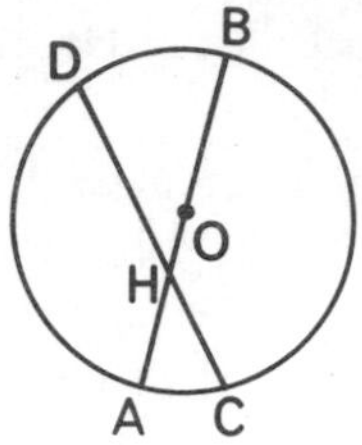

FIG. 3

Say as much as you can about the lengths of HA, OC, and HC. (In order to say something about HC, use the 'triangle inequality' in triangle OHC.)

(*d*) With radius 13 inches and OH again 2 inches long, prove that the length of HD is less than 15 inches.

(*e*) *Either* repeat (*c*) and (*d*) using different lengths for radius and OH; *or* let the lengths of radius, OH, HA, HB, HC, and HD be r, h, a, b, c, d units respectively; and prove
(i) $h+a=r$ (ii) $h+c>r$ (iii) $c>a$ (iv) $h+r>d$ (v) $d<b$

Arcs

10 If A and B are two points on the circumference of a circle, the part of the circumference from A to B is called the *arc* AB *of the circle*.

(i) There are two arcs which are entitled to be called *arc* AB. Illustrate them on a diagram; label them *major arc* AB, *minor arc* AB.

(ii) Would it be reasonable to say that the circumference of a circle is an arc of the circle?

11 (*a*) Suppose you have a rectangular card which looks rather like a square. How could you test whether it is a square, after drawing its outline on a sheet of paper?

(*b*) Suppose you have a plate which is meant to be circular but you suspect it is not. How could you test, after drawing its outline on a sheet of paper?

(*c*) In Figure 4 one of the arcs is intended to show part of a circle. Make a tracing of each arc and use these to find which is the circular arc. Then do what is necessary to obtain on your tracing

FIG. 4

paper a drawing of the complete circle. (Use nothing but Figure 4, the tracing paper and a pencil.)

12 (*a*) Figure 5 shows the circumference of a circle with centre O and two radii OP and OQ.
Suppose we made a tracing of Figure 5 lettering it O_1, P_1, Q_1. Imagine the tracing held to the original by a pin through O and

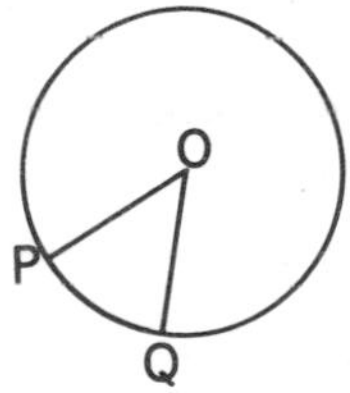

FIG. 5

O_1 and rotated about O so that P_1 and Q_1 no longer coincide with P and Q. Make sketches showing O, P, Q and possible positions for P_1 and Q_1. Your teacher will discuss with you the different relative positions possible for P, Q, P_1, and Q_1.
In *each* of these positions what, if anything, can you say about the following?

(i) angles POQ and P_1OQ_1
(ii) arcs PQ and P_1Q_1
(iii) chords PQ and P_1Q_1
(iv) angles POP_1 and QOQ_1
(v) angles POQ_1 and QOP_1
(vi) arcs PQ_1 and P_1Q
(vii) arcs PP_1 and QQ_1
(viii) chords PP_1 and QQ_1

(*b*) If the rotation of the tracing has been just sufficient to carry O_1P_1 round till it coincides with OQ, what, if anything, can you say about the following?

(i) angles POQ and POQ_1
(ii) arcs PQ and PQ_1
(iii) chords PQ and PQ_1

(*c*) Draw a figure which shows that if OP_1 coincides with OQ it is possible for chord PQ_1 to be shorter than chord PQ. (*Hint:* Make angle POQ a large obtuse angle.)

(*d*) In the figure you drew for (*c*) is it sensible to say that arc PQ_1 is double arc PQ in length? Could you express this more clearly? (Refer if necessary to question 10(i).)

To avoid ambiguity we often name an arc by means of three letters; for example, in Figure 6 it is clear what is meant when we say that arc PQQ_1 is double PRQ_1 in length.

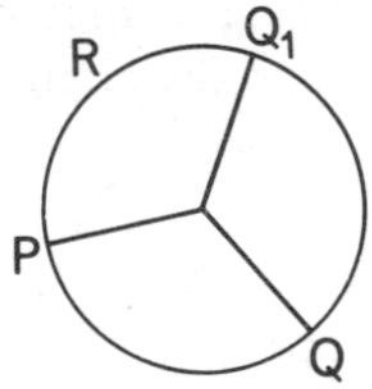

FIG. 6

Summary of the results of question 12.

A circle has centre O, and A, B, C, and D are points on the circumference.

(i) You are told that the chords AB and CD are equal. Name two equal arcs and two equal angles.

(ii) You are told that the arcs AB and CD are equal. Name two equal chords and two equal angles.

(iii) You are told that the angles AOB and COD are equal. Name two equal arcs and two equal chords.

Note.—Similar results hold if A, B and C, D are pairs of points on equal circles.

13 Draw a circle of radius 5·0 cm with centre O. Take two points A and B on the circumference, such that the size of angle AOB is between 30° and 60°. Without using a protractor, but making use of the above summary, mark on the circumference points C, D, E, and F such that angles AOB, BOC, COD, DOE and EOF are all the same size.

(i) Given that arc AB is x cm in length, write down the lengths of the arcs BCD, CDF, DEF, ACF.

(ii) Given that angle AOB $= y°$, write down the sizes of the angles 'subtended' at the centre by the arcs mentioned above.

(iii) Write down the numerical values of the following ratios:

(*a*) arc BCD: arc CDF: arc DEF: arc ACF;

(*b*) angle BOD: angle COF: angle DOF: angle AOF.

(iv) Can you find numerical values for these ratios?
chord BD: chord CF: chord DF: chord AF.

Note.—In all circles of the same size, arc length is proportional to size of angle subtended at the centre.

14 The tip of the minute hand of a clock moves round the circumference of a circle on which the sixty 'minute' positions are marked. Say which of the following statements are true and which are false:

(i) The arc joining '5 past' to '20 past' is the same length as that joining 'half-past' to 'quarter to'.

(ii) The chord joining '5 past' to '20 past' is the same length as that joining 'half-past' to 'quarter to'.

(iii) The hand turns through an angle of 6° every minute.

(iv) If the arc joining '10 past' to 'quarter past' measures 2 inches, the arc joining '10 past' to '25 past' will measure 6 inches.

(v) If the chord joining '10 past' to 'quarter past' measures $1\frac{1}{2}$ inches, the chord joining '10 past' to '25 past' will measure $4\frac{1}{2}$ inches.

(vi) The chord joining '5 past' to '25 past' is longer than the chord joining '5 past' to 'quarter past'.

(vii) The chord joining '5 past' to 'quarter to' is longer than the chord joining '5 past' to '25 past'.

(viii) The chord joining '5 past' to '25 past' is double the length of the chord joining '5 past' to 'quarter past'.

15 (i) In the clock described in question 14, if the tip of the minute hand describes $\frac{3}{8}$ of the circumference, through what angle does the hand turn?

(ii) If the minute hand turns through 48°, what fraction of the circumference does the tip of the hand describe?

(iii) The minute hand of a clock sweeps out an angle at a rate of

360° per hour. At what rate does the hour hand sweep out an angle? If there were a second hand, at what rate would it sweep out an angle?

(iv) If the second hand were the same length as the minute hand, how fast would the tip of the second hand be moving, compared with the tip of the minute hand?
What difference would it make, if the second hand were shorter than the minute hand?

(v) On a merry-go-round, the hobby-horses are arranged in threes, side by side. A child says, 'The inside and the outside horses go round in the same time, so they must be going round at the same rate.' To what extent is this statement correct, and to what extent is it incorrect?

(vi) A record-player turntable rotates at $33\frac{1}{3}$ revolutions per minute. Express this in degrees per second.
Is the needle moving along the groove at the same rate throughout the playing of a disc?

We now look at the relation between *length of chord* and *distance of chord from the centre of circle.*

16 Draw a circle, centre O, with a chord AB. On the same figure, draw carefully a line A_1B_1 to indicate a possible position of the chord AB after the figure has been rotated about O through any angle you choose.

Say what you can about the lengths or sizes of:

(i) the chords AB and A_1B_1 (ii) the arcs AB and A_1B_1 (iii) the arcs AA_1 and BB_1 (iv) the angles AOB and A_1OB_1 (v) the angles AOA_1 and BOB_1.

Figure 7 shows possible cases of the figures you have drawn.

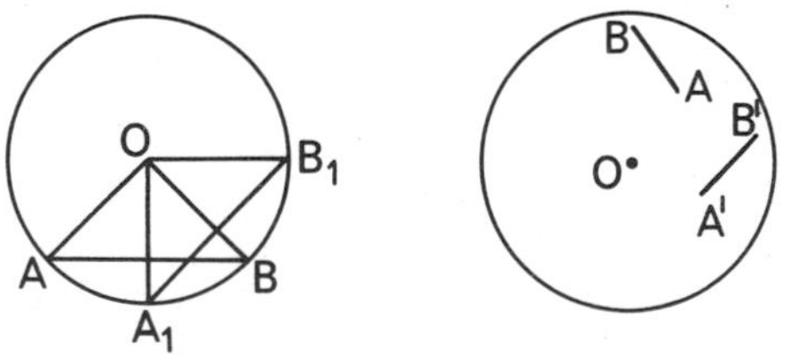

FIG. 7

17 (*a*) Suppose a circle, centre O, has two equal chords AB and A_1B_1. Name two pairs of equal arcs. Why is angle AOA_1 equal to angle BOB_1?
If the figure were rotated round O until OA lay along OA_1, where would you find (i) the point B (ii) the arc AB (iii) the chord AB?
Which, if any, of the equal chords AB and A_1B_1 is nearer to the centre of the circle?

(*b*) Now think about the arcs AA_1 and BB_1.
Are they equal in length?
What about the lengths of the chords AA_1 and BB_1?
What can you say about the distances of the chords AA_1 and BB_1 from the centre O?

18 In a certain circle, centre O, OX is drawn perpendicular to a chord, so the length of OX is the distance of the chord from the centre O. Another line OY is drawn, equal in length to OX, and a chord is drawn at right angles to OY. Think out what would happen to the two chords if the circle were rotated about O so as to bring OX into the position of OY. What does this tell you about the chords?

Note.—On the basis of questions 17 *and* 18 *we can assert:*

If two chords of a circle are equal in length, *then* they are equidistant from the centre; and
if two chords of a circle are equidistant from the centre, *then* they must be equal in length.

A note about rotation

19 Figure 8 represents a plan view of a record-player turntable, with a chalk line AB marked on it. After the turntable has turned through an angle of $x°$, the chalk line occupies the position A′B′.

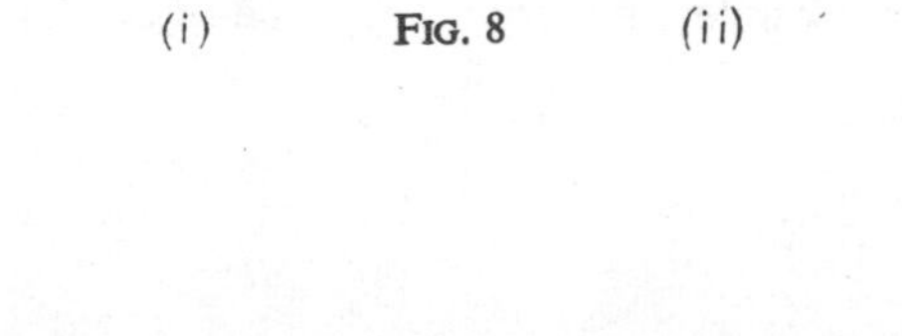

FIG. 8

(i) Name a line segment equal to OA; and one equal to OB′.
(ii) Name a triangle congruent to OAB.
(iii) State the size of angles AOA′ and BOB′.
(iv) How much has AB changed direction in its journey to the position A′B′? i.e. What is the size of the angle between AB and A′B′?

In order to answer (iv), examine Figure 8 (ii). It is easy to observe and measure the rotation of a line through the centre of the turntable, so draw POQ parallel to AB. Let the rotation through an angle $x°$ take POQ to the position P′OQ′. Name angles which have the size $x°$.

Throughout the movement what continues to be true about AB and POQ?

Copy Figure 8 (ii) and complete it to show that the angle between AB and A′B′ is $x°$.

Note.—When a plane figure is rotated through a certain angle about an axis perpendicular to its plane (as when the turntable turns about the central pin) every line in the plane rotates through an angle of the same size.

2 Regular polygons

1 See Figure 1 again (page 119). What are the sizes of the various angles at the centre?

What fraction of the circumference is each of the small arcs?

Suppose all pairs of consecutive vertices are joined. What are the sizes of all the angles in the congruent isosceles triangles?

The 9-sided polygon formed is a regular *nonagon*: all its nine sides are equal in length and all its nine angles are equal. What is the size of each of its angles?

2 Draw a 'regular octagon' in a circle of radius 4·0 cm. (What will be the size of the angle at the centre 'subtended' by each of the sides?)

3 Draw a regular pentagon (5 sides), each side being 4·0 cm long. (This time you cannot begin with the circle because you do not know its radius. Think about the five isosceles triangles which will make up the pentagon; find the angle sizes, then draw one of the triangles. One way

to finish the pentagon is to draw its 'circumscribing' circle; then use compasses to step off equal chords.)

4 Devise similar methods of drawing a regular hexagon, a regular quadrilateral, and a regular triangle. What are the usual names of the two last-named figures?

5 (*a*) Calculate the size of each angle of a regular decagon (10 sides) and a regular dodecagon (12 sides).
(*b*) What is the size of each angle of a regular polygon with 7 sides? Of one with 11 sides? Of one with 100 sides?
(*c*) By means of a similar argument, find an expression for the size of each angle of a regular polygon with n sides. Check that your formula gives the correct answer for a few values of n.
What happens if you put $n = 2$?

6 At the beginning of this chapter we said Figure 1 has cyclic symmetry of order 9 because, without turning it over, it can be 'placed on itself' in nine different ways.

From a consideration of the regular polygons you have drawn, and of other figures, write down the order of cyclic symmetry possessed by the following figures: (i) a regular octagon (ii) a regular dodecagon (iii) a square (iv) an equilateral triangle (v) a regular polygon of n sides (vi) an isosceles triangle. What kind of symmetry is possessed by an isosceles triangle?

3 Bilateral symmetry

1 The 'Big Wheel' of the fairground is not circular, yet it is called a wheel; it rotates about a centre, and it possesses cyclic symmetry. The regular polygons we met in Section 2 also possessed 'line symmetry' or 'bilateral symmetry'. A tracing of the 'spoked wheel' in Figure 9 can be picked up, *turned over*, and put down in a position of coincidence with the original figure in more than one way. How many ways can you find?

In how many of these ways do you find that one of the spokes occupies its original position? Are there any other possibilities, or must this always happen?

How many axes of symmetry has a regular pentagon? Has it any axes of symmetry other than the lines of its 'spokes'?

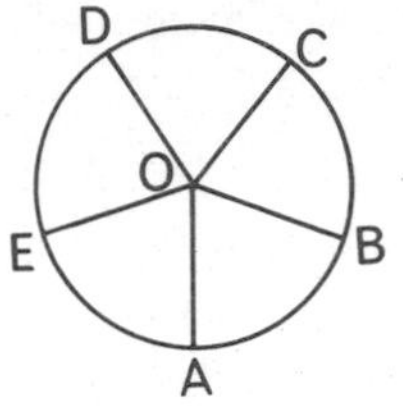

FIG. 9

2 Look at the regular octagon of Section 2, question 2. How many of its axes of symmetry pass through a vertex of the octagon? (Fewer than 8!)

Has it any other axes of symmetry? (Remember that every isosceles triangle has an axis of symmetry.) How many axes of symmetry has it altogether?

3 (i) What is the order of cyclic symmetry of the equilateral triangle and of the regular hexagon?
How many *axes* of symmetry does each figure possess?
How many of the symmetry axes of the hexagon are diagonals?
(ii) Answer the corresponding questions for the regular pentagon and the regular decagon.

4 Copy this table into your exercise books. You are to report what operation of reflection or rotation would effect the mapping on to itself of the regular nonagon ABCDEFGHI of Figure 1 (page 119), which is indicated in the first column. Check that the first two entries are correct, and complete the table.

	Mapping	Operation
	$A \to D$, $B \to E$	Anticlockwise rotation of 120° (*or* clockwise, 240°)
	$A \to D$, $B \to C$	Reflection in OG
(i)	$A \to A$, $B \to I$	
(ii)	$A \to F$, $B \to G$	
(iii)	$A \to F$, $B \to E$	
(iv)	$A \to G$	(Two answers)

Note.—In every circle we can draw a regular polygon of whatever number of sides we choose, and the resulting figure will still possess all the rotational and bilateral symmetries of the polygon. Thus a circle has all *the symmetries of every regular polygon we like to inscribe in it—both rotational and bilateral.*

Let us consider further the bilateral symmetry of a circle.

5 (i) Draw a circle, centre O, and mark two points A and B on its circumference. Make or imagine a tracing of this figure, named O_1, A_1, B_1. Think out whether it will be possible to turn over the tracing and place it face down on the original with O_1 on O and A_1 on B.
Will every point on the traced circumference fall on a point on the original circumference? Where will B_1 fall?

(ii) The original circle has a diameter which is the axis of symmetry of the isosceles triangle OAB. What happens to this diameter when we imagine the tracing turned over as above?
How is the chord AB related to this diameter of the circle?

(iii) Consider now another point C on the original circumference and its trace C_1. When the tracing is turned over, consider the positions of C and C_1 relative to the diameter which is the axis of bilateral symmetry of the triangle OAB.
What does this diameter do to the chord CC_1? What about the arc CC_1?

Note.—From the work of question 5 we have found that *this diameter (in fact every diameter) of a circle is an axis of bilateral symmetry. Thus every diameter bisects every chord which is perpendicular to it; every chord is perpendicular to the diameter through its mid-point; the perpendicular bisector of every chord passes through the centre of the circle.*

6 Draw on two-millimetre squared paper a large circle, with centre on one of the printed intersections. Mark in one of the printed diameters.

Place a ruler in the position of the perpendicular diameter. Slide it slowly keeping it parallel to itself, and watch the behaviour of the chord which the ruler suggests.

What happens when the ruler reaches the end of the diameter you draw, i.e. when it is on the point of leaving the circle? (The line of the ruler in this position is said to *touch* the circle or be a *tangent* to the circle. Note that the tangent is perpendicular to the radius it meets on the circumference.)

7 Draw a circle, centre O, and mark another point A in the interior of the circle. You are to draw, accurately, a chord which will be bisected at A. (How will it lie, in relation to the diameter through A?)

8 Draw a circle, centre O, and two parallel chords AB and CD. How many axes of symmetry must this figure have? Name a chord equal to AC; an arc equal to arc BD; an angle equal to ACD.

AD and BC are joined. Name three angles equal to ADC.

9 An infinite straight line XTY touches at T a circle with centre O. How many axes of symmetry has this figure?

A chord PQ is drawn parallel to XTY. Name two equal chords; two equal arcs; four equal angles.

10 In Figure 10, AB is a chord of a circle, centre O. L and M are points on the circumference, on the same side of AB. If arc AL = arc BM, what can we say about the straight line LM? (Consider a reflection in the diameter perpendicular to AB. What are the images of A, arc AL, and L?)

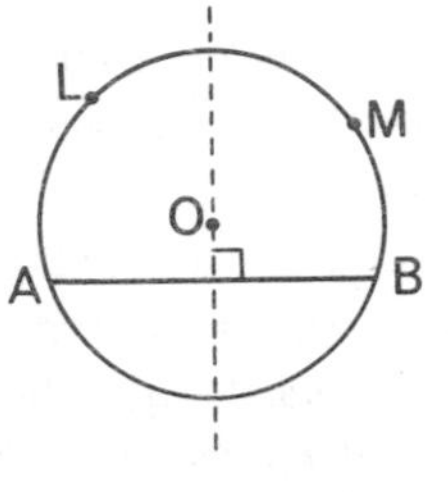

FIG. 10

Finding the centre of a circle

11 On tracing paper, draw a circle without its centre (e.g. draw round a plate or tin). Find the positions of two different diameters by folding.

12 Trace again the circular arc of Figure 4 (page 123). Find, by folding, the centre of the circle of which it is a part; complete the circle using compasses.

13 (*a*) Think of a line segment AB as a chord of a circle which has not been drawn. Say as much as you can about the centres of circles which pass through A and B.

(*b*) How many circles is it possible to draw through two given points A and B? Where will all the centres lie? Draw a diagram showing a good many members of this set of circles.
Does the set contain a largest member? a smallest member? In general, how many members are there of a specified size?

14 The line segments AB and BC (where A, B, and C are not collinear) are said to be chords of a circle which has not yet been drawn.

Where are the centres of all possible circles through A and B? Where are the centres of all possible circles through B and C?

Will it be possible to draw a circle through A, B, and C? (Note that the point you hope to use as centre will have to be equidistant from all *three* points.) If there is such a circle, draw it. If there are several such circles, draw them.

Is it *always* possible to draw a circle through three given points?

15 (*a*) Draw an acute-angled triangle ABC. Find the centre O of the circle which passes through A, B and C; and draw the circle. (*Note.—This circle is called the* circumcircle, *and* O *the* circumcentre, *of triangle* ABC.)

(*b*) Repeat for an obtuse-angled triangle ABC.

(*c*) Repeat for a right-angled triangle ABC. (If the result surprises you, have a look at the rectangle with diagonal drawn, of which the right-angled triangle ABC is one half.)

16 A, B, C, D are four points marked at random on the page (but no three are collinear). Will it always be possible to draw a circle through A, B, and C?

Write down, and discuss similarly, the other possible sets of three points.

Will it always be possible to draw a circle through the four points A, B, C, and D?

Would it ever be possible (e.g. if one or more of the points had been in a different position)?

4 Calculations using Pythagoras' theorem

1 A chord 10 centimetres long is 12 centimetres from the centre of a circle. Calculate the length of the radius of the circle.

2 A chord 12·0 centimetres long is 10·0 centimetres from the centre of a circle. What is the length of the radius of the circle?

3 OT is a radius of, and TA is a tangent to, a circle. One of these line segments measures 6 centimetres and the other measures 8 centimetres. Calculate the length of OA.

4 A circle has radius 1·7 inches. What is the perpendicular distance from the centre of every chord that is 3·0 inches long?

Describe the locus of the mid-points of such chords.

Draw an accurate diagram, showing the circle of radius 1·7 inches, and a fair number of chords each 3·0 inches long.

5 Figure 11 illustrates the penalty box on a football pitch. The penalty spot is 12 yards from the goal line, while the line of AB is 18 yards from the goal line. A circular arc AB, with centre O and radius 10 yards, is marked on the pitch. Find the length of the chord AB.

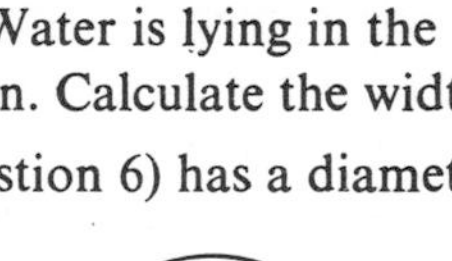

FIG. 11

6 Figure 12 shows a section through a horizontal cylindrical pipe of diameter 2 feet 6 inches. Water is lying in the pipe and is 6 inches deep at the middle of the section. Calculate the width of the water surface.

7 A water pipe (as in question 6) has a diameter of 3 feet 4 inches. The

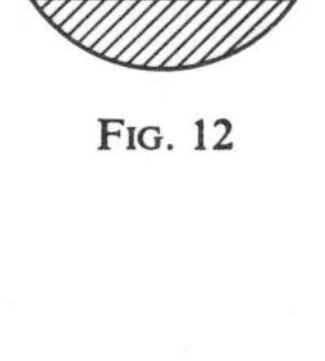

FIG. 12

width of the water surface is 2 feet. Check that the maximum depth of the water might be 4 inches. If it is *not* 4 inches, what is it?

8 In question 6 of Section 3 you looked at a whole series of chords of a circle, at steadily increasing distances from the centre of the circle. The diagram certainly suggested that 'the further from the centre, the shorter the chord.'

(i) Consider a circle of radius 10·0 centimetres. Copy and complete this table, working to three significant figures:

Distance from centre (cm)	0	1·0	2·0	3·0	4·0	5·0	6·0	7·0	8·0	9·0	10·0
Length of chord (cm)		19·9	19·6	19·1		17·3					

(ii) Draw a graph of 'length of chord' against 'distance from centre'.

(iii) For each calculation you performed in (i), you performed the steps indicated by the formula $y = 2\sqrt{(100-x^2)}$, corresponding to the mapping $x \rightarrow 2\sqrt{(100-x^2)}$.
Complete the following sentences, inserting 'increases' or 'decreases' as appropriate:
'As x increases, x^2 . . . , so $100-x^2$ . . . ,
so $\sqrt{(100-x^2)}$ . . . , so $2\sqrt{(100-x^2)}$ . . . .'
'As distance from centre increases, length of chord . . . .'
'As distance from centre decreases, length of chord . . . .'
'As length of chord increases, distance from centre . . . .'
'As length of chord decreases, distance from centre . . . .'

9 Figure 13 refers to a fixed circle. Various chords are drawn in this circle. For such a chord, of length $2c$ units and distant d units from the centre, check that c^2+d^2 is constant.

Write sentences describing how changes in the value of d affect the value of c, and *vice versa*.

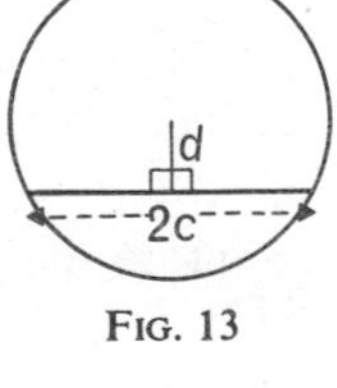

FIG. 13

5 Coordinates

1 Draw a circle, radius 7 units, with its centre at the origin O of a Cartesian diagram. Suppose P (x, y) is a point on the circumference.

Which of the following relations must be true for every point on the circumference?

(i) $x+y=7$ (ii) $x^2+y^2=49$ (iii) $x^2+y^2=196$ (iv) $x^2=49-y^2$ (v) $y^2=49+x^2$.

2 (i) In the diagram of question 1, where will we find all the points (x, y) for which it is true that $x^2+y^2=49$?

(ii) Where will we find all the points for which $x^2+y^2>49$? As a check, plot the points (5, 5) and (−6, −4).

(iii) Where will we find all the points for which $x^2+y^2<49$? As a check, plot the points (6, −3) and (−4, 5).

3 Write down an algebraic relation which expresses each of the following statements:

(i) The point P(x, y) is 3 units from the origin.

(ii) P(x, y) is more than 10 units from O.

(iii) P(x, y) lies within the circle, centre O, and radius 6 units.

Note.—For a point P *with coordinates* (x, y), *the equation* $x^2+y^2=r^2$ *is a true relation if* P *is on the circumference of a circle, centre* O, *and radius* r; *and it is not true if* P *is anywhere else.*

We say that $x^2+y^2=r^2$ is the equation of the circumference of the circle, centre O, and radius r. We often refer to it as 'the equation of the circle'.

The inequation $x^2+y^2<r^2$ is the inequation corresponding to the *interior* of this circle, and $x^2+y^2>r^2$ is the inequation corresponding to the exterior.

Note that for every single point on the plane, just *one* of these three relations is true.

4 (*a*) On a Cartesian diagram, indicate clearly the following sets of points:

(i) $\{(x, y) : x^2+y^2 < 25\}$;
(ii) $\{(x, y) : x^2+y^2 > 9\}$;
(iii) $\{(x, y) : x^2+y^2 > 9\} \cap \{(x, y) : x^2+y^2 < 25\}$;
(iv) $\{(x, y) : x^2+y^2 = 25\} \cap \{(x, y) : x = 3\}$;
(v) $\{(x, y) : x^2+y^2 < 25\} \cap \{(x, y) : x = 3\}$;
(vi) $\{(x, y) : x^2+y^2 = 9\} \cap \{(x, y) : x = 3\}$;
(vii) $\{(x, y) : x^2+y^2 = 9\} \cup \{(x, y) : x = 3\}$;
(viii) $\{(x, y) : x^2+y^2 = 25\} \cup \{(x, y) : x^2+y^2 = 9\}$;
(ix) $\{(x, y) : x^2+y^2 = 25\} \cap \{(x, y) : x^2+y^2 = 9\}$;
(x) $\{(x, y) : x^2+y^2 = 0\}$.

(*b*) Say what you can about the set of points (x, y) such that $x^2+y^2 = -10$.

5 (i) Work out the distance of the point A(3, 4) from the origin. What is the equation of the circle, centre O, which passes through A?

(ii) B(3, p) is another point on this circle. What is the value of p? C(q, 4) is another point on this circle. What is the value of q?

(iii) Using the bilateral symmetry of the circle, write down the co-ordinates of another point on the circumference.

(iv) If (4, r) is to represent a point on the circumference, write down two possible replacements for r.
Similarly for (-4, s), (t, 3), and (u, -3).

(v) Plot all the points obtained so far. Insert in the diagram all the axes of symmetry of this set of points. Does the set of points possess rotational symmetries? If so, state the angles of the rotations which conserve the set of points.

6 Repeat the procedure of question 5, starting with a point (5, 3).

7 Find the coordinates of the points of intersection of the circle $x^2+y^2 = 25$ with each of the following lines: in each case, state the length of the chord of the circle.

(i) $y = 3$	(ii) $y = 4$	(iii) $y = 4{\cdot}9$
(iv) $y = 4{\cdot}99$	(v) $y = 5$	(vi) $y = 5{\cdot}01$

6 Angle in semicircle

1 Draw a rectangle and its diagonals. Draw a circle through the vertices of the rectangle.

2 Draw a circle with two of its diameters XY and PQ. In how many ways could a tracing of this figure be placed so as to coincide with the original? What is the shape of the quadrilateral XPYQ?

3 AB is a diameter of a circle, centre O. C is another point on the circumference. Use the argument of question 2 to establish that angle ACB must be a right angle.

Note.—A diameter of a circle subtends a right angle at every point on the circumference, i.e. every 'angle in a semicircle' is a right angle.

4 PQR is a triangle, right-angled at Q. By thinking of the rectangle of which triangle PQR is one half, prove that if we draw a circle with PR as diameter, it must pass through Q.

5 PQ is a diameter of a circle, QR is a chord. PQ measures 25 centimetres, QR 7 centimetres. Calculate the length of PR.

6 XY is a diameter of a circle. YZ is a chord. YZ measures 40 centimetres, ZX 9 centimetres. Calculate the length of XY.

Summary

See page 143.

Topics to Explore

1 Look back to Chapter 3, Section 2, questi on 5*c* in which you found the size of each angle of a regular polygon of *n* sides to be $(180-360/n)°$.

(*a*) In this formula, *n* is obviously a variable on the set of natural numbers greater than 2. Just to see what happens, substitute $2\frac{1}{2}$ for *n* in the formula. If you try to draw a 'regular polygon' with an angle of 36° at each vertex, you should obtain a five-pointed star! Notice that if you travel along each of its five 'sides' in turn, you will go *twice* round the centre: perhaps this is what '$n=2\frac{1}{2}$' means!

(*b*) If you found (*a*) amusing, try $n=\frac{10}{3}$, or $n=\frac{12}{5}$. (Make your drawing a good size.)

2 Figure 1*a* shows a regular dodecagon, inscribed in a circle of radius *r* units. We want to find a formula for its area. The easiest way to do this

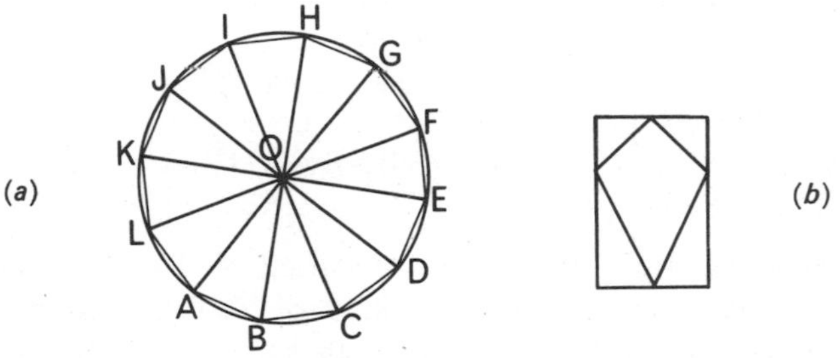

FIG. 1

is to think of it as being made up of a number of *kites* congruent to OABC. (If you have forgotten how to calculate the area of a kite, Figure 1*b* may help you.)

You will need the length of the kite diagonal AC, and you can get this by thinking about triangle OAC. Hence derive a formula for the area of the dodecagon (O is the centre of the circle).

3 Some topology—simple closed curves

Draw a closed curved—a circle, or a curve that looks like a circle, which divides the surface of the page into two regions, one inside the closed curve and one outside.

(*a*) A and C are any two points inside the curve, B and D any two points outside. Draw a straight line from A to B. How many times does the line AB cut the closed curve (see Figure 2)?

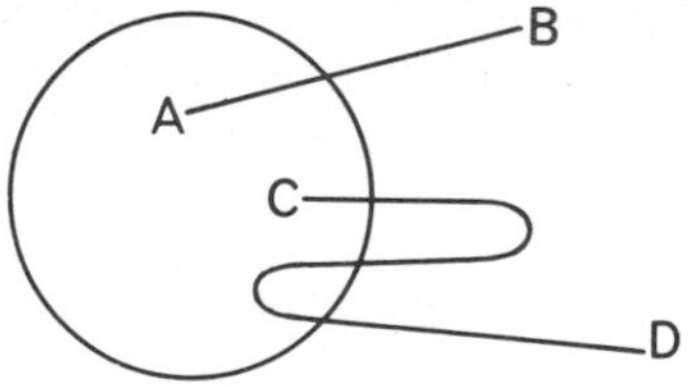

FIG. 2

(*b*) C and D are joined by a curved line. How many times does the line CD cut the closed curve? Must it be three times? Could it be seven times? Could it be four times?

(*c*) A curved line XY cuts the closed curve 16 times. What can you say about the points X and Y?

(*d*) A curved line PQ cuts the closed curve 67 times. What can you say about the points P and Q?

We are now going to consider some aspects of 'Topology' which for the time being we can regard as a kind of 'rubber sheet geometry'. We are interested in the ways in which surfaces can be twisted or stretched or otherwise deformed from one shape to another (without being torn or stuck to themselves).

(*e*) The 'circle' in Figure 3*a* can be transformed topologically, by stretching or bending but not tearing, into shapes like (*b*), (*c*), and (*d*). In (*a*), (*b*), and (*c*) it is quite clear which points are 'inside' the closed curve and which are 'outside'.
In Figure 3*d* find a method for deciding whether the point A is inside or outside the closed curve.

(*a*) (*b*) (*c*) (*d*)

FIG. 3

(*Hint.*—Choose a point B which is clearly outside the curve and draw a straight line from A to B. Why should this help you to solve the problem?)

(*f*) A long loop of string is laid in an irregular fashion on a table (see Figure 4). Five pins A, B, C, D, and E are placed as shown and the string is pulled away. Which pins will remain inside the loop and which will lie outside the loop of string?

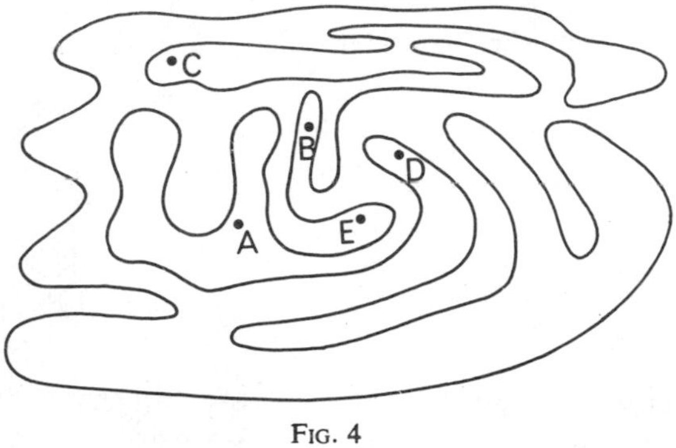

FIG. 4

(*g*) Imagine the network of lines (squared grid) in the coordinate system of Figure 5*a* to be distorted (by stretching or bending, but not by tearing or sticking parts together) so that they form the new network of Figure 5*b*.
Where will you find the points corresponding to A, B, and C in the new coordinate system?

(*h*) On diagrams similar to Figures 5*a* and 5*b* (*a*) indicate the lines

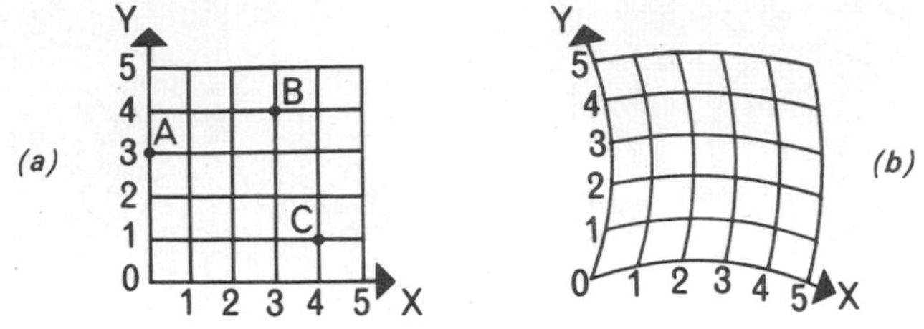

FIG. 5

(i) $x=3$ (ii) $y=2$ (iii) $y=x$ (iv) $y=2x$

(*b*) use shading to indicate:

(i) $\{(x, y): 0 \leqslant x \leqslant 2,\ 0 \leqslant y \leqslant 2\}$
(ii) $\{(x, y): 1 \leqslant x \leqslant 3,\ 2 \leqslant y \leqslant 5\}$
(iii) $\{(x, y): 0 \leqslant x,\ 0 \leqslant y,\ x+y \leqslant 5\}$

(*i*) Here is a well-known problem.
X, Y, and Z are three householders who wish to link up their central-heating systems to the gas (G), oil (O), and electricity (E) supplies. X wishes to use electricity, Y wishes to use oil, and Z

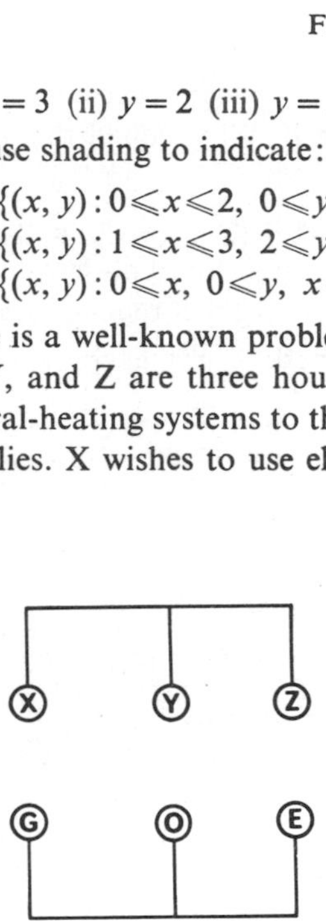

FIG. 6*a*

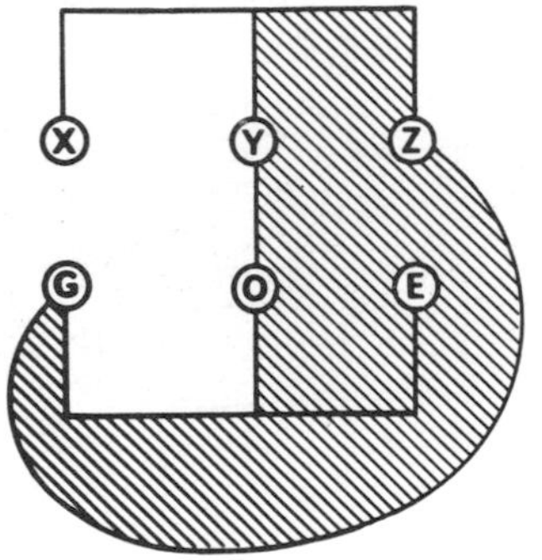

FIG. 6*b*

gas. The supply lines must not cross one another, nor must they cross any of the straight lines in Figure 6*a*. Can the problem be solved?
Figure 6*b* shows one attempt to solve the problem. Y has been joined directly to O, and Z to G. Part of the figure has been shaded

in to help you to see why X cannot be joined to E in this case. Try other solutions for yourself (*a*) with X, Y, Z, G, O, E in the positions shown; (*b*) with G, O, E interchanged in various ways.

Summary

Rotation about a point.

Let rotation about O of size $\theta°$ send A to A′, B to B′ and C to C′. Then:

(i) A′ is the image of A.
$\Rightarrow$ OA′ = OA, *and* angle AOA′ = $\theta°$, *and* O lies on the perpendicular bisector of AA′.

(ii) A′ is the image of A, *and* B′ is the image of B
$\Leftrightarrow$ A′B′ is the image of AB
$\Rightarrow$ A′B′ = AB *and* the angle between AB and A′B′ is $\theta°$.

(iii) Triangles ABC and A′B′C′ are congruent. (A figure and its image are congruent.)

(iv) O is its own image. (The centre of rotation is the only invariant point, unless θ is a multiple of 360.)

Symmetrical figures.

If a figure is mapped onto itself (is conserved) under *rotation about a point*, the point is called the *centre of rotation* and the figure is said to have *rotational symmetry* about that point.

Circle properties.

(*a*) A circle possesses rotational symmetry about its centre; hence:

(i) equal chords, equal arcs and equal angles at the centre occur together.

(ii) the length of an arc is proportional to the size of the angle subtended at the centre.

(iii) two chords are equal $\Leftrightarrow$ the chords are equidistant from the centre.

(*b*) Every diameter of a circle is an axis of bilateral symmetry; hence:

(i) a diameter perpendicular to a chord bisects the chord.

(ii) a diameter which bisects a chord is perpendicular to it.

(iii) the perpendicular bisector of a chord passes through the centre of the circle.

(*c*) Every angle in a semicircle is a right angle.

(*d*) The equation of a circle with centre the origin and radius *r* units is $x^2+y^2=r^2$.

Revision Exercises

Revision Exercise on Chapter 1

Specification of Triangles

1 Consider whether the following sets of data are sufficient to specify a triangle ABC. For each set of data, say whether it would be possible to draw a triangle with the information given; and if so, whether all the triangles that could be drawn using that set of data would be congruent. In each case the unit of length is the centimetre. The measure of the length of the side opposite angle A is denoted by a.

(i) $a = 5$, $b = 6$, $c = 7$
(ii) $a = 5$, $b = 6$, $c = 11$
(iii) $A = 35°$, $B = 65°$, $C = 75°$
(iv) $A = 35°$, $B = 65°$
(v) $A = 35°$, $B = 65°$, $c = 6$
(vi) $A = 35°$, $B = 65°$, $a = 6$
(vii) $A = 35°$, $B = 65°$, $b = 6$
(viii) $A = 35°$, $c = 6$, $b = 1$
(ix) $A = 35°$, $c = 6$, $b = 12$
(x) $A = 35°$, $c = 6$, $a = 8$
(xi) $A = 35°$, $c = 6$, $a = 6$
(xii) $A = 35°$, $c = 6$, $a = 4$
(xiii) $A = 35°$ $c = 6$, $a = 1$
(xiv) $c = 6$, $a = 4$, $C = 90°$

2 A small boat is 50 metres from a buoy. It is to travel due north on a straight course which will cause it to come 20 metres from the buoy at its nearest. Make a rough sketch, then draw a scale diagram, and use your protractor to find the bearing of the buoy from the initial position of the boat. (Is there more than one possible answer?)

3 A line AB, 30 metres long, is marked off on level ground in a park. X and Y denote two trees. Measurement yields the following information: angle XAB = 82°, angle YAB = 33°, angle XBA = 51°, angle YBA = 127°.
Make a rough sketch, then a scale diagram, and use it to find the approximate distance between the trees. Find also how far the trees are from the line of AB.

4 In a triangle ABC, AD is a median, i.e. D is the mid-point of BC. The lengths of BC, CA, and AD are 8·4, 7·6 and 7·0 centimetres respectively. Draw an accurate diagram and measure the length of AB.

5 In a triangle ABC, P is a point on BC such that AP bisects the angle BAC, AB, AP, and angle BAC measure 7·2 cm, 6·4 cm, and

58°. Draw the triangle accurately and measure the lengths of AC and BC.

6 (*a*) XY is a line of infinite length. What is the locus of points P, on one side of XY, which are 5·2 cm from XY?

(*b*) B and C are two points on XY, 6·2 cm apart. Draw triangles with altitude 5·2 cm, as follows:
(i) triangle ABC: angle ABC = 40° (ii) triangle DBC: angle DBC = 140° (iii) triangle EBC: EC is 6·8 cm long.
Work out the area of each of these triangles.

7 Draw a triangle ABC in which angles B and C, and the altitude AD measure 50°, 70°, and 10 centimetres respectively.

Revision Exercise on Chapter 2

Similar Figures

1 (*a*) Sketch two geometrical figures which have their corresponding pairs of angles equal, but are not similar.

(*b*) Sketch two geometrical figures which have the same ratio for pairs of corresponding sides, but are not similar.
In each case illustrate your answer with pairs of figures with (i) 4 sides (ii) 5 sides (iii) 6 sides.
What happens when the figures have three sides each?

2 (*a*) In Figure 1 DE is parallel to BC. Are triangles ABC, ADE similar? Justify your answer.

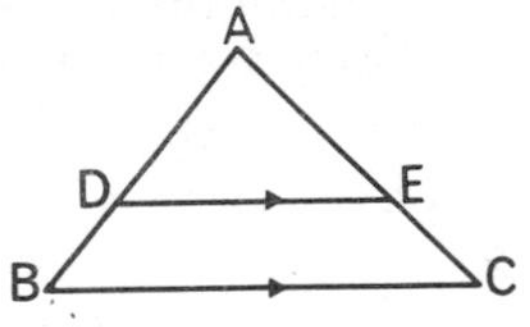

FIG. 1

(*b*) In Figure 2 XY is parallel to BC. Are quadrilaterals ABCD, AXYD similar? Justify your answer.

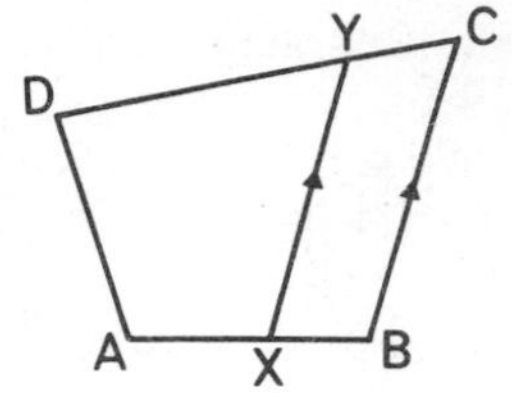

FIG. 2

3 In triangles ABC and DEF, angle A = 69°, angle B = 53°, angle E = 53° and angle F = 58°. Explain why the triangles are similar.

4 In triangles ABC and PQR, AB = 5·6 cm, BC = 4·9 cm, CA = 2·4 cm, PQ = 16·8 cm, QR = 14·7 cm, RP = 7·2 cm. Verify that the triangles are similar and name the corresponding vertices.

5 In triangles ABC and HQT, AB = 4·5 cm, BC = 7·2 cm, CA = 5·4 cm, HQ = 6·6 cm, QT = 5·5 cm, HT = 8·8 cm. Verify that the triangles are similar, and name the pairs of equal angles.

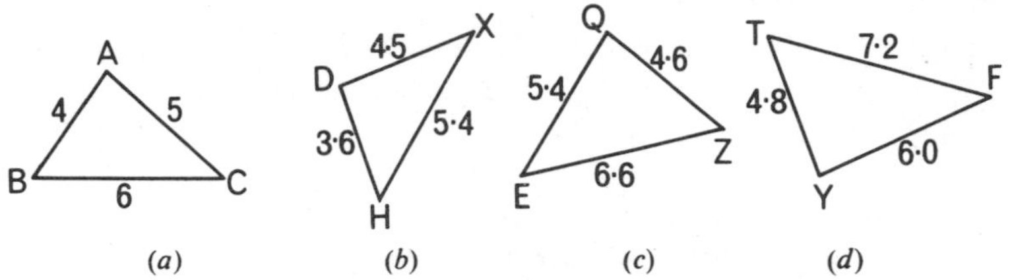

FIG. 3

6 Triangle ABC in Figure 3 is similar to two of the other three triangles. Name them.

7 If triangle PQR is an enlargement of triangle ABC with ∠P = ∠A and ∠Q = ∠B, find the enlargement ratio and the values of p and r (Figure 4).

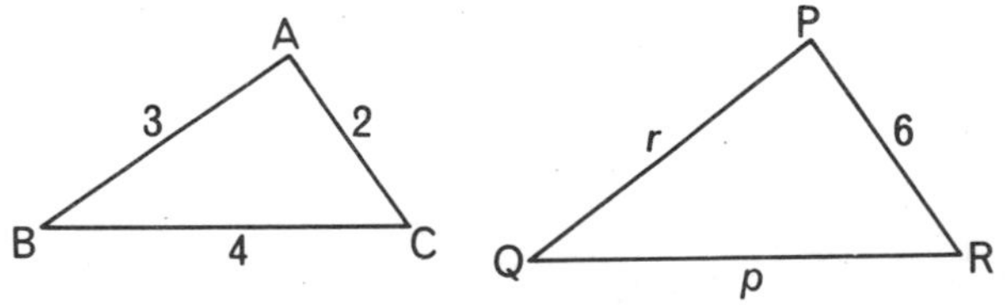

FIG. 4

8 If triangles ABC, DEF are similar with $\angle A = \angle D$ and $\angle B = \angle E$, find the values of c and d (Figure 5).

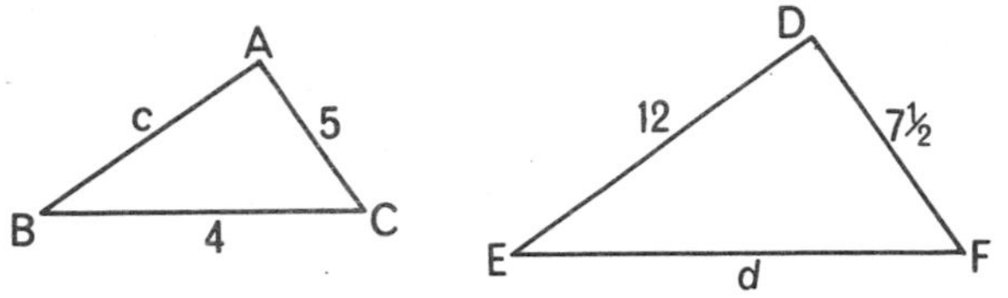

FIG. 5

9 Quadrilaterals ABCD, PQRS are known to be similar with A, B, C, D corresponding to P, Q, R, S. If PQRS is an enlargement of ABCD, state the magnification ratio. If ABCD is a reduced copy of PQRS, state the reduction ratio. Find the values of a and b.

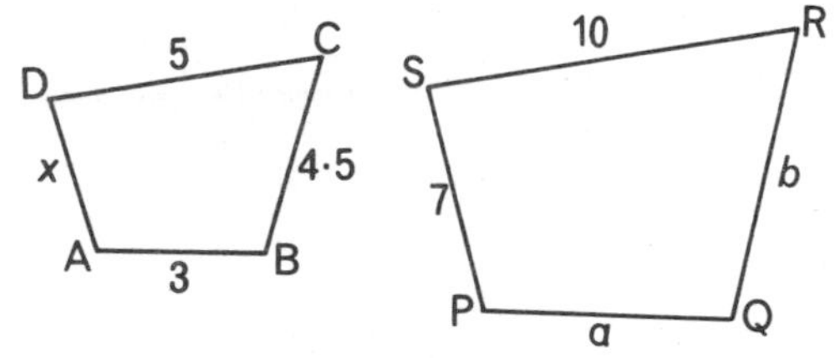

FIG. 6

Find the ratios AD:PS and AD:CD. Hence calculate the value of x in two different ways.

10 On a certain map the scale used is such that 1 inch on the map represents a distance of 200,000 inches on the earth's surface. What would be the length of a line on the map which represents a distance of 2 kilometres on the ground?

11 A model railway is made to a scale of 1:44. If the width of British Rail track is 4 ft $8\frac{1}{2}$ in, what should be the track width in the scale model? (Give your answer to the nearest tenth of an inch.)
If the length of a model engine is 6·9 inches, find the length of the real engine to the nearest foot.

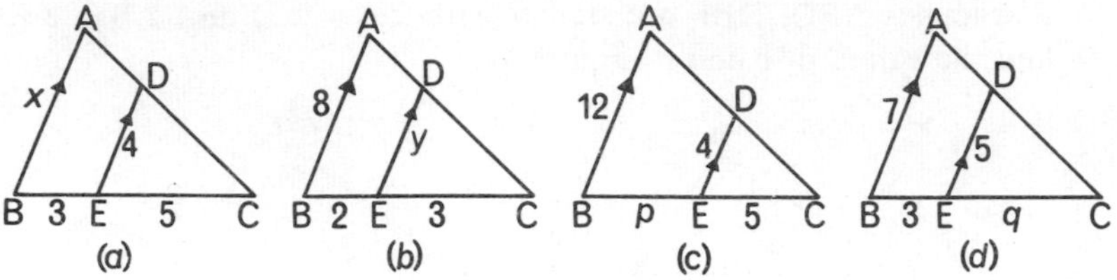

FIG. 7

12 Find the values of x, y, p, and q if all the lengths are measured in centimetres (Figure 7).
What are the values of x, y, p, and q if all lengths are measured in metres?

13 A ladder AB leans against a wall so that its upper end is 24 feet above the ground and its lower end is 10 feet out from the foot of the wall.

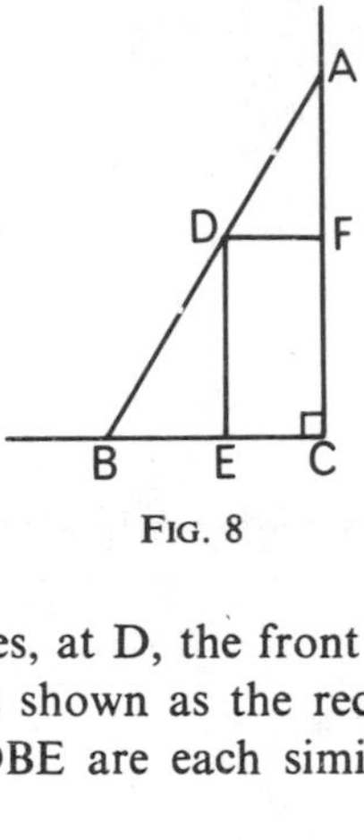

FIG. 8

The ladder just touches, at D, the front upper edge of a cupboard whose cross-section is shown as the rectangle DECF. Verify that triangles ADF and DBE are each similar to triangle ABC, then answer the following:

(i) If DF is 5 feet, show that the height of the cupboard is 12 feet.
(ii) If DF is 3 feet, calculate the height DE.
(iii) If the height DE is 6 feet, calculate the breadth DF.

14 Figure 9 shows five squares with sides 1, 2, 3, 4, and 5 units of length. Examine the areas of these five squares.

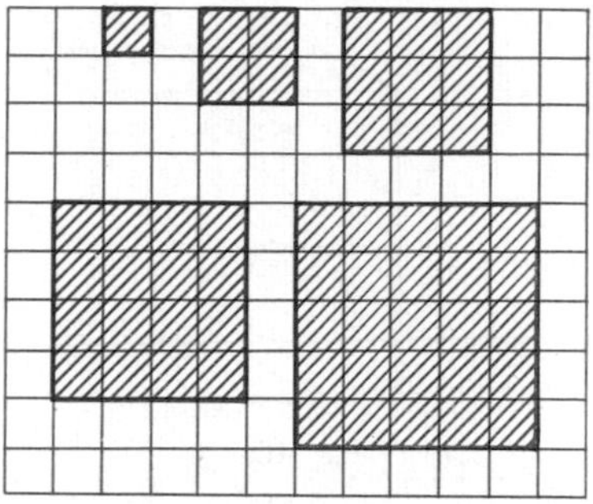

FIG. 9

State the ratio of the areas of squares whose sides are in the ratio:

(i) 2:1 (ii) 1:3 (iii) 4:1
(iv) 2:3 (v) 4:3 (vi) 2:5
(vii) m:1 (viii) 1:n (ix) m:n

15 Use suitable grids to illustrate the results of question 14 for

(i) similar rectangles (ii) similar rhombuses
(iii) similar parallelograms (iv) similar triangles

16 A photograph measures 40 mm by 30 mm. If the longer side of an enlargement is 160 mm, what is the length of the shorter side? If the small photograph cost sixpence, how much should the enlargement cost? (Assume that the cost is proportional to the area of paper used.)

17 The diagonals of two similar rectangles are 6 cm and 10 cm long. The area of the smaller rectangle is 18 cm^2. Find the area of the larger rectangle.

18 Figure 10 shows a sketch of a one-inch cube and a two-inch cube built up from one-inch cubes. Make the corresponding sketches for a three-inch and a four-inch cube. Examine their volumes.
What is the ratio of the volumes of two cubes whose edges are in the following ratios?

(i) 2:1 (ii) 1:3 (iii) 3:2 (iv) 4:1
(v) 3:5 (vi) m:1 (vii) 1:n (viii) m:n

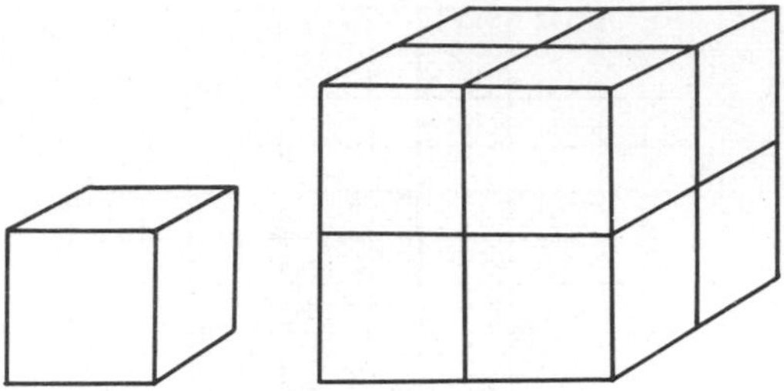

FIG. 10

19 Make sketches like those for question 18 for rectangular solids similar to one measuring 2 in by 1 in by $\frac{1}{2}$ in. Examine their volumes. State the ratio of the volumes of two similar rectangular solids whose corresponding edges are in the ratio:

(i) 2:1 (ii) 1:3 (iii) 4:3 (iv) 3:5
(v) $h:1$ (vi) $1:k$ (vii) $h:k$

20 Compare the volumes of two cubes whose edges are:

(i) 1 inch and 1 foot (ii) 1 foot and 1 yard
(iii) 1 inch and 1 yard (iv) 1 cm and 1 metre
(v) 1 cm and 1 inch

21 Two rectangular boxes have the lengths of their corresponding edges in the ratio 5:4. If the smaller box holds 1 lb of sweets, show that the larger box holds very nearly 2 lb.
If a third box, similar in shape to the 1-lb box, holds 8 lb of sweets, compare the lengths of its edges with those of the 1-lb box.

22 A new car is being designed and a model is made from the same materials using a reduction ratio of 1:10.

(i) If the overall length of the car is 15 feet, what is the length of the model?
(ii) Compare the areas of glass used for the windscreens.
(iii) If the weight of the car is 23 cwt, find the weight of the model to the nearest tenth of a pound.
(iv) If the capacity of the fuel tank is 12 gallons, show that the capacity of the model tank is nearly one-tenth of a pint.

23 The formula $V = lbh$ is used to find the volume of a rectangular solid. Find the ratio of the volumes of two similar rectangular solids whose corresponding edges are in the ratio $n:1$.

Revision Exercise on Chapter 3

The Circle

1 A land-excavating vehicle has two wheels of diameter 7 feet and two of diameter 28 inches. If the smaller wheels make one complete revolution, what fraction of one revolution is made by each of the larger wheels? What is the size of the angle through which a radial line on the larger wheel rotates about the centre of the wheel in the time taken for 2 revolutions of the smaller wheel?

2 Consider an electric meter with 3 connected circular dials A, B, and C. Each bears the numerals 0, 1, 2, . . . , 8, 9 equally spaced round the circumference. Dial A reads *units* (i.e. the hand moves from one figure to the next when 1 unit of electricity is used), B reads *tens* of units, and C reads *hundreds* of units. If electricity is being used at the rate of 1,000 units per hour, calculate the rate of rotation in degrees per minute of each of the three hands.

3 The minute hand of a town clock is 28 inches long. How many minutes will be needed for the tip of this hand to travel a distance of 22 inches? Use $\frac{22}{7}$ as an approximation for π.

4 Construct a regular hexagon with a side of length 4 centimetres.

5 Construct a regular octagon such that the distance between two opposite sides is 5 cm. (Begin by drawing a suitable isosceles triangle.) Produce each side both ways so that an eight-pointed star is formed. Letter this APBQCRDS in that order. From a consideration of the symmetry of the figure, or otherwise, state what kind of figure ABCD is, and also PQRS. Try to discover a method of construction of a regular octagon by means of two equal squares.

6 Figure 11 shows a section through a horizontal cylindrical pipe. Water is lying in the pipe, and is 18 inches deep at the middle of the section. The width of the water surface is 4 feet. Calculate the

diameter of the pipe. (Denoting the radius by r inches, find a right-angled triangle whose sides measure r, $r-18$, and 24 inches.)

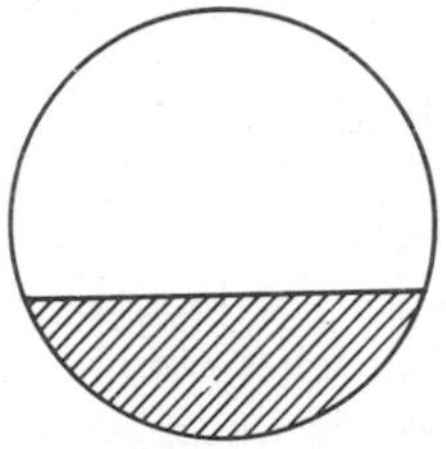

FIG. 11

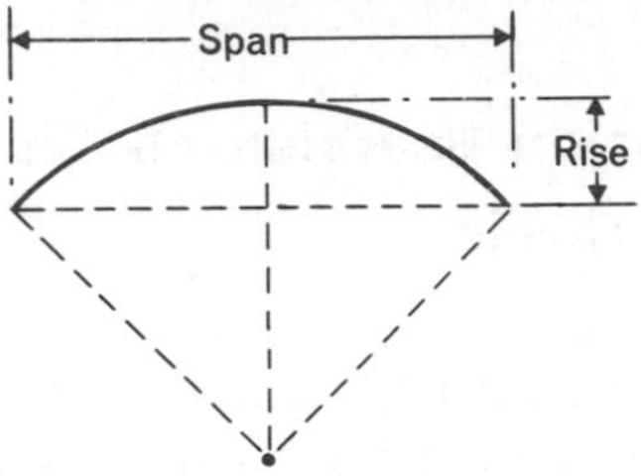

FIG. 12

7 The *span* of a bridge is the horizontal distance between the two ends, and the *rise* is the height of the centre of the bridge above the ends (see Figure 12). A humped-back bridge can be assumed to have the shape of an arc of a circle. If the span of the bridge is 20 metres and the rise is 1 metre, find the radius of this circle.

8 Arches are often composed of two arcs. Construct the following arch. Mark two points A and B so that AB represents a span of 3 metres. With A as centre and AB as radius, draw one arc of the arch. Repeat with B as centre and the same radius. Why is this called an *equilateral arch*? Which is the greater, the span or the rise?

9 Draw a diagram to indicate the part of the coordinate plane containing the set of points $\{(x, y) : x > 0,\ x^2 + y^2 < 25\}$.

10 Describe the region of the coordinate plane which contains all the points (x, y) which are members of the set of points

$$\{(x, y) : 9 \leqslant x^2 + y^2 \leqslant 16\}.$$

11 Draw a circle centre P. Take A and B two points on the circumference such that AB is not a diameter. Join AP and BP and produce these to meet the circumference again in C and D respectively. State carefully how you know that AB and DC are equal and parallel.

12 PQ and RS are two unequal parallel chords in a circle, centre O. The mid-points of these chords are X and Y respectively. Explain from symmetry why O, X, and Y must be collinear.

13 AB and BC are two non-perpendicular chords of a circle. XY is the diameter through the mid-point of BC. The line AB meets XY in H and the line HC meets the circumference again in D. Prove that chords CD and AB are equal in length.

14 A rectangle STUV is inscribed in a circle in such a way that the distances of ST and TU from the centre are equal. What type of figure is STUV?

15 In Figure 13, PQ and PR are tangents from a point P to a circle centre O. A is a point on the minor arc QR. The tangent at A to the circle intersects PQ and PR at B and C respectively. (i) What

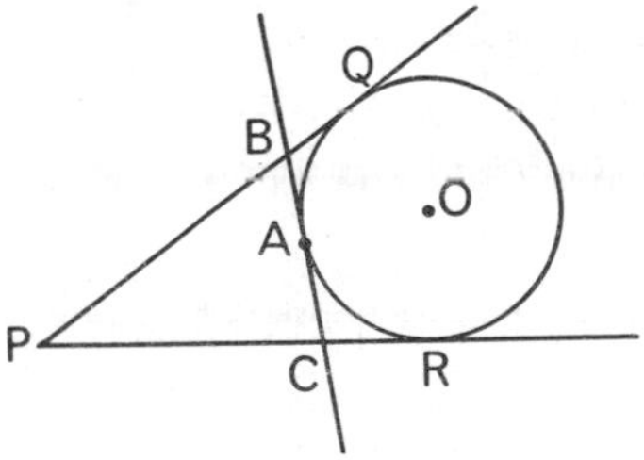

FIG. 13

special type of quadrilateral is BQOA? (ii) Repeat for figurc AORC and figure PQOR. (iii) Prove ∠ BOC = $\frac{1}{2}$ ∠ QOR. (iv) Prove ∠ BOC = 90° − $\frac{1}{2}$ ∠ QPR. (v) For what position of A is the tangent at A parallel to QR? (vi) In the case of part (v) what kind of triangle is PBC?

General Revision Exercises (Books 1-4)

General Revision Exercise 1

Reflection and Rotation

1 Using plain and/or squared paper, draw quadrilaterals as follows:

(i) with exactly one axis of symmetry, not through any vertex,
(ii) with exactly one axis of symmetry, not avoiding the vertices,
(iii) with exactly two axes of symmetry, not through any vertex,
(iv) with exactly two axes of symmetry, not avoiding the vertices,
(v) with point symmetry only (cyclic symmetry of order two),
(vi) with four axes of symmetry,
(vii) with cyclic symmetry of order four,
(viii) with no symmetry of any kind.

2 Indicate on a Cartesian diagram the straight line whose equation is $y=3$. What is the image, in this line, of each of the following points?

(i) $(-1, 3)$ (ii) $(25, 3)$ (iii) $(29, 4)$
(iv) $(-62, 0)$ (v) $(7, -4)$ (vi) $(-4, 7)$

3 (c, d) is the image of (a, b) under reflection in the line $y=3$. Which of the following are true and which are false?

(i) $c=a$ (ii) $d=b$ (iii) $c+a=6$
(iv) $d+b=6$ (v) $d=6-b$ (vi) $b=d-6$
(vii) The image of (c, d) is $(c, 6-d)$.

4 State the image of (a, b) under reflection in the line

(i) $y=10$ (ii) $x=12$ (iii) $y=-5$ (iv) $x=-7$
(v) $x=0$ (vi) $y=0$ (vii) $y=m$ (viii) $x=n$

5 (*a*) State the image, under reflection in the origin, of the points A(5, 4), B(6, −3), C(3, −6), D(−8, −1), E(0, −7), F(0, 0).

(*b*) Mark on a Cartesian diagram the point H(7, 5).
State the coordinates of A′, the image under reflection in H of the point A(5, 4).
Repeat for the other five points of (*a*).

(*c*) State the coordinates of G′, the image under reflection in H of the point G(u, v).

6 (*a*) Consider reflection in the line $x=9$. For each of the following lines, state the equation of its image in $x=9$:

(i) $x=5$ (ii) $x=10$ (iii) $x=20$ (iv) $x=-5$
(v) $y=0$ (vi) $y=7$ (vii) $y=-8$

(*b*) State the equations of the images, under reflection in the line $y=7$, of each of the lines considered in (*a*).

7 On isometric paper draw axes OX and OY such that angle XOY = 60°; use equal scales on the two axes.
Mark the points (0, 0), (4, 4), (−3, −3). Draw the line whose equation is $y=x$.
Mark the points A(0, 3), B(2, 5), C(3, 9) and the images A′, B′, C′ of these points under reflection in the line $y=x$.
Draw the line segments AC′, A′C; comment.
Draw the line segments AC, A′C′; comment.
Before you draw them, make a comment about AB′ and A′B.

8 In Figure 1, ABCD represents a square metal plate whose diagonals intersect at O. PR and QS are at right angles. What is the image, under a positive rotation of 90° about O, of (i) O (ii) D (iii) DA (iv) OS (v) PQ (vi) PR? What kind of figure is PQRS?

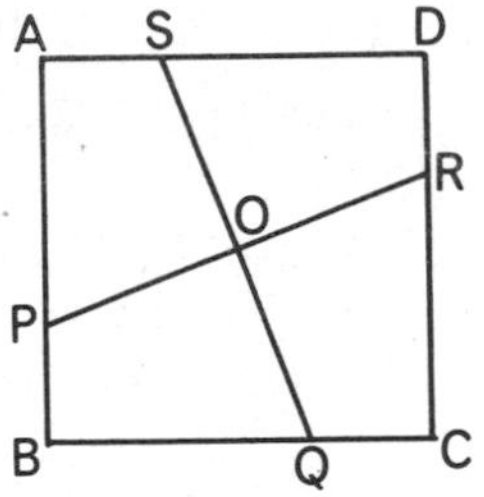

FIG. 1

Suppose PQ, QR, RS, SP were produced to intersect the lines of CD, DA, AB, BC at H, K, L, M respectively. Name a triangle congruent to QCH and one congruent to SMQ.
What kinds of figures are HRLP and HKLM?

9 Figure 2 shows a pentagram—a regular five-pointed star. What is the 'order' of the cyclic symmetry possessed by the figure? What angles of rotation would carry OA on to OB, OC, OD, OE, and OA? What

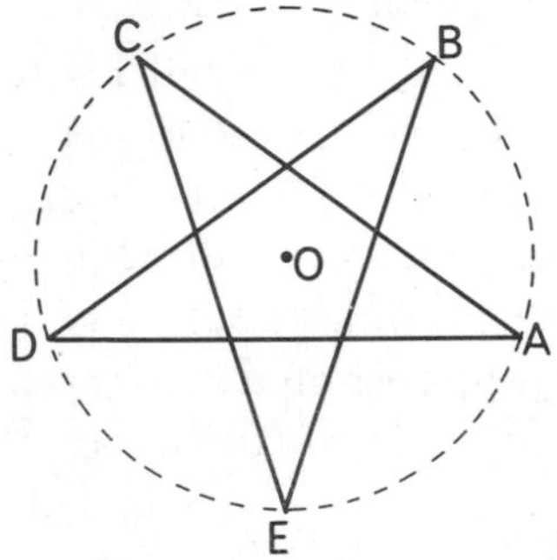

FIG. 2

positive angles of rotation would carry AC on to BD, and on to DA, and on to EB? Deduce the size of the acute angles between AC and BD; AC and DA; AC and EB.

10 Using a Cartesian diagram, write down the coordinates of the image of each of the following points, under a positive quarter-turn about O.

(i) (3, 1) (ii) (5, −2) (iii) (−6, 2) (iv) (−4, −7) (v) (x, y)

11 P(3, 1), Q(6, 2), R(7, 3), and S(4, 4) are points on a Cartesian diagram. The images of P, Q, R, S under a rotation of +90° about O are P_1, Q_1, R_1, S_1; the images of P_1, Q_1, R_1, S_1 under reflection in the y-axis are P_2, Q_2, R_2 ,S_2. Write down the coordinates of these eight points without using a figure; then check from a sketch diagram.
It is a fact that P_2, Q_2, R_2, S_2 are the images of P, Q, R, S under reflection in a certain line. Can you describe this line and write down its equation?

12 Repeat question 11, but this time P_1, Q_1, R_1, S_1 are the images of P, Q, R, S under reflection in the y-axis, and P_2, Q_2, R_2, S_2 are the images of P_1, Q_1, R_1, S_1 under a rotation of +90° about O.

13 ABCD is a parallelogram. O is the point of intersection of the diagonals. AB is produced to H and CD to K so that BH = DK. Name the images under a half-turn about O, of the line segments HC, KA, AH, and CK. Make a statement about the triangles AHC and CKA, and about the nature of the quadrilateral AHCK. Prove that KB and DH are parallel.

14 AB and AC are equal chords of a circle, centre O; P and Q are the mid-points of AB and AC.

(*a*) Describe transformations (reflection, rotation, or translation) which conserve the circle and under which (i) the image of AB is AC (ii) the image of AB is CA.

(*b*) AX is a diameter. XP and XQ produced cut the circumference at R and S respectively. By considering reflection in a certain line show that the chords XR and XS are equal in length.

15 On isometric paper draw axes OX, OY at an angle of 60°; use equal scales. Draw the triangle OAB where A is (5, 0) and B is (5, 3).

Show the positions of the images of the triangle OAB under rotations about O of 60°, 120°, 180°, 240°, 300°. State the coordinates of each of the images of A and of B.

16 (*a*) Check that the points (0, 0) and (5, 10) are members of the set $\{(x, y): y = 2x\}$.

(*b*) Find the coordinates of three other points which lie on the line whose equation is $y = 2x$.

(*c*) Write down the coordinates of the images, under reflection in the origin, of these five points. State the equation of the line which is the image, under reflection in the origin, of the line $y = 2x$.

(*d*) Write down the coordinates of the images, under reflection in the x-axis, of the same five points. State the equation of the line which is the image, under reflection in the x-axis, of the line $y = 2x$.

(*e*) Repeat (*d*) but this time consider reflection in the y-axis.

17 (*a*) Check that the points (0, 6) and (8, 10) are members of the set $\{(x, y): y = 6 + \frac{1}{2}x\}$; and find the coordinates of three other points which lie on the line whose equation is $y = 6 + \frac{1}{2}x$.

(*b*) Write down the coordinates of the images of these points under reflection in the point (0, 6); and state the equation of the line which is the image in (0, 6) of the line $y = 6 + \frac{1}{2}x$.

(*c*) Repeat (*b*) for reflection in the origin (0, 0).

(*d*) Repeat for reflection in the *y*-axis.

(*e*) Repeat for reflection in the line whose equation is $y = 6$.

(*f*) Repeat for reflection in the *x*-axis.

General Revision Exercise 2

Triangles, Parallelograms, Translation

1 ABCD is a parallelogram with its diagonals intersecting at O. GOH is a straight line meeting AB at G and DC at H. KOL is a straight line meeting AD at K and BC at L. What are the images of A, G, and L under reflection in O? Discuss the effect of giving the figure a half-turn about O. What kind of figure is GLHK? How could you ensure that GLHK is a rhombus?

2 In rectangular coordinates P is the point (1, 0), Q is (5, 1), and S is (−1, 3). Find the coordinates of the fourth vertex R of parallelogram PQRS. Where will the diagonals intersect? Draw a rectangle by drawing parallels to the *y*-axis through S and Q and a parallel to the *x*-axis through R. Deduce the area of the parallelogram from the area of the rectangle.

3 ABCD is a parallelogram, and DE and CF are drawn perpendicular to AB. DC is 6 inches long and FC is 4 inches long. Triangle FCB is given a displacement of 6 inches in the direction CD. What is the new position of the triangle? What is the area of the rectangle EFCD and of the parallelogram ABCD?

Answer the same questions if DC measures b units, FC h units and the displacement is b units in the direction CD.

4 In Figure 3, ABCD is a parallelogram with diagonals intersecting at E. Name angles in the figure equal to each of the angles marked $x°$, $y°$, $z°$, $w°$, $p°$, and $q°$.

In each case state what name can be given to the pair of equal angles.

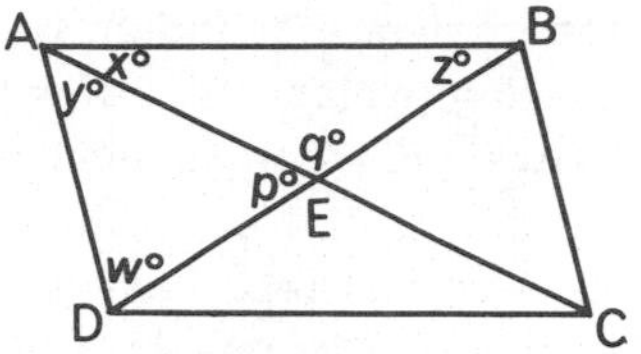

FIG. 3

What kind of parallelogram must ABCD be if (i) $x=y$ (ii) $x=z$ (iii) $p=q$ (iv) $x=z$ and $p=q$? In each case write down any other equalities between x, y, z, w, p, and q.

5 In parallelogram ABCD the bisectors of angles A and B meet at P. If angle A $=2a°$ and angle B $=2b°$, write down an equation connecting a and b. Show that angle APB is a right angle. If the bisectors of angles B and C meet at Q, of C and D at R, and of D and A at S, what kind of figure is PQRS? In what kind of parallelogram will the four bisectors not form a quadrilateral?

6 How many given measurements are required to specify a triangle ABC? Write down some sets of measurements that will do. If triangle ABC is given, how could you complete the parallelogram ABCD with your instruments? (You should be able to find more ways than one.) Do different methods of completing the figure give different parallelograms? How many measurements are required to specify a parallelogram?

7 Using the given information, draw a parallelogram ABCD, with AC and BD intersecting at O, in the following cases. State in which of these cases the information is sufficient to specify the parallelogram. Can you suggest why the information is insufficient in the other cases?

(i) AB = 4·8 cm, BC = 6·4 cm, angle ABC = 63°.
(ii) AB = 6 cm, angle BAD = 70°, angle ABC = 110°.
(iii) AC = 8 cm, BD = 6 cm, angle AOB = 100°.
(iv) AB = 4·8 cm, BC = 6·4 cm, AC = 7·2 cm.
(v) Angle ABC = 55°, angle BCD = 125°, angle CDA = 55°.
(vi) AC = 8 cm, BD = 6 cm, AB = 4·8 cm.
(vii) AB = 4 cm, BC = 6 cm, and the distance between BC and AD is 3·4 cm.

8 Take Q, the set of quadrilaterals, as the universal set.
$P = \{\text{parallelograms}\}$, $R = \{\text{rectangles}\}$, $B = \{\text{rhombuses}\}$, $S = \{\text{squares}\}$, $K = \{\text{kites}\}$, $P' =$ complement of P with respect to the universal set Q.
State which of the following sets are included in P and which in P': R, B, S, K, {kites with not all sides equal}, {quadrilaterals with one pair of parallel sides only}.
Are the following statements true or false?
(i) $R \cap B = S$ (ii) $P \cup B = K$ iii) $B \subset P \Rightarrow R \subset P$
(iv) $P \cup R \cup S \cup K = Q$ (v) $B \subset K$ (vi) $P \cap K = \emptyset$

9 An isosceles triangle has its base 4 units long on the x-axis and its vertex at the point (0, 5). If the triangle is given a displacement 4 to the right and 3 down, write down the new coordinates of the three vertices.

10 A point on the rim of a wheel rolling on a straight line describes a locus. Sketch part of the locus. If the locus is extended without limit in both directions, what is the shortest displacement that will fit the curve on to itself again?

11 A ship sails 5 kilometres in a direction S40°W and then 3 kilometres in a direction S60°W. Draw a diagram to scale, and by measurement find the total effect as a single displacement. Making the necessary measurements, express the total displacement in terms of northing and easting.

12 ABC is a triangle with BC produced to D. Calculate the sizes of angle ACB and angle ACD in the following cases
(i)A = 60°, B = 40° (ii)A = 53°, B = 47° (iii)A = x°, B = y°
State any relation you notice between angles A, B, and ACD.
(ACD is an exterior angle of triangle ABC, formed by producing one side of the triangle. Angle ACB is called the interior adjacent angle and angles A and B the interior opposite angles.)

13 In the diagram for the last question draw CE parallel to BA. Use your parallel lines to find pairs of equal angles and mark them equal. What conclusion can you draw about the exterior angle? What true relation can you write down between angle ACD and angle A, between angle ACD and angle B?

14 In triangle PQR, PQ = PR, and angle P = 40°. Calculate the size of angle Q.

15 In triangle ABC, angle B is the complement of angle C. Calculate the size of angle A.

16 In an isosceles triangle ABC, AB = AC, angle B = 75°, and BA is produced to D. Calculate the size of angle CAD. If AE bisects angle CAD, show that AE is parallel to BC.

17 In Figure 4 calculate the sizes of as many angles as you can.

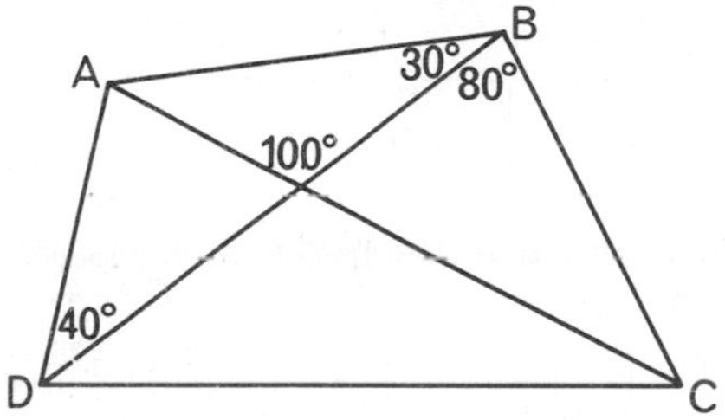

FIG. 4

18 In Figure 5 triangle ABC is right-angled at B. Show that $p+q=270$.

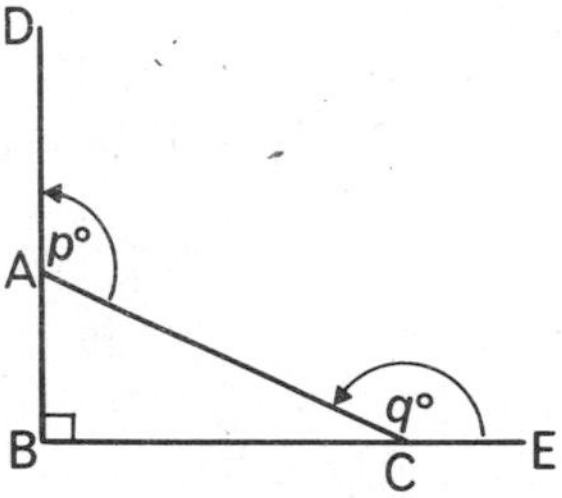

FIG. 5

19 In triangle ABC, AD bisects angle BAC and meets BC at D. Angle ABC = 46°, and angle ACB = 72°. DE and DF are drawn parallel to BA and CA to meet CA and BA at E and F respectively. Calculate the sizes of angles FAD, EAD, FDA, and EDA. What kind of triangles are FAD and EAD? What kind of figure is AEDF?

20 In the triangular tiling of Figure 6 describe how the tile ABC could be brought to the position DEF by a half-turn and a translation. Find a point O in the tiling such that a half-turn of the whole plane about O will bring ABC into the position DEF.

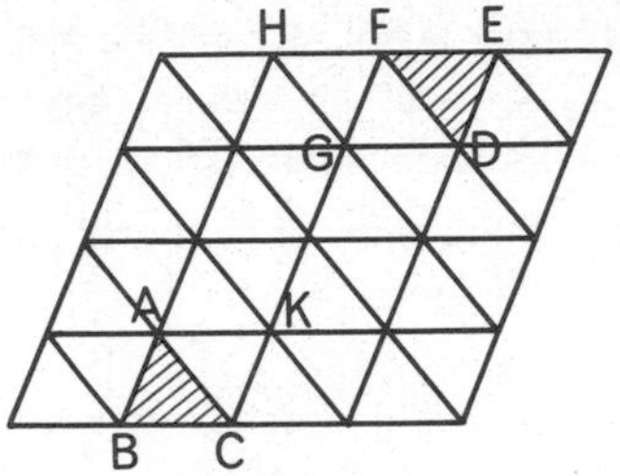

FIG. 6

What is the image of B in the point O?
What is the image of the mid-point of AC in the point O?
If we wanted ABC reflected into the position GFH, where would the centre of reflection have to be?
If the mid-point of AC is taken as the centre of reflection, what is the image of triangle ABC?
If a triangle is reflected in the mid-point of a side, what figure do the triangle and its image together form?

21 In Figure 7, PQRS is a parallelogram, ST is perpendicular to PQ; PT, TQ, and ST measure 5, $14\frac{1}{2}$, and 12 units respectively.

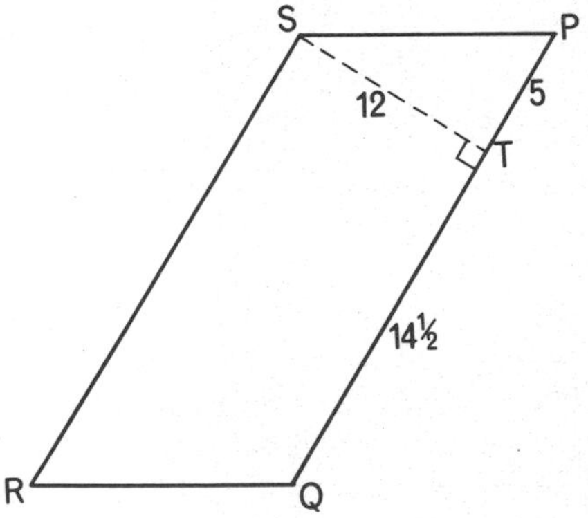

FIG. 7

Calculate (i) the area of the parallelogram;
(ii) the length of PS;
(iii) the distance between the parallels PS and QR.

22 (*a*) ABCD is a parallelogram made of four 'Meccano' strips freely jointed at the corners. AB is 12 units long and BC 8. AB is kept fixed and CD is allowed to move. What are the loci of C and D? What is the locus of the mid-point of AD? In what positions of CD will (i) ABCD be a rectangle (ii) ABCD not be a parallelogram at all? How far is the intersection of the diagonals from the mid-point of AB? What is the locus of the intersection of the diagonals?
(*b*) If AB = 12 units and BC = 12 units, what are the loci of C and D?

General Revision Exercise 3

Locus

1 Figure 8 on page 164 shows a grid of equally spaced straight lines and a set of equally spaced concentric circles with centre A.
Every point on line 2 is 2 units from BC; every point on circle 2 is 2 units from A. Verify that the point P is 5 units from BC and also 5 units from A.
Use the grid to find the locus of points whose distance from A is equal to their distance from BC. Plot a sufficient number of points and draw a smooth curve through them.
(Note the name *parabola*.)

2 Verify that the point Q is 6 units from A and 3 units from BC.
On the same diagram draw the locus of points whose distance from A is twice their distance from BC.
(Note the name *hyperbola*.)

3 Verify that the point R is 3 units from A and 6 units from BC. On the same diagram draw the locus of points whose distance from A is half their distance from BC.
(Note the name *ellipse*.)

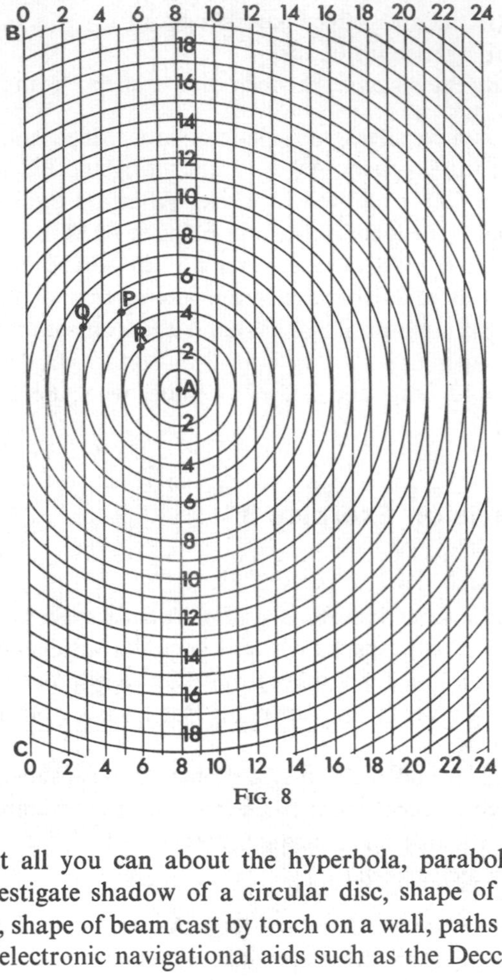

FIG. 8

4 Find out all you can about the hyperbola, parabola, and ellipse (e.g. investigate shadow of a circular disc, shape of car headlamp reflector, shape of beam cast by torch on a wall, paths of planets and comets, electronic navigational aids such as the Decca Chain).

5 Figure 9 shows a grid of two sets of concentric circles with centres A and B placed 16 units apart. (The numbers on the circles refer to the lengths of their radii.)
Verify that the point P is 3 units from A and 15 units from B.
Use the grid to plot the positions of points P such that

$$PA+PB = 18$$

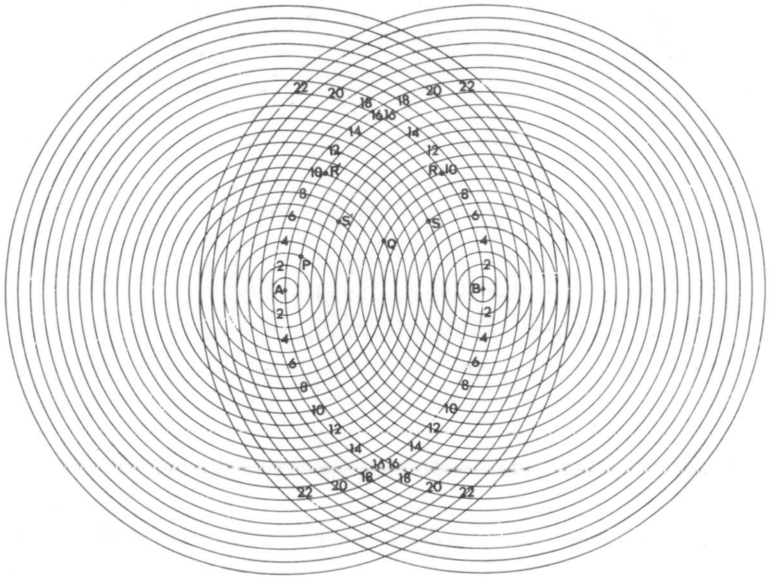

FIG. 9

Plot a sufficient number of points and draw a smooth curve through them.
(Note the name *ellipse*.)

6 In Figure 9 verify that the point R is at the intersection of circles 16 and 10.

Note that RA − RB = 6 units.

Verify also that (i) SA − SB = 6
(ii) R′B − R′A = 6
(iii) S′B − S′A = 6

Use this grid to plot the locus of points such that the difference between their distances from the two fixed points A and B is 6 units. Plot a sufficient number of points and draw two smooth curves through them.

(Note the word *hyperbola*.)

7 Indicate on one diagram the three sets of points
$\{(x, y) : x^2+y^2 = 100\}$, $\{(x, y) : x^2+y^2 < 100\}$, and
$\{(x, y) : x^2+y^2 > 100\}$

8 Indicate, each on a separate diagram, the following sets of points:

(i) $\{(x, y): x^2+y^2 < 100\} \cap \{(x, y): x > 6\}$
(ii) $\{(x, y): x^2+y^2 < 100\} \cap \{(x, y): x > -6\}$
(iii) $\{(x, y): x^2+y^2 = 100\} \cap \{(x, y): x > 6\}$
(iv) $\{(x, y): x^2+y^2 > 100\} \cap \{(x, y): x < 6\}$
(v) $\{(x, y): x^2+y^2 < 100\} \cap \{(x, y): y=0\}$
(vi) $\{(x, y): x^2+y^2 = 100\} \cap \{(x, y): y = x\}$
(vii) $\{(x, y): x^2+y^2 = 100\} \cap \{(x, y): y < x\}$
(viii) $\{(x, y): x^2+y^2 = 100\} \cap \{(x, y): y < x+10\}$
(ix) $\{(x, y): x^2+y^2 = 100\} \cap \{(x, y): 2x-3y = 30\}$
(x) $\{(x, y): x^2+y^2 = 100\} \cap \{(x, y): 3x+2y > 30\}$

General Revision Exercise 4

Special Triangles and Quadrilaterals

1 A is the point (2, 2), B is (6, 7), C is (7, 6). Calculate the lengths of AB, BC, and CA. What kind of triangle is ABC?
By reflecting in BC find the coordinates of the third vertex D of the rhombus ABDC.

2 RST is an isosceles triangle in which RT = RS = 2·5 cm and ST = [illegible]·0 cm. Calculate the area of this triangle.
Describe how by producing RS and RT you could construct a triangle whose area is 9 times the area of triangle RST.

3 By calculating gradients, show that the points (−2, 8), (0, 12), (1, 14), (4, 20) all lie on a straight line.
If P(x, y) belongs to this line, find the relationship between x and y.
B is the point (−4, 0) and C is (14, 0). Find a point T on the above line such that TB = TC.

4 Figure 10 shows two congruent rectangles, each of whose diagonals intersect at 40°.
Calculate the sizes of (i) angle RAC (ii) angle XRA.

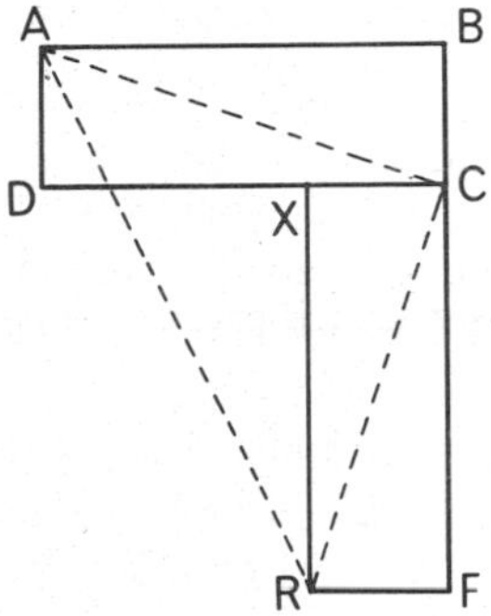

FIG. 10

5 RPQ is an isosceles triangle in which RP = RQ = 37 units and PQ = 24 units.
Calculate (i) the length of the altitude from R to PQ (ii) the area of triangle RPQ (iii) the length of the altitude from P to RQ using part (ii).

6 Figure 11 shows a square ABCD of side 4 units. AP = 1 unit. The diagonals of the square intersect at O. PO produced cuts DC at Q and BC produced at R. By rotation find the length of QC, and by similar triangles find the length of CR.

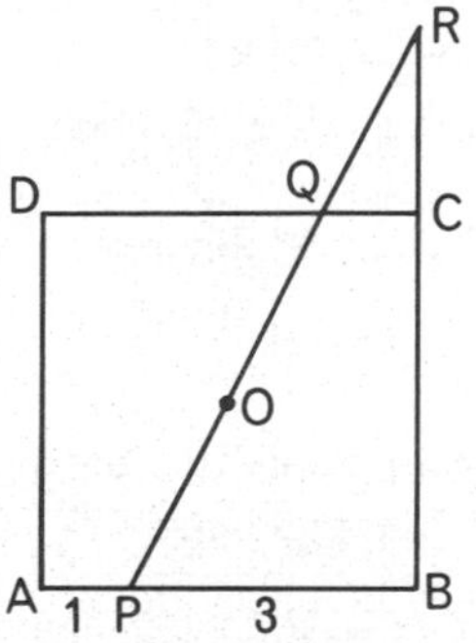

FIG 11

7 XPH is an equilateral triangle. A is a point on PH such that PA $=\frac{1}{3}$AH. XA produced meets the parallel through P to XH at T. Show that (i) PA bisects angle XPT (ii) by using similar triangles $\frac{XP}{PT}=\frac{XA}{AT}=\frac{3}{1}$.

8 XYZ is an equilateral triangle whose centre of symmetry is A. Q and S are taken on XZ and YZ respectively so that XQ = ZS. Equilateral triangles XQP and SRZ are drawn external to triangle XYZ.
Under the rotation about A which sends Z to Y, name the images of (i) XP (ii) YP (iii) angle XPY (iv) triangle XPZ.
Find the sizes of the angles between YP and XR.

9 In triangle ABC, AB = CB and angle BAC = 32°. The perpendicular bisector of AB meets AC at T and AB at Q.
Calculate the size of angle ABT.
The bisector of angle ABT meets AC at X. The image of X under reflection in QT is X′.
Calculate the size of angle BX′A.

10 Draw accurately a rhombus TSCD in which TS measures 6·2 cm and angle STC 20°.
The perpendicular bisector XY of TD meets TS at X.
Calculate the size of angle TDX.
Find the image of T after a double reflection, first in XY and then in CT.
Find the image of C after a double reflection, first in DS and then in XY.

11 AOB is a diameter of a circle with centre O. CD is a chord cutting OB at right angles at X (see Figure 12).

(i) Suppose angle OCD = 36°. Calculate the sizes of angles COD, AOD, CAD, and ODB.

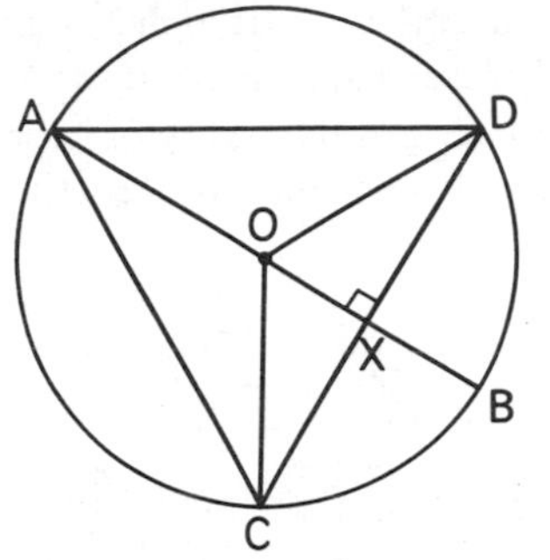

FIG. 12

(ii) Suppose the radius of the circle measures 8·0 centimetres, and CD is 10·0 centimetres. Calculate, correct to two significant figures, the length of OX, AD, and BD.

General Revision Exercise 5

Construction of Triangles, etc.

1 ABC is an isosceles triangle with AB and AC each measuring 7 cm and BC = 3 cm. Construct the triangle and measure the angles. How would you use your angle measurements to check the accuracy of your construction?

2 Is it possible to construct a triangle ABC with AB and AC each 4 cm long and BC 9 cm long?
The sides of a triangle are a, b and c cm long. A triangle with $b = c = 4$ is drawn. Complete the following statements:
(i) $a >$ . . . . . (ii) . . . . . $< a$.
Combine your answers in the form . . . . . $< a <$ . . . . .

3 In triangle DEF, DE and DF are equal in length and the base EF is 2·5 cm long. State (if possible) (i) the shortest length that DE can have in order that a triangle can be drawn, (ii) the greatest length DE can have.

4 In triangle ABC, angle C is a right angle, BC is 3·4 cm long and AB 5 cm. Construct triangle ABC accurately.

5 Figure 13 shows a number of triangles ABC each with AB = 5 cm and angle B = 47° (refer back to question 4).
What is the shortest length that AC can have in order that a triangle ABC may be drawn? State another length for AC which will give only one triangle ABC.

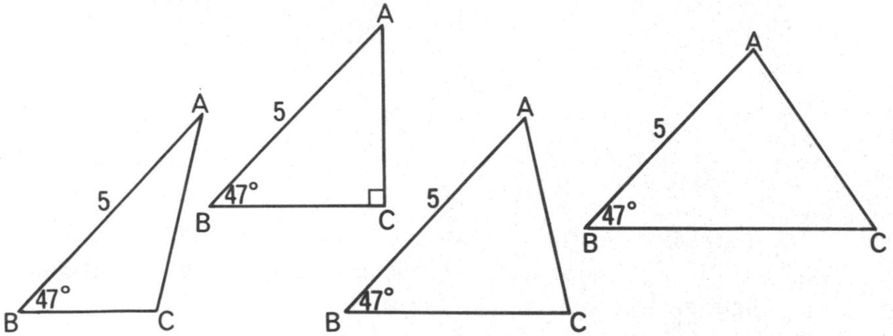

FIG. 13

State in the form of an inequality all the possible lengths of AC which will each give one triangle only.
What lengths for AC will each give two possible triangles ABC? (Give your answer in the form of a double inequality.)

6 In triangle ABC, AB measures 5 inches and AC is 4 inches. State the greatest and least lengths that BC may have in order that a triangle ABC may be drawn.

7 A framework of rods is in the shape of a parallelogram ABCD freely jointed at A, B, C, and D. If a fifth rod is attached from B to D, the framework becomes rigid. Explain why.
Would the framework become rigid if the fifth rod was attached to the mid-points of AD and AB?
If two points on AB and AD were joined by a fifth rod, would the framework be rigid, whichever points were chosen?

8 ABCD is a framework of rods in the shape of a quadrilateral freely jointed at A, B, C, and D. How could the framework be made rigid?
Is one extra rod sufficient?

9 ABCD is a given quadrilateral whose diagonals AC and BD measure 6·3 cm and 5·4 cm respectively. Suggest other information which would be needed in order to draw the quadrilateral.

10 A and B are two coastguard stations, A being 5 miles due north of B. In order to find the position of a ship C in distress, observations are made from A and B. The bearing of C from A is 30° east of south, and the bearing of C from B is 50° east of north. Find the distance of C from A and also from the shore-line AB.
(Make a scale drawing using a scale of 1 inch to two miles.)
What are the distance and bearing of C from a lifeboat station D, 4 miles due south of B?

11 A surveyor drawing a map of a district wishes to determine the position of a church tower A. He knows the position of two landmarks B and C one mile apart; C is due east of B. He has a theodolite for measuring angles. What measurements would he make in order to fix the position of the church?
Suppose he finds angle B = 43° and angle C = 37°. How far is A from B and from C?
(Use a scale of 1 inch to 1,000 yards.)

12 Having found the position of the church A in question 11, how could the surveyor fix the position of another landmark D (see Figure 14*a*)?

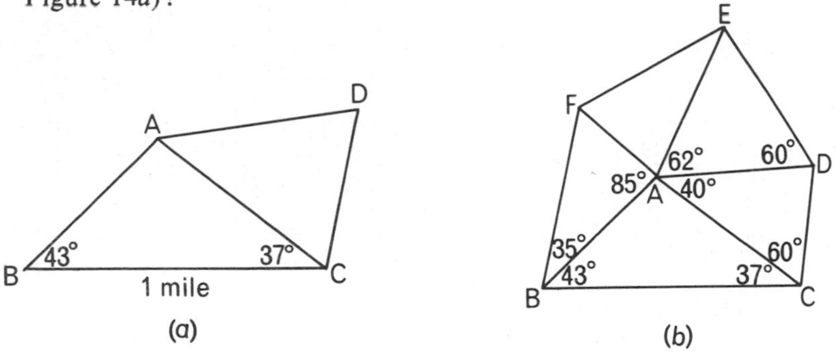

FIG. 14

13 The information shown in Figure 14*b* (not drawn to scale) was obtained by the surveyor. A, B, C, D, E, and F are important land-

marks in the same district. Draw an accurate map showing these six places and find the distance between E and F.
(Use a scale of 1 inch to 1,000 yards.)

14 Draw a parallelogram whose diagonals measure 7·5 cm and 10·0 cm, and intersect at 110°.

15 Draw a rhombus whose diagonals measure 7·5 cm and 10·0 cm.

16 Draw a rhombus, whose sides are 7·5 cm, in which one diagonal measures 4·5 cm.

17 Draw a kite ABCD in which AC measures 7·5 cm, angle A 142°, and angle C 68°.

18 Draw a kite ABCD in which BC measures 4·5 cm, CD 6·5 cm, and angle C 114°.

19 Draw kites of two different shapes, for which the side lengths are 4 cm and 6 cm, and one diagonal measures 5 cm.

Arithmetic

CHAPTER 1 Using a Slide Rule

1 Ruler addition and subtraction

Exercise 1—Practical

1 Cut out two rectangular strips of card, each 1 inch wide and 8 inches long, and mark them off in inches and half inches, edge to edge. Figure 1 shows how you can use these strips to *add* two numbers. We call the upper marked strip the C scale and the lower one the D scale.

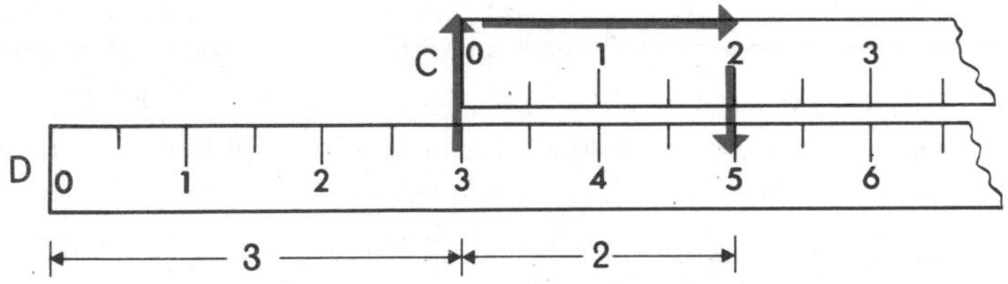

FIG. 1

You can see that to add 3 and 2 we set 0 on the C scale opposite 3 on the D scale, and read off the sum on the D scale opposite 2 on the C scale.

2 Use the two scales in this way to find:

(i) $4+3$ (ii) $5+3$ (iii) $2+2{\cdot}5$ (iv) $3{\cdot}5+1{\cdot}5$

Look at Figure 1 again and you will see that the two scales also give $5-2$. The D scale simply acts as a number line.

3 Use the two scales to give:

(i) $8-3$ (ii) $5-1$ (iii) $4{\cdot}5-2{\cdot}5$

Let a and b represent two numbers. The diagrams for their addition $a+b$ and for their subtraction $a-b$ are shown in Figure 2.

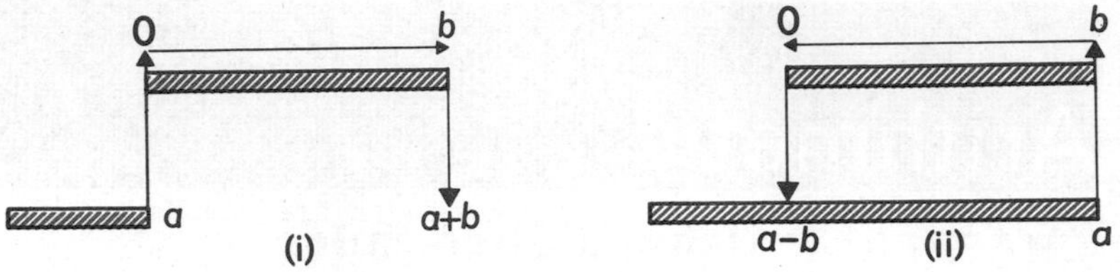

FIG. 2

Notice that when we use the scales in the way described above, the first number and the sum or difference appear on the D scale.

2 From addition to multiplication

You have found in your study of numbers that the same laws are true for the operations of addition and multiplication. We have:

	Addition	*Multiplication*
	Sum $= a+b$	Product $= a \times b$
Commutative laws	$a+b=b+a$	$a \times b = b \times a$
Associative laws	$(a+b)+c=a+(b+c)$	$(a \times b) \times c = a \times (b \times c)$
Identity elements	$a+0=a=0+a$	$a \times 1 = a = 1 \times a$

We have used the two scales for addition. How can we adapt them for multiplication? We find that if in Figure 3(i) we replace 0 (the identity element for addition) by 1 (the identity element for multiplication), and the sum $a+b$ by the product $a \times b$ we obtain:

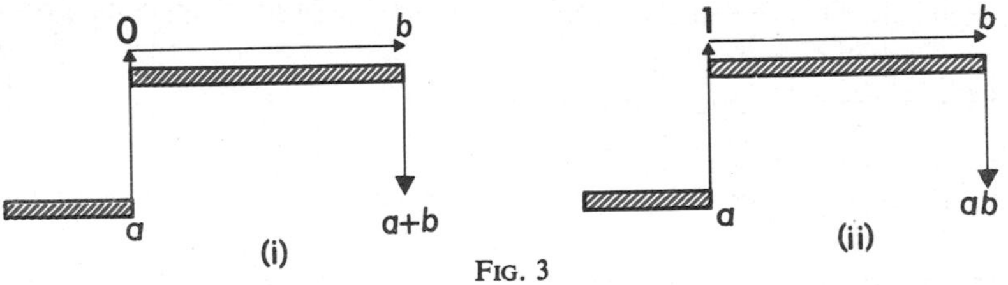

FIG. 3

We must therefore change the number scales so that the first number is 1, as shown in Figure 4(ii). We can now choose any number we want as a replacement for p; suppose we take 2. It follows at once from

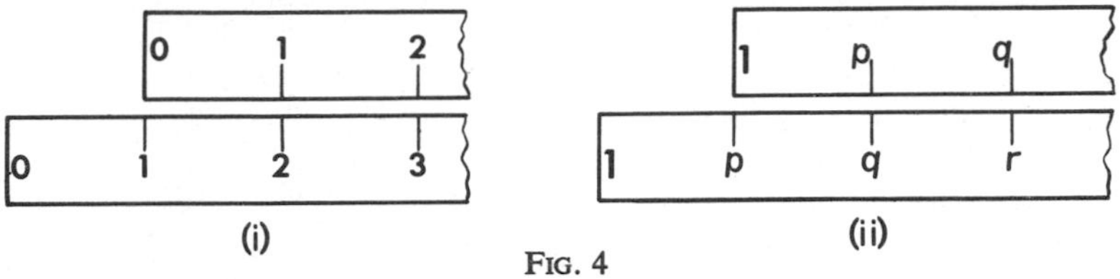

FIG. 4

Figure 3(ii) that 4 must be taken as the replacement for q. What number then replaces r?

You should now be able to continue the sequence of numbers. Suppose we had replaced p by 3. What numbers would then have to be taken as replacements for q and r?

Exercise 2—Practical

1 Use the reverse sides of the strips you had in Exercise 1. Mark them off in inches, edge to edge, but insert the numbers 1, 2, 4, . . . of the sequence obtained above (starting at the extreme left-hand edge of each strip).

2 Use these strips and Figure 3(ii) to verify that:

(i) $4 \times 8 = 32$ (ii) $16 \times 4 = 64$ (iii) $2 \times 32 = 64$ (iv) $8 \times 16 = 128$

3 Adapt Figure 2(ii) to show a scheme for dividing one number by another. Use your strips to find the quotients:

(i) $8 \div 2$ (ii) $64 \div 4$ (iii) $32 \div 32$ (iv) $128 \div 4$

Find some other products and quotients.

3 Calibrating the multiplication scales

The scales you have made can be used for multiplication and division involving the numbers 1, 2, 4, 8, . . . , but what about numbers like 3, or 7, or 29?

In Section 2 we noted the correspondence between the elements of the set $\{0, 1, 2, 3, 4, \ldots\}$ under addition and the elements of the set

{1, 2, 4, 8, 16, . . .} under multiplication. This mapping can be shown thus:

Numbers to be added:	0	1	2	3	4	. . .
	↕	↕	↕	↕	↕	
Numbers to be multiplied:	1	2	4	8	16	. . .

Figure 5 shows the graph of the mapping of one set onto the other.

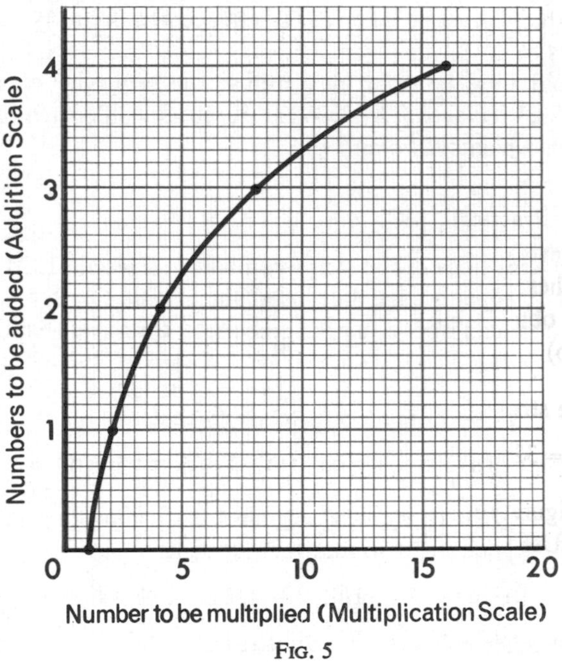

FIG. 5

The points lie on a smooth curve and it is reasonable to assume that for any number on the multiplication scale we can obtain from the graph the corresponding number on the addition scale. For example, 10 on the multiplication scale corresponds to 3·3 approximately on the addition scale, so you can mark 10 on your strip of card, 3·3 inches from the left-hand end.

Exercise 3

Calibrate your strips as indicated above to show each whole number from 1 to 16. Mark also the positions of 1·5 and 2·5. Use your strips to calculate the products and quotients below. Remember that the positions of the numbers on your scales are approximate and therefore your answers will also be approximate.

1 2×3	2 3×5	3 4×4	4 7×2
5 $6 \times 2{\cdot}5$	6 $4 \times 1{\cdot}5$	7 $8 \times 1{\cdot}5$	8 $2{\cdot}5 \times 2{\cdot}5$
9 $12 \div 4$	10 $16 \div 8$	11 $9 \div 3$	12 $12 \div 6$
13 $16 \div 10$	14 $10 \div 2{\cdot}5$	15 $6 \div 1{\cdot}5$	16 $13 \div 2{\cdot}5$

4 The slide rule

Look at your slide rule. Notice the C and D scales, which are like the ones you have been using. Place the hairline on the *cursor* over 2 on the D scale, then move the *slide* until the 1 on the C scale is under the hairline. You will find it helpful to hold the *body* of the slide rule in such a way that you can lever the slide very slowly for the last adjustment. Place the hairline on the cursor over 3 on the C scale, and read off the number on the D scale which is under the hairline. Now place the hairline over 4 on the C scale and read off the corresponding number on the D scale.

The C and D scales contain the whole numbers from 1 to 10, with the divisions between these accurately subdivided as follows:

1 to 2, divided into tenths, and each tenth divided into tenths;
2 to 4, divided into tenths, and each tenth divided into fifths;
4 to 10, divided into tenths, and each tenth divided into halves.

In order to give you some practice in reading numbers accurately on the scales, the letters in the following diagrams indicate numbers on the C or D scale.

Exercise 4

Read off, or write down, the numbers corresponding to the letters shown in the diagrams in questions 1–3 (Figures 6–8).

1

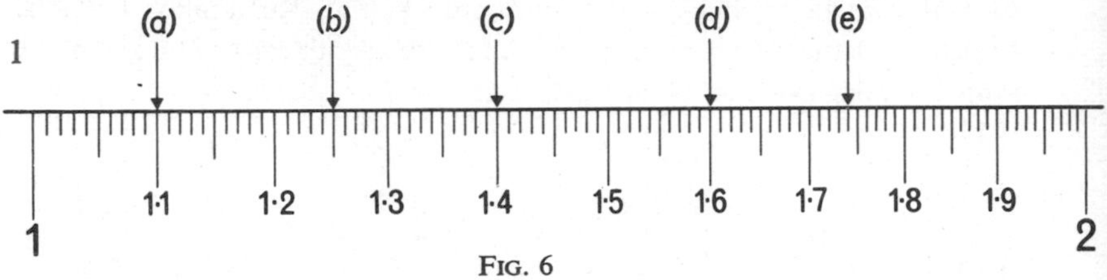

FIG. 6

2

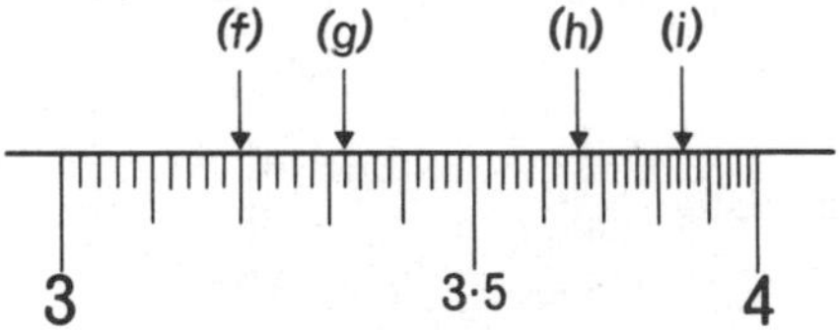

FIG. 7

3

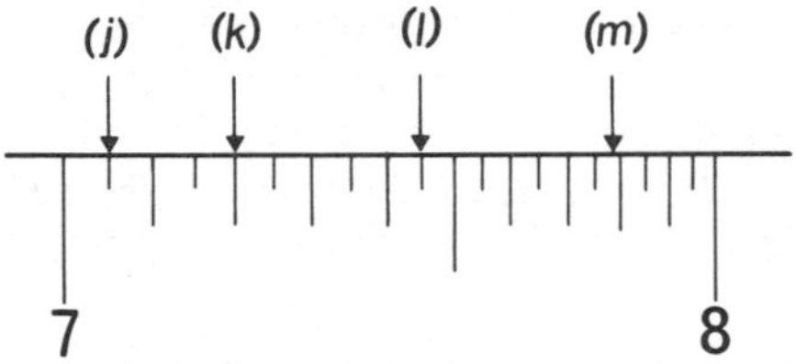

FIG. 8

4 Setting the cursor first, slide the C scale to the right until the 1 is opposite each of the following numbers on the D scale in turn. In each case read off, or write down, the number on the D scale corresponding to 2 on the C scale.

(*a*) 1·6 (*b*) 3·1 (*c*) 4·5 (*d*) 1·24 (*e*) 2·22 (*f*) 4·9

What kind of calculation have you been making here?

Note.—From the above exercise you will notice that 3-figure accuracy is the best you can expect to obtain when using a slide rule.

5 Multiplication and division

Look at the numbers 1, 2, 3, 4, . . . , 10 on each of the C and D scales on a slide rule. From Figure 9(i) we can find the product 2 × 3·5 as in Figure 9(ii) by moving the slide (and scale C) to the right until 1 on scale C is opposite 2 on scale D, then looking along scale C to 3·5 and reading off the product on scale D.

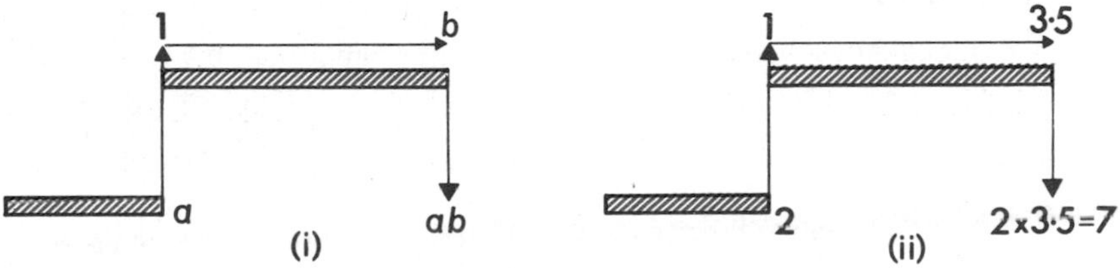

FIG. 9

When the slide rule is used in this way, the first and final numbers are on scale D.

It is important to remember that all that the slide rule is giving is the *sum of two lengths*, one on the C scale and the other on the D scale; that these lengths represent numbers, as on the number line; and that the rule is calibrated in such a way that the *product* of the two numbers results.

Exercise 5

Use a slide rule to calculate the following products:

1 2 × 3	2 2 × 5	3 3 × 2·5	4 3 × 1·2
5 4 × 2·5	6 4 × 1·6	7 5 × 2	8 5 × 1·8
9 1·4 × 2·5	10 1·8 × 5	11 $2{\cdot}2^2$	12 $3{\cdot}14^2$

From Figure 10(i) we can find the quotient 6·8 ÷ 2 as in Figure 10(ii). Note that here the slide rule gives us the *difference of two lengths*.

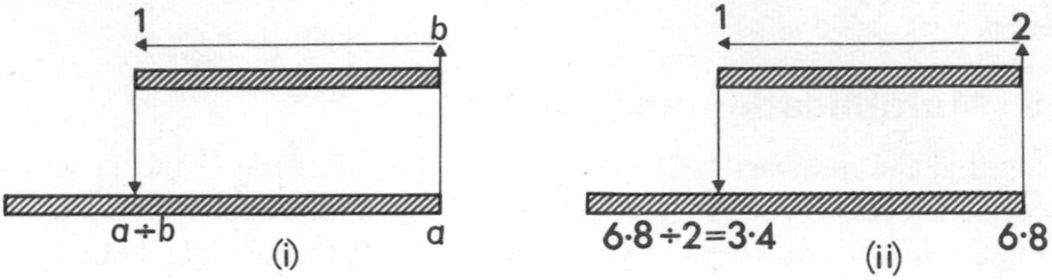

FIG. 10

Exercise 6

Use a slide rule to calculate the following quotients:

1 $10 \div 5$	2 $8 \div 4$	3 $7 \div 2$	4 $10 \div 4$
5 $10 \div 2{\cdot}5$	6 $8 \div 6$	7 $8 \div 7$	8 $4 \div 2{\cdot}5$
9 $5 \div 3$	10 $3{\cdot}5 \div 2{\cdot}5$	11 $3{\cdot}14 \div 2$	12 $3{\cdot}14 \div 3$

6 Squares and square roots

If your slide rule has an A scale, use the hairline on the cursor to find the relationship between a number on the A scale and the corresponding number on the D scale.

Exercise 7

Use the A and D scales to write down the square roots of:

1 30 2 66 3 3 4 1·54 5 20 6 88

Use the A and D scales to write down the squares of:

7 9 8 3·6 9 5·1 10 7·2 11 1·9 12 1·08

7 Rough estimates

Now that you know how to use a slide rule, you are ready to work out harder calculations such as

$$28 \times 13 \qquad 594 \div 33 \qquad 0{\cdot}063 \times 0{\cdot}0088 \qquad \frac{365 \times 3{\cdot}14 \times 8{\cdot}5}{6{\cdot}25 \times 60}$$

But the slide rule does not show you where the decimal point should be placed in the answer, so you must first be able to give a rough estimate of the answer.

We do this by writing each number with only one significant figure, and calculating an approximation for the answer.

Example 1.
$$\begin{aligned} & 28 \times 13 \\ & \doteqdot 30 \times 10 \\ & = 300 \end{aligned}$$

Example 2.
$$\begin{aligned} & \frac{594}{33} \\ & \doteqdot \frac{600}{30} \\ & = 20 \end{aligned}$$

Example 3.
$$\begin{aligned} & \frac{365 \times 3{\cdot}14 \times 8{\cdot}5}{6{\cdot}25 \times 60} \\ & \doteqdot \frac{400 \times 3 \times 8}{6 \times 60} \\ & = \frac{400 \times 24}{360} \\ & \doteqdot \frac{400 \times 20}{400} \\ & = 20 \end{aligned}$$

Example 4.
$$\begin{aligned} & 0{\cdot}063 \times 0{\cdot}0088 \\ & \doteqdot 0{\cdot}06 \times 0{\cdot}009 \\ & \doteqdot 0{\cdot}0005 \end{aligned}$$

Exercise 8

Give rough estimates of the answers to questions 1–14. Your estimates may not agree with those given in the book, but the positions of the decimal points should be the same.

1 37×29 2 $38{\cdot}9 \times 2{\cdot}4$ 3 $31{\cdot}7 \times 0{\cdot}48$

4 $8{\cdot}7 \times 0{\cdot}07$ 5 $0{\cdot}0536 \times 0{\cdot}429$ 6 $3{\cdot}14 \times 281$

7 $289 \div 48$ 8 $83{\cdot}7 \div 5{\cdot}8$ 9 $6{\cdot}37 \div 248$

10 $0{\cdot}48 \div 6{\cdot}9$ 11 $\dfrac{2{\cdot}89 \times 760}{46{\cdot}3}$ 12 $\dfrac{3{\cdot}14 \times 1{,}040}{29 \times 0{\cdot}68}$

13 $5 \times 8{\cdot}9^2$ 14 $67 \times 76 \times 0{\cdot}94$

15 Estimate the area of a rectangle 7·56 centimetres long and 2·14 centimetres broad.

16 Estimate the area of a square of side 0·23 centimetres.

17 Estimate the volume of a cuboid 3 feet 8 inches long, 2 feet 4 inches broad, and $10\frac{1}{2}$ inches high.

18 Estimate the perimeter of a plot of ground with straight boundary walls of lengths 180 yards, 135 yards, 256 yards, 93 yards, and 106 yards.

19 Mount Everest is 29,002 feet high, and the deepest part of the Pacific Ocean is 36,198 feet deep. Estimate each of these in miles (1 mile = 5,280 feet).

20 The circumference of a planet is 6·28 times its radius. Taking the radius of the earth to be 3,960 miles, estimate its circumference. Taking the moon's radius to be 1,081 miles, estimate its circumference.

Exercise 9

In the following examples, find a rough approximation, and then calculate the product using a slide rule:

1 11 × 19	2 13 × 18	3 21 × 18
4 3·2 × 25	5 4·1 × 190	6 3·7 × 2·1
7 1·16 × 5·63	8 1·08 × 6·09	9 7·14 × 106
10 421 × 0·219	11 1·2 × 0·78	12 123 × 456

Exercise 10

Again find a rough estimate, and then calculate the quotients in the following:

1 190 ÷ 13	2 380 ÷ 18	3 594 ÷ 33
4 7·8 ÷ 2·3	5 97 ÷ 4·8	6 385 ÷ 204
7 79·4 ÷ 3·5	8 824 ÷ 41	9 3·87 ÷ 15·8
10 0·43 ÷ 0·19	11 0·007 ÷ 6·2	12 0·86 ÷ 0·029

If you try to multiply 7 by 5 you will finish up off the scale. Since you are taking care of the decimal point separately, it is possible to set the

7 opposite 10 instead of opposite 1, and then to read off the product opposite 5 on the D scale.

This is shown in the second diagram of Figure 11(i), where a is set opposite 10 and the product is read opposite b.

In division, the quotient will be found opposite either 1 or 10 on the C scale, as indicated in Figure 11(ii).

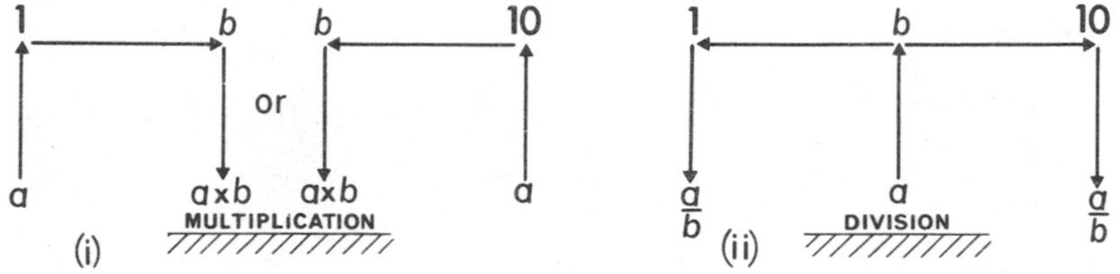

FIG. 11

Exercise 11

Work out the following by slide rule:

1 7×5	2 78×83	3 $4{\cdot}9 \times 9{\cdot}6$
4 $0{\cdot}83 \times 0{\cdot}75$	5 $2{\cdot}76 \times 94{\cdot}7$	6 $63 \div 8$
7 $3 \div 6$	8 $100 \div 33{\cdot}3$	9 $0{\cdot}87 \div 0{\cdot}092$
10 $2{\cdot}8 \div 79{\cdot}3$	11 $0{\cdot}046 \div 0{\cdot}725$	12 $0{\cdot}24 \div 6{\cdot}28$

8 Successive multiplication and division

When you have to perform successive multiplication and/or division, each calculation is done in turn; and since the product or quotient is always on the D scale, it is set ready to act as the a in the next calculation. If you have both multiplication and division to do, take them alternately, starting with division. Try it, and you will see why. You may discover short cuts; for example, a calculation which is very common in proportion can be done as follows:

$$\frac{7{\cdot}54 \times 3{\cdot}26}{5{\cdot}93}$$

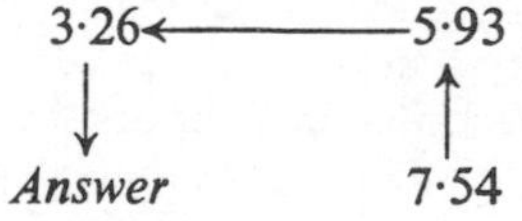

Note how easy it is to use a slide rule to calculate a percentage.

Example. Express 43 as a percentage of 262.

$$\text{Percentage} = \frac{43}{262} \times 100 \qquad \frac{40 \times 100}{300}$$

$$= 16{\cdot}4 \qquad \doteqdot 10$$

Exercise 12

Use a slide rule for each of the following:

1 $\dfrac{2{\cdot}8 \times 3{\cdot}7}{1{\cdot}9}$ 2 $\dfrac{47 \times 19}{73}$

3 Calculate the area of a rectangle 3·78 cm long and 2·79 cm broad.

4 Give the square roots of (i) 29 (ii) 1,650.

5 Express as percentages (i) $\frac{4}{7}$ (ii) $\frac{5}{8}$ (iii) $\frac{8}{9}$ (iv) $\frac{5}{32}$ (v) $\frac{9}{16}$

6 $\dfrac{5{\cdot}2 \times 6{\cdot}8}{7{\cdot}7}$ 7 $\dfrac{35{\cdot}6}{16{\cdot}1 \times 3{\cdot}82}$

8 Calculate the area of a square of side 8·8 in.

9 The area of a rectangle is 3·96 in^2 and its breadth is 0·92 in. Calculate its length.

10 £1 is equivalent to 2·78 dollars. How many dollars can be obtained with £686?

11 A profit of 13% is made on goods costing £789. What was the selling price (to the nearest £)?

12 A loss of 7% is made on goods costing £893. Find the selling price (to the nearest £).

13 $4{\cdot}8 \times 7{\cdot}6 \times 0{\cdot}6$ 14 $\sqrt{\dfrac{5{\cdot}7}{2{\cdot}5}}$

15 Calculate the volume of a cuboid of length 1·6 m, breadth 1·4 m, and height 0·7 m.

16 A cuboid has volume 15·2 in^3, length 7·8 in, and breadth 3·9 in. Calculate its height.

17 An aircraft flies 2,790 miles in 6 hours 45 minutes. Calculate its average speed.

18 A car travels 393 miles at an average speed of 38·5 mph. How long does its journey take?

19 27 books weigh 6·5 kg. Find the weight of 37 similar books.

20 $6{\cdot}8^2 \times 3{\cdot}4^2$

21 $\dfrac{36 \times 49}{25 \times 31}$

22 For further practice, calculate the answers to questions 1–16 in Exercise 8.

CHAPTER 2 Length, Area, and Volume associated with the Circle

1 The circumference of a circle

Exercise 1—Practical

1 (*a*) Draw a circle of radius 1 unit and, by 'stepping' the radius round the circumference, inscribe a regular hexagon in the circle, as shown in Figure 1.

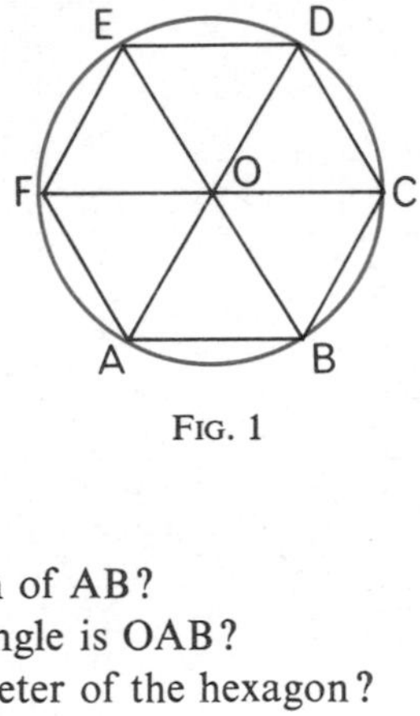

FIG. 1

(*b*) What is the length of AB?

(*c*) What kind of triangle is OAB?

(*d*) What is the perimeter of the hexagon?

(*e*) What is the length of the diameter of the circle?

(*f*) Is the length of the circumference of the circle greater than, or less than, the perimeter of the hexagon?

(*g*) What is the value of the ratio $\dfrac{\text{perimeter of the inscribed hexagon}}{\text{length of the diameter of the circle}}$?

From the answers to the above questions it should be seen that *the length of the circumference of a circle is more than 3 times the length of its diameter.*

2(*a*) Draw a square of side 2 units.
You are now going to inscribe a circle in this square, i.e. draw a circle which fits exactly inside the square. Where must the centre of this circle lie? What is the length of the radius of this circle? What is the length of the diameter of the circle? What is the perimeter of the square?

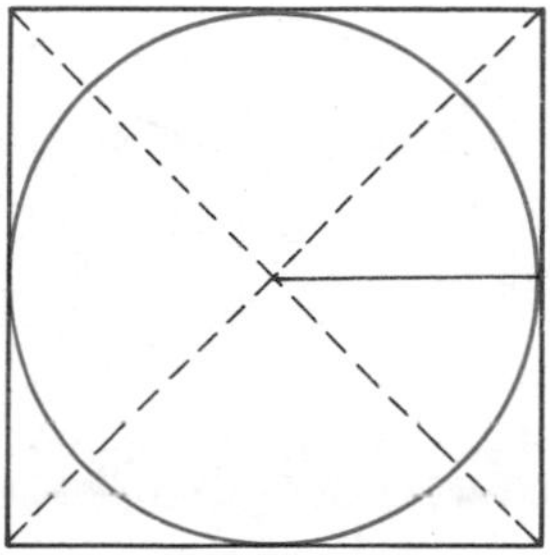

FIG. 2*a*

Which is greater, the perimeter of the square or the length of the circumference of the circle?

What is the value of the ratio $\dfrac{\text{perimeter of square}}{\text{length of diameter of circle}}$?

From the answers to the above questions, it should be seen that *the length of the circumference of a circle is less than* 4 *times the length of its diameter.*

From questions 1 and 2 it is clear that *the length of the circumference of a circle is between* 3 *and* 4 *times the length of the diameter of the circle.*

2(*b*) (This may be taken as an alternative to question 2*a*.)
Draw a circle as in question 1, but this time draw lines perpendicular to the radii at A, B, C, D, E, F to form a hexagon circumscribing the circle as shown in Figure 2*b*.
Is the length of the circumference of the circle greater than, or less than, the perimeter of this hexagon?
What are the sizes of angles AOB, POB, BOQ, POQ?
What kind of triangle is triangle OPQ?
If the length of PB is x units, what are the lengths of PQ and OP?

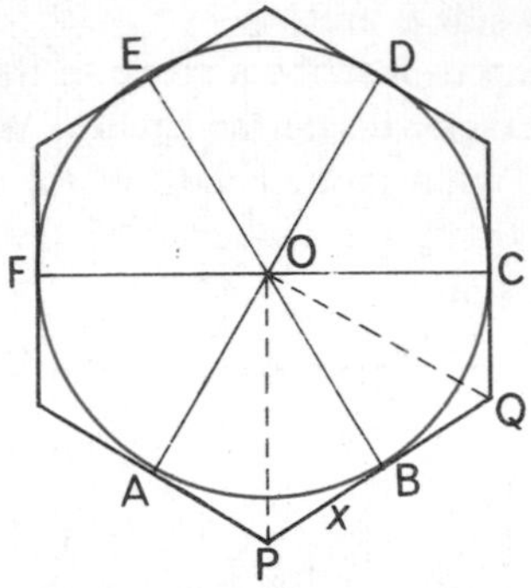

FIG. 2*b*

We can now write down, using Pythagoras' theorem,

$$(2x)^2 = x^2+1^2$$
$$\Leftrightarrow 4x^2 = x^2+1$$
$$\Leftrightarrow 3x^2 = 1$$
$$\Leftrightarrow x^2 \doteqdot 0{\cdot}333$$
$$\Leftrightarrow x \doteqdot 0{\cdot}58$$

since x represents a positive number.

Can you now write down the perimeter of the hexagon?

What is the value of the ratio $\dfrac{\text{perimeter of the circumscribed hexagon}}{\text{length of the diameter of the circle}}$?

It can now be seen that *the length of the circumference of a circle is less than* 3·48 *times the length of its diameter.*

From questions 1 and 2 it is clear that *the length of the circumference of a circle is between* 3 *and* 3·48 *times the length of the diameter of the circle.*

3(*a*) Here you will require several circular or cylindrical objects, e.g. bicycle wheel, tin, chalk circle drawn on the floor, etc. Devise methods of measuring the diameter and the circumference of each of these (using tape measure, string, etc.). Copy and complete the table.

Length of diameter	Length of circumference	$\frac{\text{Length of circumference}}{\text{Length of diameter}}$

(*b*) Calculate your average for the ratio $\frac{\text{circumference}}{\text{diameter}}$ and then find the average result for the whole class.
(Note that it is unlikely that your measurements will be correct to more than 3 significant figures, and in fact the third significant figure is not dependable.)

Formula for the length of the circumference

The approximate results above suggest that the ratio $\frac{\text{length of circumference}}{\text{length of diameter}}$ is the same for all circles. This is in fact so, and the ratio is called π (the Greek letter p, pronounced 'pie'), so we can say that

$$\frac{C}{d} = \pi,$$

where C represents the length of the circumference and d represents the length of the diameter in the same units. Then $C = \pi d$, and since $d = 2r$, where r represents the length of theradius, $C = 2\pi r$.

2 Approximations for π

The number π cannot be expressed exactly as a vulgar or decimal fraction; it is an *irrational number*, and is placed on the number line between 3·141 and 3·142.

Approximations for π are 3·14 correct to 3 significant figures
3·142 correct to 4 significant figures
3·1416 correct to 5 significant figures

The fraction $\frac{22}{7}$ when expressed as a decimal is equal to 3·142857 . . . ; correct to 3 significant figures this is 3·14 and correct to 4 significant figures it is 3·143. Therefore π may be taken to be $\frac{22}{7}$ *when we require to work only to 3 significant figures*. But remember than when π is taken to be $\frac{22}{7}$, we must not give more than 3 significant figures in any result obtained.

Historical Note

For many centuries—probably since man invented the wheel, and realized that a 'tyre' was desirable to prevent wear—interest has been shown in this number which we now call π. In the Bible, in I Kings vii. 23, you will find that the Jews of King Solomon's time apparently took π to be 3; you may find in the school library books which give the story of how better and better approximations for π were obtained. By using electronic computers it was actually worked out in 1961 to 100,265 decimal places!

3 Calculations involving circumferences of circles

Where it is clear that by *circumference* we mean *length of circumference*, etc., we shall use this shorter form.

The circumference of a circle is given by $C = \pi d$ or $C = 2\pi r$.

The use of a slide rule is helpful. Some slide rules have the position of π marked on each scale.

Example 1.—Find the circumference of a wheel whose diameter is 23 centimetres.

In $C = \pi d$ put $d = 23$

Then
$$C = 3{\cdot}14 \times 23$$
$$= 72{\cdot}2$$

Circumference is approximately 72 cm.

Example 2.—A wheel has a radius of 14 inches. How many times will it rotate in travelling $\frac{1}{4}$ mile without slipping?

(You can verify by rolling a wheel along the floor or a coin along the desk that the distance travelled in one revolution is equal to the circumference.)

In $C = 2\pi r$ put $r = 14$

Then $C = 2 \times \frac{22}{7} \times 14$

$= 88$

Circumference $\doteqdot$ 88 inches

Distance travelled $= \frac{1}{4}$ mile

$= 440$ yd

$= 440 \times 36$ in

Number of revolutions $= \dfrac{440 \times 36}{88}$

$= 180$ approximately

Example 3.—The distance round the edge of a circular pond is 100 yards. Find the radius of the pond.

First Method

Replacing C by 100 in $C = 2\pi r$

$100 = 2 \times 3{\cdot}14 \times r$

$\Leftrightarrow 100 = 6{\cdot}28r$

$\Leftrightarrow \quad r = \dfrac{100}{6{\cdot}28}$

$= 15{\cdot}9$

Radius $\doteqdot$ 15·9 yards

Alternative Method

$C = 2\pi r$

$\Leftrightarrow r = \dfrac{C}{2\pi}$

Replacing C by 100

$r = \dfrac{100}{1} \times \dfrac{1}{2} \times \dfrac{1}{3{\cdot}14}$

$= \dfrac{50}{3{\cdot}14}$

$= 15{\cdot}9$

Radius $\doteqdot$ 15·9 yards

Exercise 2

Use 3·14 or $\frac{22}{7}$ as an approximation for π.

1 Find the circumferences of the circles whose diameters are

(i) 28 ft (ii) 3 ft 6 in (iii) 20 yd
(iv) 7 cm (v) 49 m (vi) 4 cm

2 Calculate the circumferences of circles with radii

(i) $52\frac{1}{2}$ yd	(ii) 1 ft 9 in	(iii) 14 cm
(iv) 2 in	(v) 5 m	(vi) 100 cm

3 Find the diameters of circles whose circumferences are

(i) 220 yd	(ii) 2 ft 9 in	(iii) 88 cm
(iv) 8 m	(v) $\frac{1}{2}$ mile	(vi) 6 cm

4 The diameter of an old halfpenny was 1 inch. What was its circumference?

5 The centre-circle of a football pitch has a radius of 10 yards. What is the length of the white line forming this circle?

6 The 'circle' in a hockey pitch has a radius of 16 yards. What is the length of the white line marking the 'circle'? (The 'circle' is actually a semicircle.)

7 A car wheel turns 50 times. If the diameter of the wheel is 16 inches, how far has the car travelled (to the nearest foot)?

8 A sports master wants to mark out a circular $\frac{1}{4}$-mile running track. What radius should he use?

9 A hot-water cistern has a circumference of 2 metres. What is its diameter?

10 (i) Find the circumferences of circles of radii (*a*) 5·0 cm (*b*) 8·0 in (*c*) 100 yd.

(ii) Calculate, correct to two significant figures, the circumference of the earth, assuming its radius to be 4,000 miles.

(iii) Calculate the distance travelled by the earth round the sun in one year, assuming that it moves in a circle of radius 93,000,000 miles. Give your answer in the $a \times 10^n$ form, with a correct to two significant figures.

11 Figure 3 shows the plan of a football pitch, with semicircular areas behind the goals. If the pitch is 120 yards long and 80 yards broad, what is the length of one lap of the track surrounding the pitch?

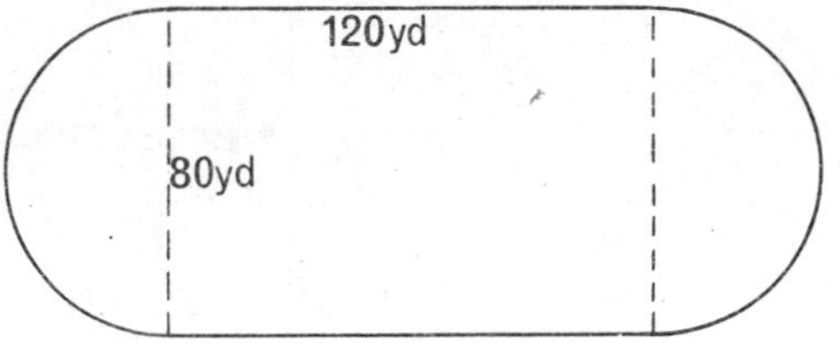

FIG. 3

12 If a wheel rotates 80 times in travelling $\frac{1}{4}$ mile, what is its diameter?

13 What is the perimeter of Figure 4, in which angle AOB is a right angle, and AB is an arc of a circle, centre O, of radius 4 cm?

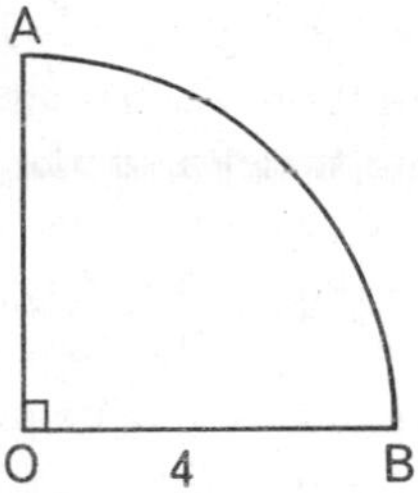

FIG. 4

14 Look back at Figure 1. What is the size of angle AOB? What fraction is this of one revolution? What fraction of the circumference is the arc AB? If the radius of the circle is 1 cm, find the length of the arc AB.

15 Find the circumference of a circle of radius 14 cm. Calculate the lengths of the arcs of this circle which are cut off by drawing at the centre angles of (i) 30° (ii) 40° (iii) 120° (iv) 270°

4 The area of a circle

Exercise 3—Practical

1 Draw the largest circle you can inside a square of gummed paper of side 10 cm. Divide this circle into sectors by drawing angles of 30° at the centre as shown in Figure 5. Bisect one of these sectors.

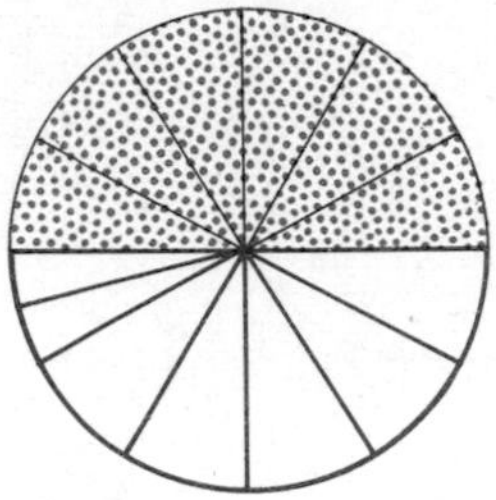

FIG. 5

FIG. 6

Now cut out all the sectors and stick them side by side as in Figure 6. Approximately what shape is Figure 6? Can you suggest how this shape could be made even more nearly a rectangle? If the radius of the circle is r, what is the breadth of the 'rectangle'? What is the length of the 'rectangle'? What is the area of the 'rectangle'?

It will be seen that, by taking a very large number of sectors of the circle, the shape of Figure 6 will become indistinguishable from a rectangle, and that its breadth is r units and its length is $\frac{1}{2}C$ units, i.e. $\frac{1}{2} \times 2\pi r = \pi r$ units, so that the area of the circle is given by $r \times \pi r$ square units, or

$$A = \pi r^2$$

Note.—Since $r = \frac{1}{2}d$, $r^2 = \frac{1}{2}d \times \frac{1}{2}d = \frac{1}{4}d^2$, *so the formula for the area of a circle can be written* $A = \frac{1}{4}\pi d^2$; *this form is often used by engineers since with callipers they find it easier to measure the diameter of a circle than the radius.*

2 Draw a circle of radius 5 cm on 2-mm squared paper. By counting squares in a quarter-circle find an estimate of the area of the circle. (You should consider what allowance to make for 'broken' squares.) Verify that this confirms the result $A = \pi r^2$. Repeat for circles of various radii.

3 Use the values of A and r obtained in question 2 to draw a graph to illustrate the relationship between A and r^2.

4 Use the values of C and r obtained in Section 1, question 3, to draw a graph to illustrate the relationship between C and r.

5 What do you notice about the shape of the graphs in questions 3 and 4?

Notice that since $A = \pi r^2$, A is directly proportional to r^2. What is the relationship between C and r?

5 Calculations on the areas of circles

The area of a circle is given by $A = \pi r^2$, or $A = \frac{1}{4}\pi d^2$.

Example 1.—Find the area of a circle whose diameter is $3\frac{1}{2}$ feet.

$$d = 3\tfrac{1}{2} = \tfrac{7}{2} \qquad A = \pi r^2$$

$$r = \tfrac{7}{4} \qquad\qquad = \tfrac{22}{7} \times \tfrac{7}{4} \times \tfrac{7}{4}$$

$$= \tfrac{77}{8}$$

$$= 9\tfrac{5}{8}$$

The area is $9\frac{5}{8}$ ft^2 or 9 ft^2 80 in^2, approximately.

Example 2.—The area of a circular pond is 67 m^2. Find the diameter of the pond.

First Method

$$A = \pi r^2$$

Replacing A by 67, $\quad 67 = 3{\cdot}14r^2$

$$\Leftrightarrow r^2 = \frac{67}{3{\cdot}14} = 21{\cdot}3$$

$$\Leftrightarrow \quad r = \sqrt{21{\cdot}3} \text{ as } r \text{ represents a positive number.}$$

$$\doteqdot 4{\cdot}62 \text{ (from tables)}$$

Since A was the measure in m^2, r is the measure in m. So the radius is 4·62 m approximately and the diameter is 9·2 m.

Alternative Method

$$A = \pi r^2$$

$$\Leftrightarrow r^2 = \frac{A}{\pi}$$

$$\Leftrightarrow \quad r = \sqrt{\frac{A}{\pi}}$$

Replacing A by 67, $r = \sqrt{\frac{67}{3 \cdot 14}}$

$$= \sqrt{21 \cdot 3}$$

$$\doteqdot 4 \cdot 62$$

The radius is 4·62 m, so the diameter is 9·2 m.

Exercise 4

1 Find the areas of the circles given by

radius	(i) 7 yd	(ii) 1 ft 2 in	(iii) 2 cm
diameter	(iv) 28 m	(v) 1 yd	(vi) 6 cm

2 Find the area of the shooting 'circle' on a hockey pitch, given that its radius is 16 yards. (The 'circle' is actually a semicircle.)

3 The diameter of an old halfpenny was 1 inch. Find the area of one surface of the halfpenny.

4 Find the radii of the circles whose areas are

(i) 154 in^2 (ii) $9\frac{5}{8}$ yd^2 (iii) 22 cm^2 (iv) 4840 m^2

5 Find the total areas of Figures 3 and 4 in Exercise 2.

6 Find the areas of the shaded portions of the following figures. (Assume all angles to be right angles which appear to be so.)

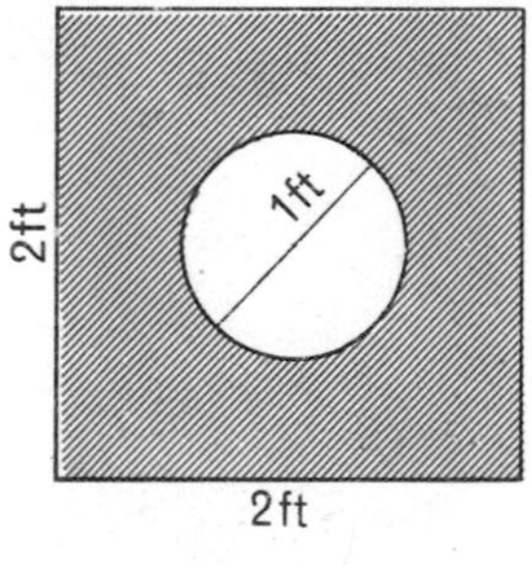

FIG. 7

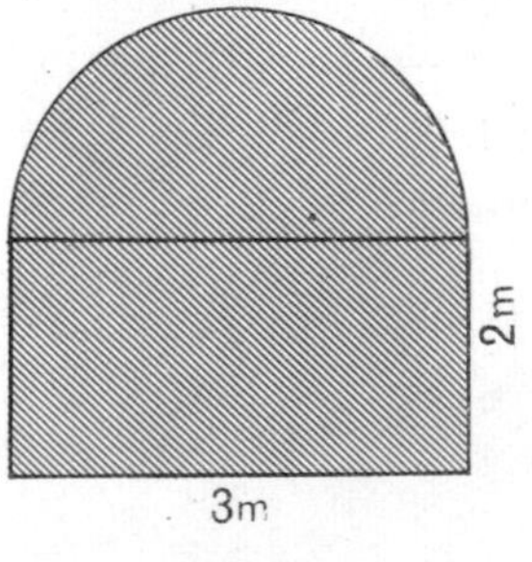

FIG. 8

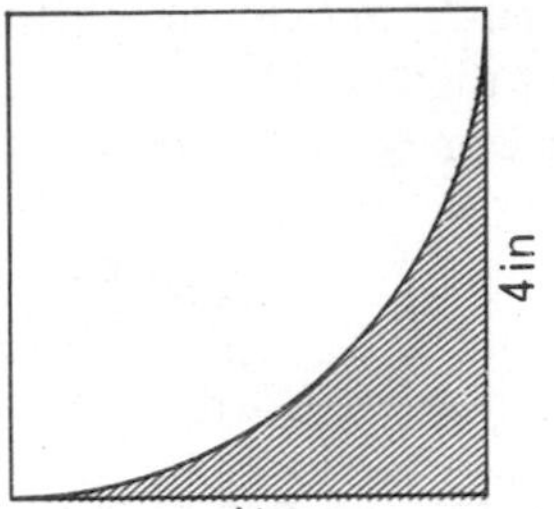

FIG. 9

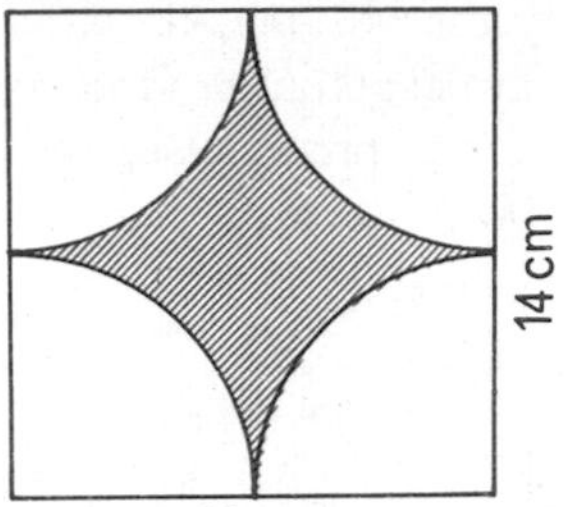

FIG. 10

7 A square lawn 20 feet long has a circular lily-pond in the middle, of diameter 10 feet. Find the area of the grass. (Draw a diagram.)

8 Milk-bottle tops are made by cutting as many circles as possible of diameter 2 inches out of a strip of aluminium 12 feet long and 2 inches broad. What percentage of the aluminium is wasted?

9 (i) Find the areas of circles of radii (*a*) 10 cm (*b*) 5·0 yd.
(ii) The diameter of a circular window is 1 foot 6 inches. Find the area of glass in the window.

10 Find the diameter of a circular ink-blot which covers an area of 2·0 cm^2.

11 A circular garden plot has an area of 100 ft^2. Find its diameter.

12 The ratio of the radii of two circles is 2:1. What is the ratio of (i) their circumferences (ii) their areas?

6 The volume of a prism and a cylinder

We know that the measure of the volume of a cuboid in cubic units is given by the formula $V = Ah$ where A is the measure of the area of the base in square units and h is the measure of the height in units.

Figure 11 shows a cuboid. Its volume can be found from the formula $V = Ah$. Let us cut it vertically down through the diagonal as shown by the shading. We have now formed two equal triangular *prisms*: strictly speaking prisms of this kind are called *right prisms* to show that the ends are at right angles to the parallel edges. These can be placed together side by side to form the triangular prism shown in Figure 12.

Clearly the volume, the area of the base, and the height of this new prism are exactly the same as those of the cuboid.

So, for a prism also, the volume can be found from the formula $V = Ah$.

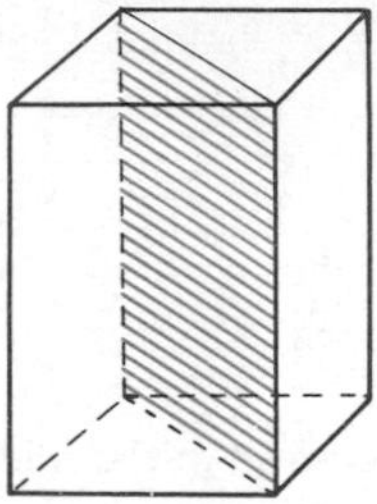

FIG. 11

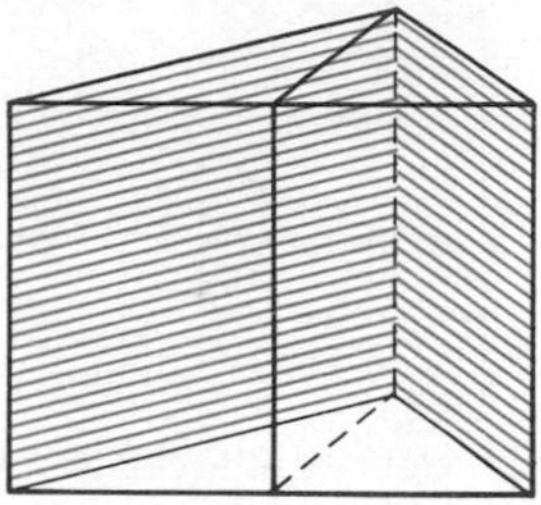

FIG. 12

Figure 13 shows a hexagonal prism. It can be divided into triangular prisms as shown. (You can verify this by fitting together six 'Toblerone' packets.) The volume of each of these can be found from the formula $V = Ah$, so that the volume of the hexagonal prism is $6Ah$ square units. But $6Ah$ can be written $(6A)h$ and $(6A)$ square units is clearly the area of the base of the hexagonal prism. So the volume of a regular hexagonal prism is also given by *area of base* × *height*.

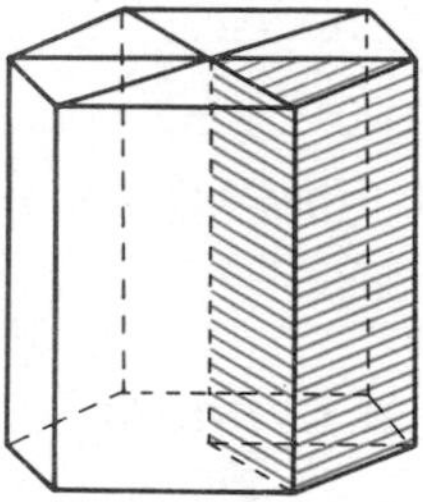

FIG. 13

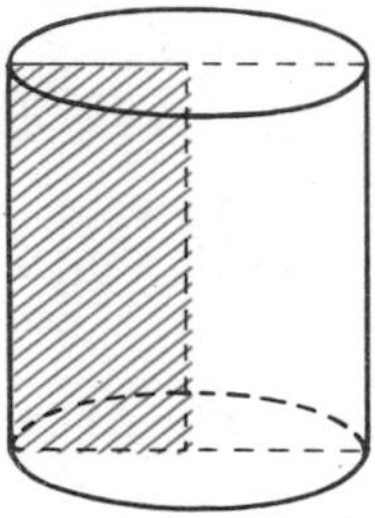

FIG. 14

Imagine that we continue to increase the number of sides on the ends of such a prism. Ultimately we will obtain a prism such as is shown in Figure 14 where the ends have become indistinguishable from circles. In this case the prism is indistinguishable from a *cylinder*.

The formula for the volume, $V = Ah$, still holds. Since the area of the end, A, is now the area of a circle, πr^2, the volume of a cylinder is given by the formula

$$V = \pi r^2 h$$

Exercise 5

1 Complete the following table referring to cylinders:

	(i)	(ii)	(iii)	(iv)	(v)	(vi)	(vii)
Radius	7 in	1 ft 2 in	2 m	3 cm	2 cm	3 ft 6 in	
Height	3 in	6 in	1 m	4 cm			2 ft 4 in
Volume					176 cm^3	150 ft^3	66 ft^3

2 A cylindrical tin of custard powder is $3\frac{1}{2}$ inches tall and has a diameter of $3\frac{1}{2}$ inches. What volume of powder can it hold?

3 A cylindrical tin of drinking chocolate is 3 inches in diameter and 5 inches tall. How many such tins can be filled from a cubical box of side 1 foot?

4 It is required to make a cylindrical can which will hold 1 litre of water.

(i) If the diameter is to be 10 cm, what must the height of the can be?
(ii) If the height is to be 11 cm, what must the diameter of the can be?

5 How many gallons of petrol can be stored in a cylindrical tank of diameter 4 ft and length 7 ft? (1 ft^3 = $6\frac{1}{4}$ gal)

6 A cylindrical tower is 200 feet high and its internal diameter is 20 feet. Find its volume. (Use 3·14 for π and give your answer in the $a \times 10^n$ form.)

7 Calculate the radius of a cylinder of volume 484 cm^3 and height 14 cm.

8 Find the height of a cylinder of volume 231 cm^3 and radius $1\frac{3}{4}$ cm.

7 The surface area of a cylinder

Examine a cylindrical can which has a paper wrapping, or a cylindrical packet of sweets. You can see that it has three surfaces, two of which are flat (plane) and one curved. Use a knife to slit the wrapping along its length and separate each of these surfaces. You will see that the curved surface can actually be flattened out. When flattened, what is its shape?

Take a cylinder; wrap a piece of paper round it, and trim this off with scissors until it fits the curved surface of the cylinder exactly. Now unwrap and look at the shape of the paper when flattened out. Do you think you could fit a flat sheet of paper on to the curved surface of a sphere?

You will see that the curved surface of a cylinder can be unwrapped to give a rectangle. Can you see the connection between the breadth and length of this rectangle and the dimensions of the cylinder? Can you now draw a net for making a cylinder from cardboard?

Figure 15 shows the net for making a cylinder. If the radius is r units and the height of the cylinder is h units, what is the circumference of one end? What are the length and breadth of the rectangle?

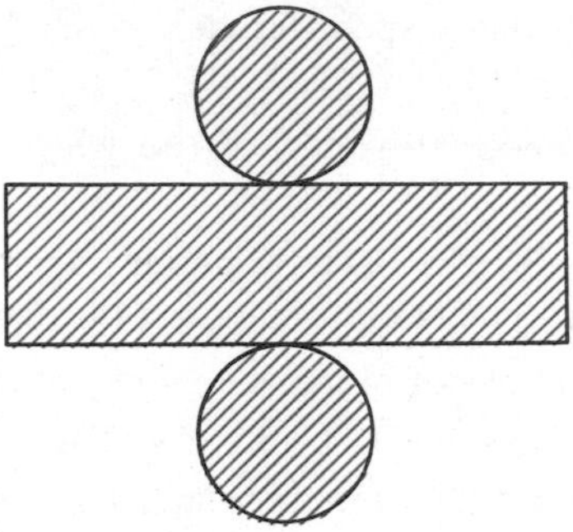

FIG. 15

Exercise 6

1 You are going to make a cylinder from cardboard. If the radius of the end is $1\frac{3}{4}$ inches, what will be the circumference of that end? If now the height of the cylinder is to be 3 inches, what are the dimensions of the rectangle in the net? You can now draw and cut out the three parts necessary as shown in Figure 16. (You may find it helpful to have tabs as shown; this will make it easier to stick the parts together.)

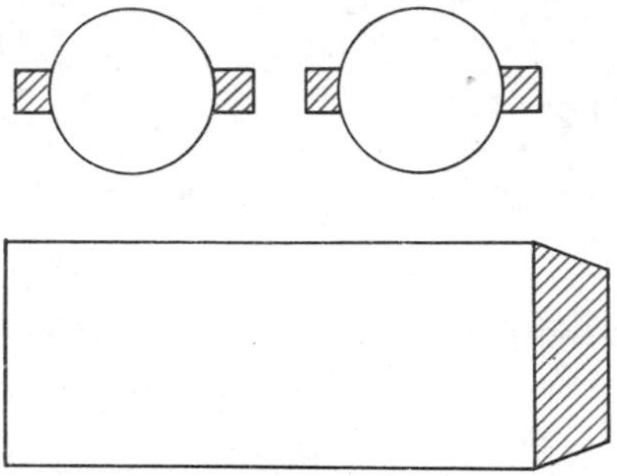

FIG. 16

2 Work out the total surface area of the cylinder constructed in question 1. What would the area be if you had made a cylindrical can with no lid?

3 Repeat questions 1 and 2, this time making a cylinder of height 6 cm and radius of base 6 cm.

4 By studying Figure 15, write down formulae for (i) the surface area of a cylinder with a lid (ii) the surface area of a cylinder with no lid (iii) the area of the curved surface of a cylinder.

5 You have found in question 4 that the curved area of a cylinder is given by $A = 2\pi rh$. Use this formula to calculate the curved areas of cylinders with these dimensions:

	(i)	(ii)	(iii)	(iv)
Height	10 in	5 cm	14 cm	1 yd
Radius of base	7 in	4 cm	6 cm	1 ft 6 in

6 A cylindrical cardboard carton, closed at both ends, is 20 cm high and has radius 14 cm. What area of cardboard is necessary to make it, assuming that there are no overlaps at the joins?

7 A cylindrical water tank is open at the top. Its height is 4 feet and its diameter is 1 foot 2 inches. Calculate its total surface area.

8 A closed cylindrical tank can hold 1,375 gallons of petrol. The radius of its base is 3 feet 6 inches. Calculate the total surface area of the tank. (1 cubic foot = $6\frac{1}{4}$ gallons.)

Summary of results

The value of the ratio $\frac{\text{circumference}}{\text{diameter}}$ is the same for all circles and is denoted by π.

Approximations for π are 3·14 (correct to 3 significant figures)
3·142 (correct to 4 significant figures)
$\frac{22}{7}$

Circumference of a circle: $C =$ ~~$2\pi r$~~ πd.
Area of a circle: $A = \pi r^2$
Volume of a prism: $V = Ah$
Volume of a cylinder: $V = \pi r^2 h$

CURVED SURFACE AREA OF A CYLINDER $= 2\pi rh$.
TOTAL SURFACE AREA OF CYLINDER $= 2\pi Rh + 2\pi R^2$.

CHAPTER 3 Applications of Percentages—Discount, Profit and Loss, Interest

1 Revision of percentages

Example 1.—Express (i) 15% as a common fraction, (ii) $\frac{7}{8}$ as a percentage.

(i) $15\% = \dfrac{15}{100} = \dfrac{3}{20}$

(ii) $\frac{7}{8} = \frac{7}{8} \times 100\% = 87\frac{1}{2}\%$

Example 2.—Calculate $37\frac{1}{2}\%$ of £1·75; $3\frac{1}{2}\%$ of £7·84

$$\begin{aligned} 37\tfrac{1}{2}\% \text{ of } £1{\cdot}75 &= \frac{37\frac{1}{2}}{100} \times £1{\cdot}75 \\ &= \frac{75}{200} \times £1{\cdot}75 \\ &= \tfrac{3}{8} \times £1{\cdot}75 \\ &= \tfrac{1}{8} \times £5{\cdot}25 \\ &= £0{\cdot}65\tfrac{1}{2} \end{aligned}$$

$$\begin{aligned} 3\tfrac{1}{2}\% \text{ of } £7{\cdot}84 &= \frac{3\frac{1}{2}}{100} \times £7{\cdot}84 \\ &= 3\tfrac{1}{2} \times £0{\cdot}0784 \\ &= 0{\cdot}2352 \\ &\quad + 0{\cdot}0392 \\ &\quad\;\; 0{\cdot}2744 \\ &= 27\tfrac{1}{2} \text{ pence} \end{aligned}$$

Example 3.—In the first half of a football season a team obtained 26 points out of a possible 40. What percentage is this?

$$\text{Required percentage} = \frac{26}{40} \times 100\% = 65\%$$

Exercise 1

1 Express the following percentages as fractions:

(*a*) 20% (*b*) 185% (*c*) $\frac{1}{4}\%$ (*d*) $2\frac{1}{2}\%$ (*e*) $12\frac{1}{2}\%$ (*f*) 7·5% (*g*) 0·4% (*h*) $8\frac{1}{3}\%$

2 Express the following fractions as percentages:

(*a*) $\frac{3}{4}$ (*b*) $\frac{4}{25}$ (*c*) $2\frac{1}{3}$ (*d*) $\frac{1}{80}$ (*e*) $\frac{5}{8}$ (*f*) 0·8 (*g*) 0·03 (*h*) 1·17

3 A fraction may be expressed as a common fraction, as a decimal fraction, or as a percentage. Thus $\frac{3}{4} = \frac{75}{100} = 0{\cdot}75$, or 75%.

Copy and complete this table.

Vulgar fraction	*Decimal fraction*	*Percentage*
$\frac{11}{20}$	...	...
...	0·17	...
...	...	42%
...	0·008	...
$\frac{1}{3}$	...	...
...	...	$122\frac{2}{9}$%

4 A boy scored 114 out of 150 in English and 104 out of 160 in mathematics. Find his percentage mark in each.

5 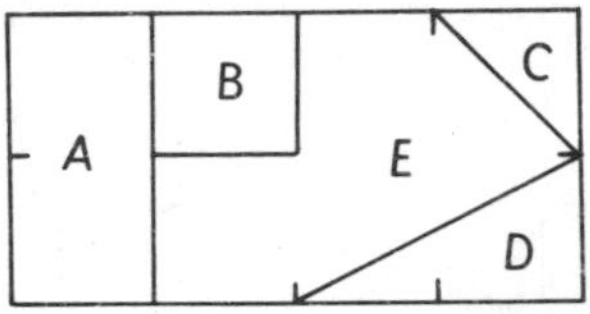

The rectangle shown measures 4 units by 2 units. What is its area? Calculate the percentage which each of the areas A, B, C, D, E is of the whole area. (The sides are divided into units.)

6 Calculate (i) 5% of £1 (ii) $2\frac{1}{2}$% of £1 (iii) $12\frac{1}{2}$% of £1

7 A man's hotel bill amounts to £12·75. To this must be added a 10% 'service' charge. What must he actually pay?

8 A school team plays 16 matches, winning 12 and drawing 2 of them. Allowing 2 points for a win and 1 for a draw, calculate the percentage of the total possible points gained.

9 It is estimated that the cost of living rose 3% in the course of a year. What actual increase does this impose on the weekly expenses

of a household which amounted to £9·40 at the beginning of the year?

10 In 1964 a man's salary was £900 per annum. In 1965 it was increased by 4%. Find his new monthly salary.

* * * * * * *

Notice that $1 = \frac{2}{2} = \frac{3}{3} = \frac{4}{4} = \frac{8}{8} = \frac{25}{25} = \ldots;$
these are all equivalent forms of the number 1.

In particular, $100\% = \frac{100}{100} = 1.$

Any percentage greater than 100 represents a number greater than 1, and any percentage less than 100 represents a number less than 1.

Example.—24% of a certain number is 102. What is the number?

$$24\% \text{ of the number} \longleftrightarrow 102$$

$$100\% \text{ of the number} \longleftrightarrow 102 \times \frac{100}{24}$$

$$= 425$$

Exercise 2

1 80% of a number is 56. What is the number?

2 110% of a number is 198. What is the number?

3 $16\frac{2}{3}\%$ of a sum of money is 28 pence. What is the sum?

4 Find the weight of which $12\frac{1}{2}$ oz is $62\frac{1}{2}\%$.

5 Imported watches are subject to a duty of 15%. Calculate the duty-free cost of a watch which is worth £11·50 after duty has been paid on it.

6 A girl sets aside $7\frac{1}{2}$ pence each week towards holiday expenses. If this is 15% of her pocket money how much pocket money does she receive each week?

7 In an examination a boy scores 104 marks, which is 65% of the possible total. Out of what total was the examination marked?

8 After an increase of 12% on the original price an article cost 56 pence. Find the original price.

9 When purchase tax of 45% is added to the basic price a car costs £841. Find the basic price.

10 After travelling 54 miles a motorist estimates that he still has 70% of his journey to do. What is the total length of his journey?

11 A man contributes 6% of his income to a pension fund. If this contribution amounts to £8·70 per month find his annual salary.

12 A Building Society agrees to make a loan of £2,941 towards the cost of a house. If this represents 85% of the purchase price find the value of the house.

2 Discount and commission

Example 1.—During sale time a shop allows 20% discount on all purchases. What will a customer pay for a coat normally priced at £12·87½?

$$\text{Discount} = \frac{20}{100} \times £12{\cdot}87\tfrac{1}{2} = £2{\cdot}57\tfrac{1}{2}$$

$$\text{Sum paid} = £12{\cdot}87\tfrac{1}{2} - £2{\cdot}57\tfrac{1}{2}$$

$$= £10{\cdot}30$$

or

$$100\% \text{ of normal price} \longleftrightarrow £12{\cdot}87\tfrac{1}{2}$$

$$80\% \text{ of normal price} \longleftrightarrow £12{\cdot}87\tfrac{1}{2} \times \frac{80}{100}$$

$$= \frac{£103{\cdot}00}{10}$$

$$= £10{\cdot}30$$

Example 2.—An agent received £15·50 commission on sales which he made. If the rate of commission was $2\frac{1}{2}\%$ what was the value of the sales?

$$\text{Since } 2\tfrac{1}{2}\% = \frac{1}{40}, \ \frac{1}{40} \text{ of the value of sales} = £15{\cdot}50$$

$$\frac{40}{40} \text{ of the value of sales} = £15{\cdot}50 \times 40$$

$$\text{Value of sales} = £620$$

or

$$2\tfrac{1}{2}\% \text{ of the sales} \longleftrightarrow £15{\cdot}50$$

$$100\% \text{ of the sales} \longleftrightarrow £15{\cdot}50 \times \frac{100}{2\frac{1}{2}}$$

$$= £15{\cdot}50 \times \frac{200}{5}$$

$$= £620$$

Exercise 3

1 Express the following percentage discounts as rates per £: (*a*) 40% (*b*) $12\frac{1}{2}\%$ (*c*) $16\frac{2}{3}\%$ (*d*) $3\frac{1}{3}\%$ (*e*) $1\frac{1}{4}\%$

2 Express the following discounts as percentages: (*a*) 25 pence in the £ (*b*) 12p in the £ (*c*) 75p on £50 (*d*) 35p on £2·50 (*e*) 3p on $7\frac{1}{2}$p.

3 What will I pay for a coat marked at £18·95 if I am allowed discount of 20 pence in the £.

4 A store's advertisment reads: 'Shop-soiled goods—$66\frac{2}{3}\%$ reduction'. What will be paid for articles usually sold for (*a*) £1·35 (*b*) £7·83 (*c*) £0·98?

5 An agent collects rents amounting to £560 for a landlord and gives him £553, retaining the balance as commission. What rate of commission did he charge?

6 A salesman is given $2\frac{1}{2}\%$ commission on sales over £500 in value. What did he actually receive for selling goods worth £960?

7 A commercial traveller receives a basic weekly wage of £7, plus commission at the rate of $1\frac{1}{4}\%$ on the value of goods which he sells. Find how much he is paid in a week when he sells £680 worth of goods.

8 During a sale a firm sold goods at a reduction of 20% on the marked price. A customer pays £9·60 for a coat and 104 pence for a shirt. Find the marked prices of these two items.

9 A manufacturer allows shopkeepers a discount of $2\frac{1}{2}\%$ for prompt payment of accounts. What would 3 shopkeepers actually pay if their bills amounted respectively to £42, £13·50, £63·59?

10 A firm's sales representative receives a basic wage of £15·50 per week, plus commission of 4% of the value of goods sold over £10,000. In a certain year he sold goods worth £23,000. Calculate his average weekly wage for the year, taking 1 year = 52 weeks.

11 Find the value of the goods sold if an agent whose rate of commission is $3\frac{1}{2}\%$ actually receives £81·90.

12 A broker charges £19·75 for handling business valued at £7,900. What rate per cent does he charge?

3 Percentage as a basis of comparison; percentage composition

Example 1.—In a general election there was a 78% poll in a constituency of 38,000 votes. Of the votes cast 49% went to Mr White, 36% to Mrs Black and the rest to Miss Gray. How many votes did Miss Gray receive?

$$\text{Number of votes cast} = \frac{78}{100} \times 38{,}000 = 29{,}640$$

Of these Miss Gray received 100%−49%−36% = 15%

$$\text{Number voting for Miss Gray} = \frac{15}{100} \times 29{,}640$$

$$= 4{,}446$$

Example 2.—For a bowling green a grass seed mixture contains (by weight) 85% Chewing's Fescue and 15% Brown Top Bent. Find the weight of each in $2\frac{1}{2}$ lb of the mixture.

$$\begin{aligned}\text{Weight of Chewing's Fescue} &= 85\% \text{ of } 2\tfrac{1}{2}\text{ lb}\\ &= \frac{85}{100} \times \frac{5}{2}\text{ lb}\\ &= 2\tfrac{1}{8}\text{ lb}\\ &= 2\text{ lb } 2\text{ oz}\\ \text{Weight of Brown Top Bent} &= 2\text{ lb } 8\text{ oz} - 2\text{ lb } 2\text{ oz}\\ &= 6\text{ oz}\end{aligned}$$

Exercise 4

1 The cost of an article increases from 20p to 23p. Find the percentage increase. Express the new price as a percentage of the old.

2 Express as percentages
  (i) an increase of $12\frac{1}{2}$p in £1
  (ii) a decrease of $7\frac{1}{2}$p in 45p
  (iii) a loss of 2 min in 1 hr
  (iv) a gain of 5 lb in $7\frac{1}{2}$ st (to nearest 1%)

3 A machine is accurate to within $\frac{1}{2}$%. If it is set to cut strips of metal of length 10 cm, between what limits must the lengths lie?

4 A garden of area $\frac{1}{4}$ acre is made up as follows: flowers 50%, vegetables 30%, lawn 10% and the remainder paths. Find the number of square yards occupied by each (1 acre ≑ 4,840 square yards).

5 A grass seed mixture for a sports ground consists of 50% ryegrass, 45% Fescue, and 5% Dogstail. How many ounces of each are there in $3\frac{3}{4}$ lb of the mixture?

6 A town council which built 780 houses in 1964 plans to build 117 more houses in 1965 than in the previous year. Express the 1965 figure as a percentage of that for 1964.

7 A fertiliser consists of 50% sulphate of ammonia, 25% sulphate of iron and 25% superphosphate, by weight. How much of each is there in $3\frac{1}{2}$ lb of the fertiliser?

8 In a small town the comparative figures for births, marriages, and deaths in 1963 and 1964 are shown in the table below:

	Births	*Marriages*	*Deaths*
1963	320	100	260
1964	302	107	235

In each case express the 1964 figure as a percentage (to the nearest 1%) of the corresponding 1963 figure.

9 Concrete consists of 60% sand, 20% stones and 20% cement by volume. How many cubic feet of each are contained in 1 cubic yard of concrete?

10 An alloy is made by mixing copper and zinc in the ratio 5:3. What is the percentage composition of the alloy?

11 Excluding wages, salaries, and materials, the expenses of a manufacturing company in a certain year are as follows:—rent 35%, machinery 30%, transport 25%, office equipment $2\frac{1}{2}$%, miscellaneous $7\frac{1}{2}$%. If the amount paid in rent is £1,470 find the cost of the other items.

12 During the last election in a constituency of 40,000 voters, there was a 65% poll. How many actually voted?
Of the votes recorded 43% went to the Labour candidate, 39% to the Conservative, and the remainder to the Liberal. How many voted Liberal?

13 In another constituency 72% of the voters recorded their votes, 51% of which went to the Conservative. How many did he receive, if there were 45,000 voters on the roll?

14 The approximate figures for the population of Orkney in 1861 and 1961 are as follows:

	Males	*Females*
1861	15,000	17,500
1961	9,000	9,700

Calculate to the nearest 1 % (i) the percentage the 1961 total population is of the 1861 total population and (ii) what percentage of the population was female in 1861 and in 1961.

4 Profit and loss

Actual profit and loss

A *shopkeeper* buys goods either direct from the *manufacturer* or through a *wholesaler*, and sells (*retails*) them to the *customer*.

If he sells his goods at a higher price than he paid for them then he makes a *profit* or *gain*.

If, for some reason, his selling price is less than his cost price then he sustains a *loss* on the transaction.

Thus Profit = selling price − cost price

and Loss = cost price − selling price

Example.—A confectioner bought $\frac{1}{2}$ gross Easter Eggs at $6\frac{1}{4}$ pence each. He sold half of them at $7\frac{1}{2}$ pence each and, after Easter, disposed of the rest at $4\frac{1}{2}$ pence. Find his gain or loss on the deal.

$$\begin{aligned} \text{Total cost price} &= 72 \times 6\tfrac{1}{4}\text{p} = £4{\cdot}50 \\ \text{Total selling price} &= (36 \times 7\tfrac{1}{2})\text{p} + (36 \times 4\tfrac{1}{2})\text{p} \\ &= 36 \times 12\text{p} \\ &= £4{\cdot}32 \\ \text{Loss} &= 18\text{p} \end{aligned}$$

Exercise 5

1 A dealer bought 50 sheep at an auction sale for £5·50 each and sold them privately at £6·30 each. Find his total profit.

2 A stationer bought 150 Christmas decorations for £3·50. He sold as many as he could before Christmas at 4p each but was left with 20 which were then useless. What was his gain or loss on the deal?

3 A bookseller bought 4 dozen copies of a book at 42p each. At what price was each book sold if his profit was £3·84?

4 A tea merchant mixes 110 lb tea costing £24 with 130 lb costing £27. He packages the mixture into $\frac{1}{4}$-lb cartons costing 4p per dozen, and sells the cartons at $7\frac{1}{2}$p each. Find his total profit.

5 A florist bought 200 bulbs at $4\frac{1}{2}$p each. 140 of them were classed as top size and sold at $6\frac{1}{2}$p each. The remainder were put in bowls, three to a bowl, and sold at $52\frac{1}{2}$p per bowl. If the bowls cost him $27\frac{1}{2}$p each, and if the total cost of the bulb fibre was 65p, find his total gain.

Percentage profit and loss

For comparison purposes it is customary to express the actual profit or loss in the form of a percentage. This is sometimes taken as a percentage of the *Cost Price* although it is common trade practice for a shopkeeper to reckon his profit as a percentage of the *Selling Price*.

In all examples which follow you should assume that the gain or loss is to be expressed as a *percentage of the Cost Price unless it is otherwise stated*.

Example 1.—An article is bought for 20 pence and sold for 25 pence. Express the gain as a percentage of (a) the cost price; (b) the selling price.

$$\text{Actual gain} = 25\text{p} - 20\text{p} = 5\text{p}$$

$$(a)\ \text{Gain as a percentage of cost price} = \frac{5}{20} \times 100\% = 25\%$$

$$(b)\ \text{Gain as a percentage of selling price} = \frac{5}{25} \times 100\% = 20\%$$

Example 2.—Sugar bought at £2·80 per cwt is sold at 2 lb for $5\frac{1}{2}$ pence. Find the percentage profit.

$$\text{Cost price per cwt} = £2{\cdot}80$$

$$\text{Selling price per cwt} = 56 \times 5\tfrac{1}{2}\text{p} = £3{\cdot}08$$

$$\text{Actual gain} = 28\text{p}$$

$$\text{Percentage gain} = \frac{\text{actual gain}}{\text{cost price}} \times 100\%$$

$$= \frac{28}{280} \times 100\% = 10\% \text{ of cost price}$$

Exercise 6

Calculate the profit or loss as a percentage of the *Cost Price* in questions 1 to 4.

	Cost Price	*Selling Price*
1	30 pence	35 pence
2	£8·75	£8·05
3	£1·12 per stone	$13\frac{1}{2}$ pence
4	£1 per gallon	14 pence

Calculate the profit or loss as a percentage of the *Selling Price* in numbers 5 to 8.

	Cost Price	*Selling Price*
5	62 pence	75 pence
6	£61·20	£72
7	£4·95 per yd²	$62\frac{1}{2}$ pence per ft²
8	£4·48 per cwt	$3\frac{1}{2}$ pence

9 Articles cost £7·50 per dozen to make and are sold at 75 pence each. Calculate the gain as a percentage of (*a*) the cost price (*b*) the selling price.

10 Caster sugar is bought for £6·72 a cwt and sold at $6\frac{1}{2}$ pence per lb. Find the percentage profit.

11 A shopkeeper estimates that, after paying all expenses, his profit is 2·3% of his takings. If his takings average £750 per week find his estimated annual income from his business.

12 A roll of linoleum 4 yards wide and 40 yards long was bought for £67·20 and sold at 49 pence per yd². Find the gain or loss per cent.

To calculate the Selling Price

Example.—A bookseller bought 20 copies of a novel for £10·50 and priced them so as to gain $33\frac{1}{3}$% on his outlay. Find the marked selling price of each copy.

$$\text{Cost price of one copy} = \frac{£10{\cdot}50}{20} = 52\tfrac{1}{2} \text{ pence}$$

Profit = $33\frac{1}{3}\%$ of $52\frac{1}{2}$ pence = $\frac{1}{3}$ of $52\frac{1}{2}$ pence = $17\frac{1}{2}$ pence
Selling price = $52\frac{1}{2}$ pence + $17\frac{1}{2}$ pence = 70 pence

Exercise 7

Find the Selling Price in each of the following 5 questions given that the gain or loss is reckoned as a percentage of the Cost Price.

	Cost Price	*Gain or Loss %*
1	£15	10% Gain
2	$62\frac{1}{2}$ pence	16% Gain
3	£1·25	24% Loss
4	72 pence	$33\frac{1}{3}\%$ Gain
5	£1·53	$16\frac{2}{3}\%$ Loss

6 Articles bought for £6·48 per gross are sold at a gain of $33\frac{1}{3}\%$. Find the selling price of each.

7 A man bought a car for £840 and spent another £40 on extra fittings. Later he sold it at a loss of 35% on his total outlay. Find the selling price of the car.

8 An education authority requires 25 gross of a certain type of exercise book which costs the contractors 3p each to manufacture. If the contractor makes a profit of 10% find the cost of the exercise books to the authority.

9 Two different qualities of tea costing 28 pence and $32\frac{1}{2}$ pence per lb are blended in the ratio of 5:4. The mixture is sold at a gain of 25%. Find the selling price per lb.

10 Television sets are bought for £48 each and marked for sale to gain 20% on the cost price. Find the marked price. Most of the sets are sold at this price but when a new model is introduced the dealer is forced to clear the remainder at £37·80 each. Express the loss

sustained by selling at this price as a percentage of (*a*) his cost price (*b*) his new selling price (nearest $\frac{1}{2}$%).

11 A manufacturer makes 10,000 toys of a certain type at a total cost of £450. Find the average cost of manufacturing one such toy. The manufacturer sells them to a wholesaler at a gain of $16\frac{2}{3}$% of his cost price. Find how much the wholesaler pays for 50. The wholesaler in turn sells them to a shopkeeper at 6p each. What is the wholesaler's profit reckoned as a percentage of what they cost him?

5 Interest

'Buy National Savings Certificates: annual yield over 3% free of income tax.'

'Dunaber Trustee Savings Bank: Special Investment Department. 5% interest.'

'Invest with the City of Duncaldy: $6\frac{1}{4}$% Mortgage Loans.'

'Post Office Savings Bank: interest $2\frac{1}{2}$%—first £15 free of tax.'

'Fortune Unit Trust: estimated yield $4\frac{3}{4}$%.'

Almost every newspaper carries advertisements such as these. They are designed to encourage people to save some of their money and to invest these savings with a bank, or a local authority, or with a business company.

The money which a person invests is called the *Principal* and in return for the use of this principal the lender receives a certain sum called the *Interest*. This interest is usually calculated as a percentage of the principal.

If the rate of interest is 4% per annum the lender receives £4 for every £100 which he lends for a year. If he lends £280 for a year the interest is 4% of £280 = £11·20 and at the end of the year the principal amounts to £291·20, i.e. the *Amount* is £291·20.

In the same way, when a person borrows money from a bank or a building society he must pay interest on the loan. Thus if a building society's rate of interest is $6\frac{1}{4}$%, for every £100 which the borrower has on loan at the beginning of a year he must pay £$6\frac{1}{4}$ interest at the end of the year.

Example.—Calculate the amount of £1,240 invested for one year at a rate of interest of $4\frac{1}{4}\%$ per annum.

$$\begin{aligned} \text{Interest} &= 4\tfrac{1}{4}\% \text{ of } £1{,}240 \\ &= \frac{4\frac{1}{4}}{100} \times £1{,}240 \\ &= £52{\cdot}70 \\ \text{Amount} &= £1{,}292{\cdot}70 \end{aligned}$$

$$\begin{array}{r} £12{\cdot}40 \\ 4 \\ \hline 49{\cdot}60 \\ 3{\cdot}10 \\ \hline 52{\cdot}70 \\ 1{,}240{\cdot} \\ \hline 1{,}292{\cdot}70 \end{array}$$

Exercise 8

1 Find the annual interest payable on the following principals invested at the rates stated:

	(i)	(ii)	(iii)	(iv)	(v)
Principal	£500	£225	£40	£1,040	£62·50
Rate of interest	3%	4%	$2\frac{1}{2}\%$	$6\frac{1}{4}\%$	$3\frac{1}{2}\%$

2 Find the *amount* of each of the following principals invested for a year at the interest rates given:

	(i)	(ii)	(iii)
Principal	£200	£70	£2,340
Rate of interest	$2\frac{3}{4}\%$	5%	$3\frac{2}{3}\%$

3 To pay for new machinery a firm borrows £5,000 for a year from a bank, the rate of interest being $6\frac{1}{2}\%$. What sum must be repaid at the end of the year?

4 The annual interest for a loan at 5% is £7·50. Find the amount of the loan.

Simple interest

Let us consider the interest gained from a principal of £100 invested at 5% per annum.

Interest for the first year = 5% of £100 = £5.

If this £5 interest is paid out to the investor the principal will still be £100 for the second year and the interest for the second year will again be £5.

Interest of this type, i.e. interest which is paid out each year leaving the principal unaltered, is called *Simple Interest.*

Example.—Find the simple interest on £42·50 invested for 8 months at $3\frac{1}{2}\%$ per annum.

$$\begin{aligned}\text{Interest for 1 year} &= 3\tfrac{1}{2}\% \text{ of } £42{\cdot}50\\ &= £1{\cdot}4875\\ \text{Interest for 8 months} &= \frac{8}{12}\times £1{\cdot}4875\\ &= £0{\cdot}99\end{aligned}$$

$$\begin{array}{r} £0{\cdot}425\\ 3\\ \hline 1{\cdot}275\\ 0{\cdot}2125\\ \hline 1{\cdot}4875\\ 2\\ \hline 3)2{\cdot}9750\\ \hline 0{\cdot}9917\end{array}$$

Exercise 9

Find the Simple Interest in questions 1–4.

1 £150 invested for 6 months at 3% per annum.

2 £75 invested for 10 months at 4% per annum.

3 £181 invested for 8 months at $3\frac{1}{2}\%$ per annum.

4 £425 invested for 4 months at $3\frac{3}{4}\%$ per annum.

5 A man borrowed £300 from a bank at 6% per annum. How much must he repay altogether at the end of 9 months?

6 A shopkeeper was due to pay an account of £80 by a certain date. He was charged interest at the rate of $4\frac{1}{2}\%$ per annum after that date. How much interest had he to pay if payment was made 8 months after the required date?

7 A Government raised £2,500,000 by issuing a new stock, bearing interest at $3\frac{1}{4}\%$ per annum. What interest must the Government pay out at the end of each six months?

8 If £P is invested for T years at R% per annum, show that the simple interest, £I, is given by $I = \dfrac{PTR}{100}$.

Use this formula to find the interest on

(i) £250 in 2 months at 5% per annum

(ii) £440 in 6 months at $2\frac{1}{2}$% per annum

(iii) £125 in 4 months at 7% per annum.

Compound interest

When money is deposited in a bank for a period greater than one year it is customary for the interest to be added at the end of every year. For example if a principal of £100 is deposited, and gains interest at the rate of 5% per annum, then at the end of one year the interest is £5. This is added to the original principal so that the [redacted] for the second year will be 5% of £105, that is £5·25. Now the principal for the third year will be £110·25, and so on.

This is an example of *compound interest*. Notice that, in compound interest, the principal increases every year, so that the interest also increases every year.

Notes

(1) *Interest is normally calculated only on complete pounds of principal.*

(2) *Since the calculation often becomes complicated, a calculating machine may be found useful; in practice bankers read off the actual interest from ready reckoner tables.*

(3) *Remember, a quick way to calculate, for example,* 3% *of* £342 *is to write:*

$$\frac{3}{100} \times £342 = 3 \times £3{\cdot}42 = £10{\cdot}26.$$

Example.—Calculate the compound interest on £450 for 3 years at 4% per annum.

First principal	= £450	$\frac{4}{100} \times 450 = 4 \times 4{\cdot}5$
First interest	= 18	$= 18{\cdot}0$
Second principal	= 468	$\frac{4}{100} \times 468 = 4 \times 4{\cdot}68$
Second interest	= 18·72	$= 18{\cdot}72$
Third principal	= 486·72	$\frac{4}{100} \times 486 = 4 \times 4{\cdot}86$
Third interest	= 19·44	$= 19{\cdot}44$
Amount	= 506·16	
Original principal	= 450	
Compound interest	= £56·16	

Exercise 10

Calculate the compound interest on

1 £500 for 2 years at 4% p.a.
2 £800 for 3 years at 2% p.a.
3 £340 for 2 years at 3% p.a.
4 £575 for 2 years at 5% p.a.
5 £642 for 3 years at 6% p.a.
6 £483 for 4 years at 3% p.a.
7 Calculate the compound interest on a deposit of £640 for 3 years if the rate per cent per annum is 4% for the first year, 5% for the second year and 6% for the third year.

When the rate per cent is fractional the calculation becomes very tedious, e.g. $2\frac{3}{4}\%$ of £346 $= \frac{2\frac{3}{4}}{100} \times £346 = £2{\cdot}75 \times 3{\cdot}46$.

In this case a calculating machine is a help. Use a calculating machine to find the compound interest in questions 8 to 10.

8 £587 for 2 years at $3\frac{1}{2}\%$ p.a. 9 £1,256 for 3 years at $4\frac{1}{4}\%$ p.a.

10 £650 for 4 years at $6\frac{3}{4}\%$ p.a.

Reminders

1 $p\%$ of a quantity $N = \dfrac{p}{100} \times N.$

2 The percentage that A is of $B = \dfrac{A}{B} \times \dfrac{100}{1}\%$

CHAPTER 4 Statistics

1 Measurements, samples, and populations

In Book 2 we saw that information about numbers could be illustrated and its meaning quickly grasped by drawing pictographs, bar charts, pie charts, and line graphs. In each case we were concerned with the *measure* of a quantity which could be measured or counted.

In this chapter we shall first deal with more methods of depicting measurements. The set of items which have the characteristic in which we are interested is called a *population*, and the set of items actually measured is called a *sample* of that population. For example, if we are interested in the ages last birthday of Scottish pupils in their second year at school, the *population* is the set of all Scottish pupils in their second year, and the *sample* is the set of second year Scottish pupils whose ages we actually know. In this particular case the measurement must be a whole number (of years), and we shall consider this type of measurement in Sections 1–3.

Exercise 1 (Mainly for revision)

1 Figure 1 is a pictograph of the cost of education in Scotland in 1962–1963. The sums of money are in millions of £s and the volumes of the money-bags indicate the expenditure.

(i) In which part of the educational system was the greatest amount of money spent?

(ii) Which single item cost most?

(iii) Compare the total general expenditure, expenditure on salaries, and expenditure on buildings.

(iv) What percentage of the total expenditure was made on the training of teachers?

	Primary Schools	Secondary Schools	Special Schools	School Meals and Milk	Further Education	Training of Teachers	Libraries, Recreational Education and Youth Service
General Expenditure	£17M	£14M	£1M	£7M	£8M	£2M	£2M
Salaries	£23M	£25M	£1M		£4M	£1M	
Buildings	£6M	£9M			£5M	£1M	

FIG. 1

2 In Scotland there are public schools (managed by local education authorities), grant-aided schools (run by boards of governors receiving grants from the Scottish Education Department), and independent schools (run by boards of governors without any aid from public funds).

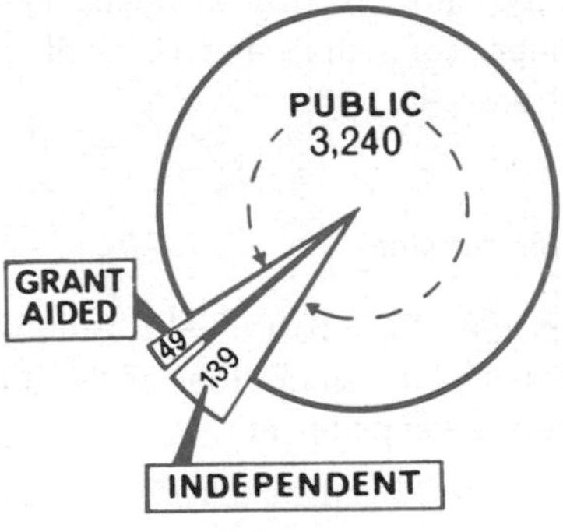

FIG. 2

The pie chart in Figure 2 shows the number of each of these types of school in 1962.

(i) What is the total number of schools?

(ii) What percentage of the schools are grant-aided?

3 The number of pupils attending the above schools in 1962 was: public schools 870,000; grant-aided schools 22,000; independent schools 18,000 (to two significant figures in each case).
Show this information on a pie chart.

4 The line graphs in Figure 3 indicate the primary and secondary-school populations in Scotland in each year from 1952 until 1962.

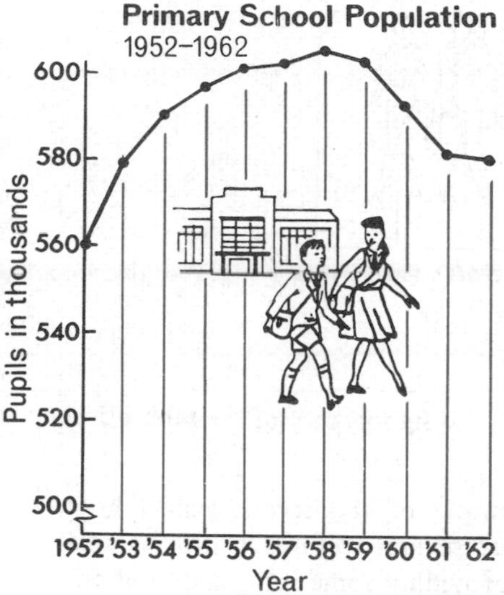

FIG. 3(*a*)

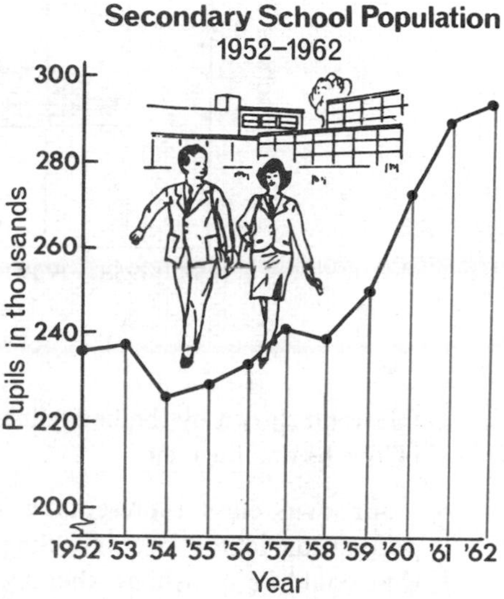

FIG. 3(*b*)

(i) The first graph shows the 'bulge' in the primary-school population. In which year did it reach its peak? What relation is there to the bulge in the second graph?

(ii) In which year was the secondary-school population least? Estimate the population in this year.

(iii) Calculate approximately the percentage increase in the secondary-school population between 1954 and 1962.

5 Figure 4 is not unrelated to Figure 3. It shows the supply and demand for teachers in the years 1957–62.
Give as much general information as you can from this figure, e.g.

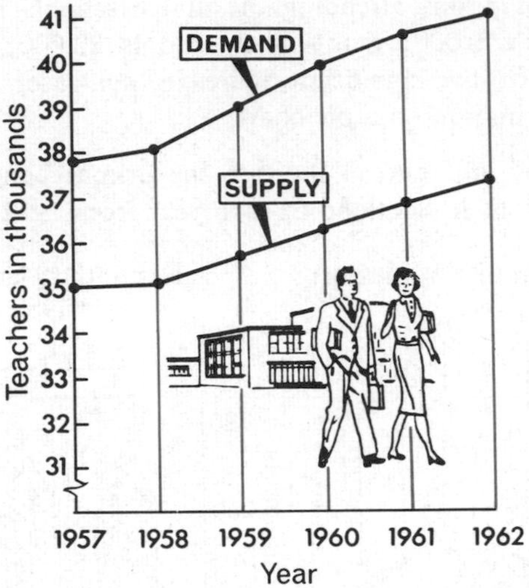

FIG. 4

the trend shown by the heavy lines, the significance of the separation of the heavy lines, etc.

6 Your own class represents a sample of the second-year school population in the country. Suggest several features of this sample that could be measured, thereby providing some information about the population.

2 Frequency tables

The number of items in a sample may be quite large. For example, the marks in a class test were called out in alphabetical order of the pupils' names as follows:

7	6	4	6	8	3	5	5	6	1	4	4	7
7	5	9	5	4	6	3	6	2	4	5	3	5
6	5	6	4	5	5	6	3	4	5	8	7	7

Notice that the mark 8 occurs twice, 7 occurs five times, 6 occurs eight times, and so on.

The information can be shown more clearly in a *frequency table*.

Score		Frequency
1	/	1
2	/	1
3	////	4
4	~~////~~ //	7
5	~~////~~ ~~////~~	10
6	~~////~~ ///	8
7	~~////~~	5
8	//	2
9	/	1
10		0
	Total	39

As you can see the original information has been transferred to the table as 'tally marks'. It is convenient in practice to use every fifth tally mark in a given score to 'cross out' the previous four, thus making it easy to count up the tally marks for each score in groups of five. The total number of tally marks for each score is called the *frequency* of the score and is entered in the frequency column. It should be noted that the tally marks give a rough picture of the distribution of marks.

The score that occurs most often, i.e. 5, is called the *mode* or *modal score* of the distribution.

Exercise 2

1 The number of goals scored by football teams in the Scottish Summer Cup on 1st May, 1965 was

1 4 2 0 2 1 1 3 3 1 3 1 0 0 3 0

Construct a frequency table. What is the modal score?

2 The classes in four primary schools contained the following numbers of pupils:

35	38	40	29	30	34	42	37	35	36	31	37
28	30	36	34	33	39	30	36	39	37	30	38
40	39	37	35	33	31	30	34	41	40	38	37
28	31	32	37	33	38	40	38	39	38	37	30

Make a frequency table. What is the mode?

3 Construct a frequency table of the number of children in the families of members of your class.

4 Make a frequency table for the following scores in one round of a golf competition:

72	69	71	76	80	71	70	68	74	75	71	76	69	75
70	72	74	70	69	79	75	74	70	76	75	73	80	75

What is the modal score?

5 Collect some statistics from a book or newspaper and arrange them in a frequency table.

3 Class intervals

When we have to consider a large number of different measurements, it is usual to group the information in *class intervals*.

Here are some examination marks:

42	73	54	58	85	52	48	54	60	54
58	48	70	52	53	53	53	60	25	55
60	55	50	53	75	58	52	45	65	68
58	57	82	30	55	49	57	63	72	28

We might decide to group the marks in class intervals of 5, starting at 25. This means that the first group would include 25, 26, 27, 28, 29, and the second group 30, 31, 32, 33, 34, and so on.

The frequency table is:

Marks		Frequency
25–29	//	2
30–34	/	1
35–39		0
40–44	/	1
45–49	////	4
50–54	~~////~~ ~~////~~ /	11
55–59	~~////~~ ////	9
60–64	////	4
65–69	//	2
70–74	///	3
75–79	/	1
80–84	/	1
85–89	/	1
	Total	40

Since the data, or information, have been classed together we can note, not the mode, but the *modal class*, i.e. the class interval in which the greatest frequency of marks occurs. In the above example the modal class would be 50–54 marks.

Exercise 3

1 Make frequency tables for the information given above, using class intervals of 1, 3, 10, and 20. (Perhaps you could share this work with your neighbour.) By comparing these tables decide whether you think 5 was a good choice of class interval. What is the disadvantage (*a*) of too small a class interval (*b*) of too large a class interval?

2 Make a frequency table for the following marks in a mathematics examination:

44	54	85	92	73	57	99	91	96	74	75	70
83	49	57	52	64	67	73	82	90	70	89	91
52	64	73	82	59	50	65	79	82	89	53	52

Group the marks in class intervals of 5, starting at 40.

3 The distribution of royalty money to 37 Scottish football league clubs for season 1964–65, in £s, was:

4,720	4,000	4,000	4,000	3,920	3,680	3,600	3,520
3,440	3,200	3,200	3,200	3,200	3,120	3,120	2,960
2,960	2,880	2,880	2,640	2,640	2,560	2,560	2,560
2,560	2,560	2,400	2,320	2,320	2,240	2,000	1,920
1,920	1,680	1,520	1,120	560			

Make a frequency table for the above, grouping the amounts in suitable class intervals. Compare your table with your neighbour's and discuss how to choose the most suitable class interval.

4 Make a frequency table for the information given about the number of pupils in primary school classes in Exercise 2, question 2. Group the numbers in threes. What is the modal class?

4 Histograms

Frequency distributions can be illustrated by means of histograms in which the frequency in each class is represented by a rectangle, *the area of the rectangle being proportional to the frequency.* When equal class intervals are chosen, the height of the rectangle is proportional to the frequency.

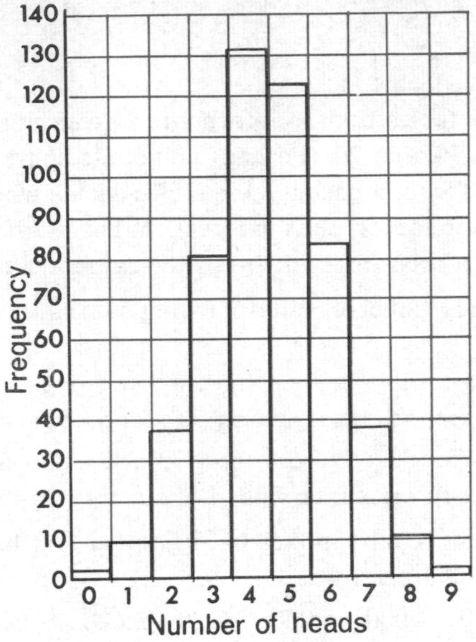

FIG. 5

In a number of trials, 9 coins were tossed together and the following data (illustrated in Figure 5) were obtained:

Number of heads	0	1	2	3	4	5	6	7	8	9
Frequency	2	9	36	80	131	122	83	37	10	2

Note that the probability of obtaining exactly 3 heads

$$= \frac{\text{number of trials in which exactly 3 heads were obtained}}{\text{total number of trials that took place}}$$

$$= \frac{80}{512} = \frac{5}{32} = 0{\cdot}16$$

Exercise 4

1 The number of children of school age in each household in a certain street was required for a census. Illustrate the information obtained as a histogram.

Number of children in household	0	1	2	3	4	5	6
Frequency	4	9	44	26	7	1	1

What is the probability that a household visited at random in the street will contain exactly two children of school age?

2 Illustrate as a frequency table and as a histogram the final scores in the Schweppes British Professional Close Golf title (1965), given below. Group the scores in class intervals of 2.

286	286	289	290	292	292	292	293	293	293
294	294	294	295	296	296	296	296	297	297
298	298	298	298	298	299	299	299	299	300
301	301	302	302	302	302	302	303	304	305

3 The first-year pupils in a school were asked the number of coins they had with them, and the following information was obtained:

Number of coins	0	1	2	3	4	5	6	7	8	9	10	11	15	17	19	22
Frequency	13	4	13	6	11	10	8	4	1	5	5	4	2	1	1	1

Illustrate this information as a histogram with 23 class intervals. Now draw another histogram with the same first 11 class intervals, and then with two class intervals of 6, for 11–16, and 17–22; remembering that the area of each rectangle is proportional to the frequency it represents, what will the heights of the last two rectangles be?

4 Repeat question 3 using data from your class, and choosing suitable class intervals.

*   *   *   *   *   *   *

So far we have been studying measurements which are whole numbers. If we now consider the height of a boy at different ages we shall be dealing with a different type of measurement, since the boy's height does not increase instantaneously from one whole number of inches to the next, but progressively takes up intermediate measurements.

We can conveniently represent such measurements in frequency tables and by histograms, grouping the heights in suitable class intervals. Here are the height measurements of the 34 pupils of a third-year class in a Scottish school. A class interval of 2 inches is chosen, and for convenience we assume here that 4 ft 8 in to 4 ft 10 in includes heights of 4 ft 8 in but not 4 ft 10 in, and similarly for the other intervals.

Height	4 ft 8 in to 4 ft 10 in	4 ft 10 in to 5 ft 0 in	5 ft 0 in to 5 ft 2 in	5 ft 2 in to 5 ft 4 in	5 ft 4 in to 5 ft 6 in	5 ft 6 in to 5 ft 8 in
Frequency	3	8	4	9	6	4

The histogram is shown in Figure 6, and we can see that it shows two distinct peaks.

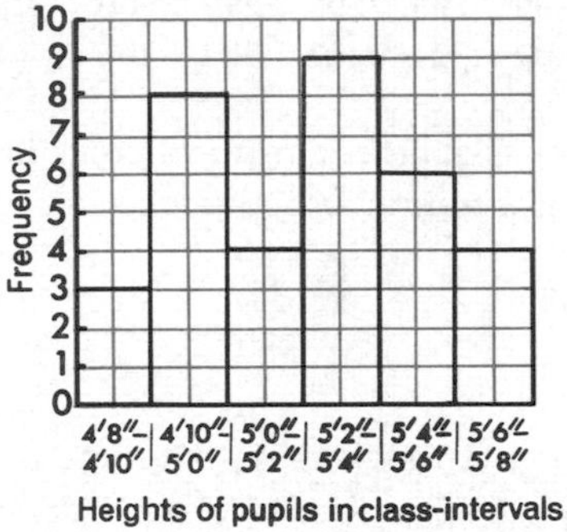

FIG. 6

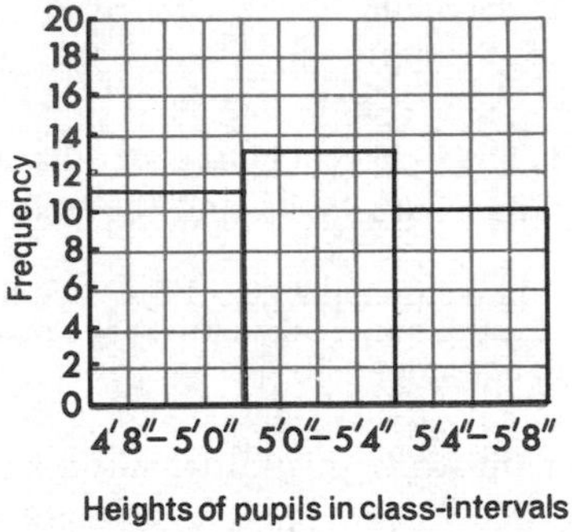

FIG. 7

Figure 7 is the histogram drawn for the same heights, but this time a class interval of 4 inches has been taken. You can see that with too large a class interval important and interesting features of the distribution may not be apparent; with too small a class interval the regularity of a distribution may be missed.

5 Frequency polygons

Another way of showing a frequency distribution is by means of a frequency polygon. Here we draw ordinates, or 'uprights', through the mid-points of the class intervals on the horizontal axis, with heights proportional to the frequencies. The lines joining the points at the tops of the ordinates form the frequency polygon.

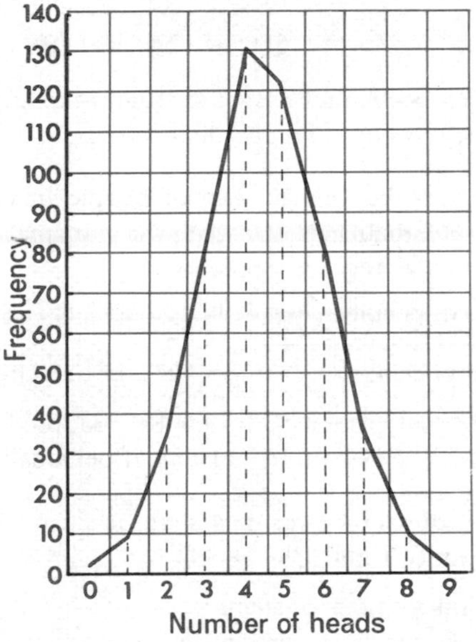

FIG. 8

Figure 8 shows the frequency polygon for the data obtained from the experiment of tossing 9 coins a number of times.

Exercise 5

1 Draw a histogram and frequency polygon (on the same diagram) for the information given regarding the ages in years and months of first-year pupils in a school; 12, 2-12, 4 here includes pupils 12 years 2 months old, but not those aged 12 years 4 months, and so on.

Age in years and months	12, 2 -12, 4	12, 4 -12, 6	12, 6 -12, 8	12, 8 -12, 10	12, 10 -13, 0	13, 0 -13, 2	13, 2 -13, 4	13, 4 -13, 6	13, 6 -13, 8
Frequency	10	18	27	28	37	40	25	9	1

2 The heights in inches of pupils of a first-year class were:

48	52	57	53	59	62	58	58	61	60
50	55	54	59	60	59	59	62	60	49
53	57	58	60	59	58	57	60	59	58
52	59	57	61	61	59	58	59	59	57

Make a frequency table, and draw a histogram of the heights. Show also the frequency polygon for the distribution.

3 A first-year class noted the number of people in cars passing the school one day at lunchtime. Illustrate the information obtained as a histogram and as a frequency polygon.

Number of people in car	1	2	3	4	5	6
Number of cars	35	27	12	22	12	2

What is the probability that a car selected at random from this sample will contain (i) exactly 1 person (ii) exactly 4 persons?

4 The number of blooms on sweet-pea stems is shown in the following frequency polygon of Figure 9.

(i) Find the total number of stems.

(ii) What is the mode of the distribution?

(iii) What is the probability that a stem selected at random from this sample will contain (*a*) exactly 3 blooms (*b*) at least 3 blooms?

5 Draw a pie chart and a frequency polygon to illustrate the distribution of 'intelligence' in a section of the population, as indicated by a verbal reasoning test:

Intelligence quotient	55–69	70–84	85–99	100–114	115–129	130–144
Percentage of population	2	14	34	34	14	2

What is the probability that a person selected at random from this sample will have an intelligence quotient (I.Q.) of (i) 130–144 (ii) 85–99?

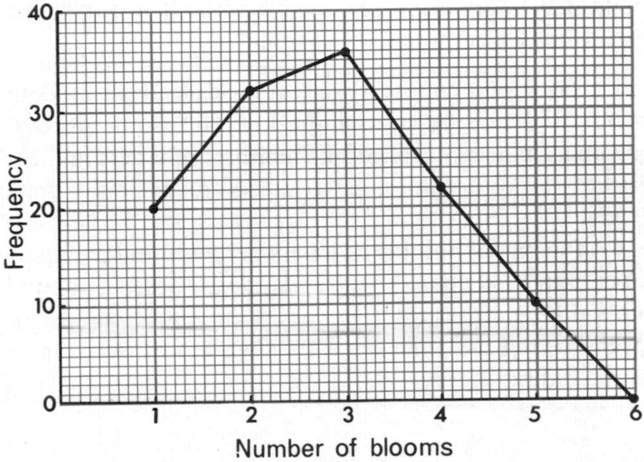

FIG. 9

6 The results of the Scottish First and Second Division league football matches on Saturday, 27th February, 1965 were as follows:

SCOTTISH LEAGUE—DIVISION I

Aberdeen	2	Dunfermline	2
Celtic	2	Kilmarnock	0
Dundee Utd.	3	Airdrie	2
Hearts	1	Dundee	7
Morton	3	Hibernian	2
Motherwell	0	Partick	2
Rangers	1	St. Mirren	0
St. Johnstone	1	Clyde	0
Third Lanark	1	Falkirk	2

SCOTTISH LEAGUE—DIVISION II

Albion Rovers	2	East Fife	2
Ayr	0	Berwick	1
Brechin	1	Stirling Alb.	3
Cowdenbeath	4	Montrose	2
E. S. Clydebank	3	Arbroath	1
Forfar	0	Dumbarton	2
Raith	0	Hamilton	2
Stenhousemuir	2	Qn. of South	1
Stranraer	4	Alloa	0

From the results illustrate as a histogram the number of goals scored by each team.

7 A class project. Each pupil, or pair of pupils, should select a paragraph

in a newspaper or book and count the number of times each letter occurs in the paragraph. The results for the whole class should be combined, and given in the form of a frequency polygon or a histogram.

Why might the information obtained be useful in (*a*) decoding a message (*b*) constructing the Morse code?

8 (*a*) Select a book and choose a page at random from it. Count the numbers of letters in each of the first 100 words on the page. Draw up a frequency table of the numbers of letters in the words. Illustrate the information as a histogram and as a frequency polygon.
What is the modal number of letters per word in the passage you have chosen? Compare your results with those of a pupil who chose a different passage.

(*b*) Repeat 8(*a*) but this time count the numbers of words in each of the first 100 sentences.

6 Mean

The *average* of a set of numbers was studied in Book 3.

Suppose that John had marks of 75, 80, 81, 90, 84 in English, French, Latin, mathematics, and science respectively.

The total number of marks he obtained $= 75+80+81+90+84$

$$= 410$$

$$\text{His average mark} = \frac{410}{5} = 82$$

If in the same examinations James had marks of 72, 84, 86, 60, 56, the total number of marks he obtained $= 72+84+86+60+56$

$$= 358$$

$$\text{His average mark} = \frac{358}{5} = 71{\cdot}6$$

John's average mark of 82 compared with James's average mark of 71·6 describes John's greater success in the examinations, without giving the complete list of marks.

The *average* of a set of numbers or measures found in this way is strictly called the *arithmetic mean* of the numbers or measures. In statistics it is always called the *mean.* It is

$$\frac{\text{the sum of all the measures}}{\text{the number of measures}}$$

It follows that the sum of all the measures is the product of the mean and the number of measures.

The mean gives a *central measure* which is useful for comparing measurements of different samples. For example, the mean height of the male inhabitants of East Africa is 5 ft 7 in, and the mean height of the men of the Watutsi tribe is 5 ft 10 in.

When we say that a batsman has scored an average of 14·4 runs in 21 completed innings at cricket, we know that his total number of runs for the 21 innings is 302, since the total number of runs scored

= mean score × number of innings
= 14·4 × 21
= 302 (to the nearest whole number, of course)

Exercise 6

1 Find the mean of the following test scores:

(*a*) 3 4 5 5 4 3 6 7 8 4
5 6 8 9 9 7 5 6 6 7

(*b*) 6 7 8 5 7 8 9 6 7 8
5 8 9 7 8 6 9 8 5 7

2 Find the mean amount of pocket money received each week by members of your class.

3 The mean number of chimneys on a row of 59 houses was 3·8. Find the total number of chimneys in the road.

4 The number of hours of sunshine recorded daily in a city during the last fortnight of April 1965 was:

3·8	7·8	5·7	2·0	3·4	7·2	4·1
4·9	6·3	0·8	1·3	7·9	7·6	5·2

What was the mean daily number of hours of sunshine for the city over this period?

5 In a class of 35 pupils it was found that the mean number of times each pupil went to the pictures in a week was 0·57; find the total number of attendances at the pictures during the week.

6 The duration, in minutes, of telephone calls made by a business man on a certain day was:

3	7	10	2	4	8	11	9	6	3
2	4	8	15	14	10	8	7	4	7

Calculate the mean duration of his calls.

7 Mean from a frequency table

We can extend the frequency table to facilitate the calculation of the mean as shown in the following example.

The number of goals scored by Scottish First and Second Division football clubs on 24th April, 1965, was:

3, 2, 2, 2, 4, 0, 3, 1, 0, 2, 4, 0, 5, 1, 1, 1, 2, 0, 2, 2, 2, 1, 0, 0, 4, 0, 0, 1.

To calculate the mean number of goals scored per team, construct the following table:

Number of goals	Frequency		Number of goals × frequency
0	~~////~~ ///	8	0
1	~~////~~ /	6	6
2	~~////~~ ///	8	16
3	//	2	6
4	///	3	12
5	/	1	5
	Totals	28	45

Mean number of goals $= \frac{45}{28} = 1{\cdot}6$, correct to 2 significant figures.

Exercise 7

1 Draw up a frequency table for the number of children in the families represented by the pupils in your class. Calculate the mean number of children per family.

2 A machine is designed to pack a commodity in 20-oz cartons. As a check on its accuracy, a sample of packets is taken at regular intervals throughout the day, and the packets are weighed to the nearest tenth of an ounce. The following histogram shows the distribution of the weights of the packets in a sample.

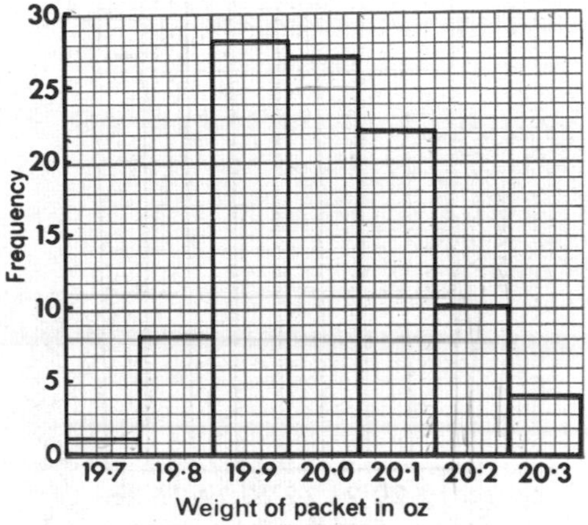

FIG. 10

(i) How many packets are there in the sample?
(ii) Find the mean weight of the packets.
(iii) What is the probability that a carton selected at random from the sample will have a weight (to the nearest tenth of an ounce) of 20·0 oz?

3 Measure the heights of the pupils in your class, to the nearest centimetre and calculate the mean height. Illustrate as a histogram.

4 Calculate the mean number of coins the members of your class have with them.

5 Two second-year classes in a school were asked how many textbooks they had with them in class, and the results are shown below. Calculate the mean number of textbooks per pupil.

Number of textbooks	0	1	2	3	4	5	6	7	8	9	10
Frequency	0	1	1	7	9	10	10	11	8	2	2

6 The histogram in Figure 11 shows two classes' estimates of the length of a given line. The teacher said the line was 2·3 in long. Were the classes good at estimating length? What was the mean estimate?

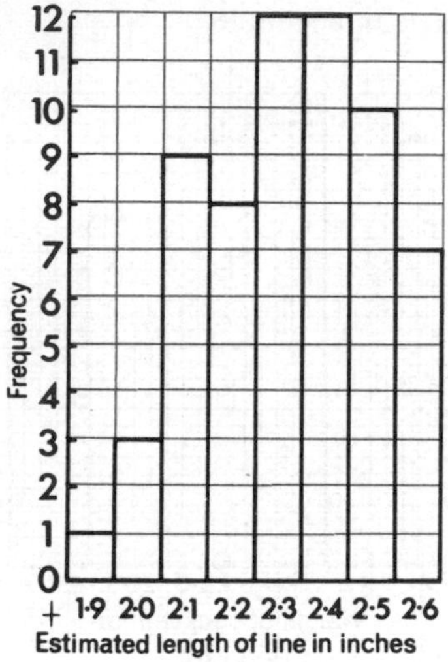

FIG. 11

7 The following table gives the number of textbooks carried by each pupil in a certain class on a certain day.

4	12	2	8	9	9	4	2	3	10	3		
8	3	9	6	11	3	10	2	6	11	5		
8	6	2	5	8	10	1	3	8	9	11	6	

Draw up a frequency table showing the number of pupils carrying 1, 2, 3, . . . books and calculate the mean number of books carried per pupil. Draw a histogram to illustrate the distribution. Can you suggest an explanation for the unusual shape of this distribution? Calculate to the nearest whole number the percentage of pupils (i) who were carrying fewer than 4 books (ii) who probably did not go home for lunch that day.

8 A golfer playing on a nine-hole golf course scores as follows: 6 3 4 7 5 5 4 3 6. He keeps his score in this way: 'One over five; one under five; two under five; five; five; five; one under five; three under five; two under five. Total score: 43.' Study this until you understand it and apply the same idea to the following scores:

(i) 4 4 5 5 3 6 7 5 6
(ii) 3 4 5 4 6 5 6 2 4 5 6 6 5 3 4 5 5 4

9 In a rifle-shooting competition, the target consisted of a bull's-eye, scoring 10, surrounded by nine rings scoring 9, 8, 7, and so on. A miss scored 0. The results of the competition are shown in Figure 12.

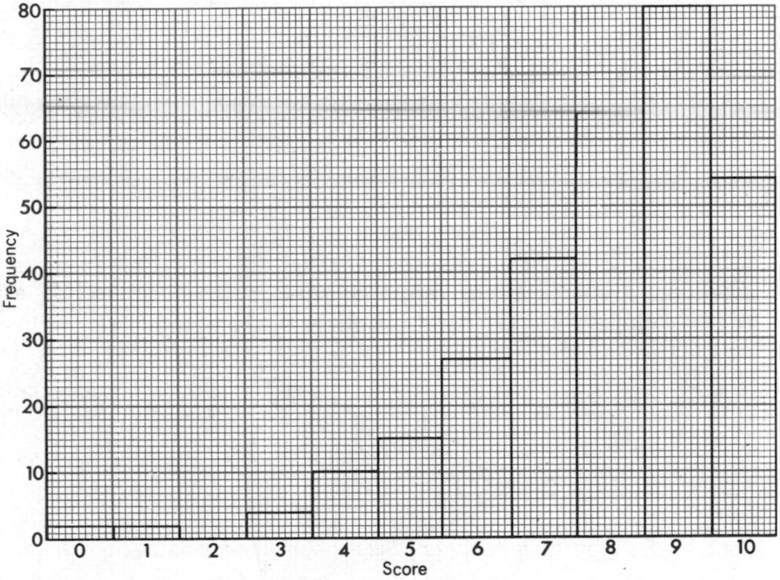

FIG. 12

Form a frequency table and calculate (i) the total number of shots (ii) the mean score per shot. If there were 30 competitors, how many shots did each fire? What percentage of the total shots (*a*) were bull's-eyes (*b*) scored less than 6? What was the average number of bull's-eyes per competitor?

Revision Exercises

Revision Exercise on Chapter 2

The Circle

1 Figure 1 shows a rectangle from which a quarter-circle has been removed at each corner. Find the area and the perimeter of the figure.

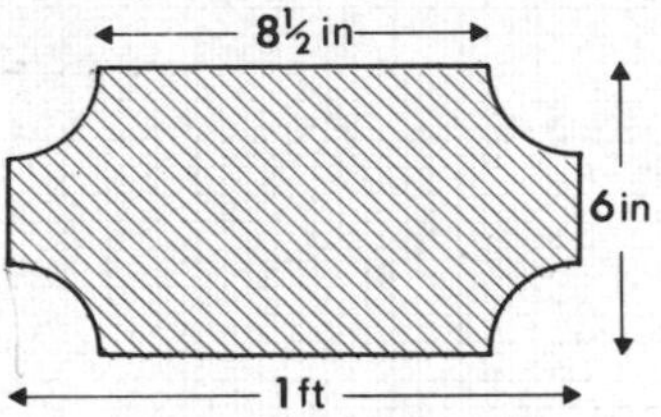

FIG. 1

2 AB is an arc of a circle, centre O, with radius 5 cm. Angle AOB is 45°. Calculate the area and perimeter of the figure OAB.

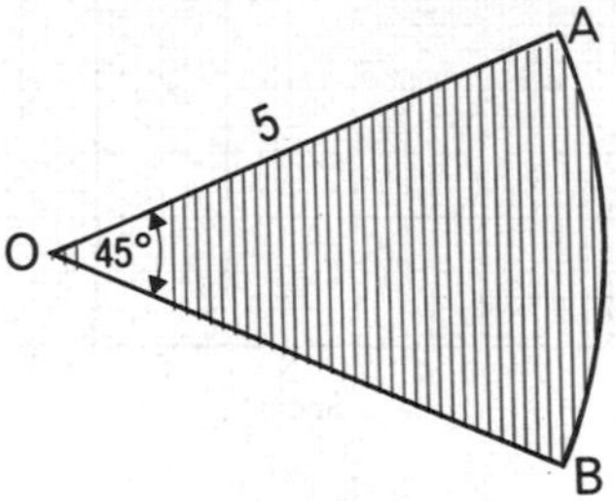

FIG. 2

3 A motor-car wheel has a diameter of 1 foot 2 inches.

(*a*) How far does the car travel in 100 revolutions of the wheel?

(*b*) How many revolutions does the wheel make while the car travels 1 mile?

4 The moon is 238,000 miles from the earth. How many miles does the moon travel in going once round the earth, assuming that it follows a circular path?

5 An artificial satellite is travelling in a circular orbit 1,040 miles above the earth's surface and completes one revolution in 2 hours. If the radius of the earth is 3,960 miles, find the speed of the satellite in mph.

6 If an artificial satellite has a speed of 11,000 mph and completes one revolution of the earth in 6 hours, find its height above the earth's surface, assuming that it has a circular orbit and that the radius of the earth is 3,960 miles.

7 A rectangular lawn 30 feet long and 16 feet broad has two circular flower-beds cut out of it, each of diameter 10 feet. Find the area of the grass to the nearest square foot.

8 In order to make lids for tin cans, the largest possible circular discs are cut out of a strip of tin 240 cm long and 7 cm broad. If as many discs as possible are cut, how much of the strip is wasted?

9 How many gallons of water does a cylindrical hot-water tank hold if its radius is 1 foot 9 inches and its height is 4 feet? [1 ft^3 = $6\frac{1}{4}$ gal]

10 A cylindrical block of brass has a volume of 8·0 cubic centimetres.

(*a*) Find the height if its radius is 3·0 cm.
(*b*) Find its radius if its height is 3·0 cm.
Give answers correct to 2 significant figures.

11 Find the volume of coffee contained in a cylindrical tin of radius 7·7 cm and height 16·8 cm.
Find also the area of a label which will fit round this tin, allowing 2 cm for overlap.

12 A merry-go-round consists of two rings of space-ships which complete 4 revolutions per minute. If the radius of the outer ring is 14 yards and the radius of the inner ring is $10\frac{1}{2}$ yards, calculate the speeds of the space-ships in the two rings in yards per minute.

13 A rectangular tank measuring 12 feet by 8 feet by 11 feet is half-filled with water. The water is allowed to flow into a cylindrical tank of radius 4 feet. Find the height to which the water will rise in the cylinder, assuming that its axis is vertical.

14 Circular discs of diameter 1 inch are cut out of a sheet of cardboard 3 feet long and 5 inches broad. How many discs can be cut, and what percentage of the cardboard sheet is wasted?

15 Making the necessary measurements, calculate the total surface area (i) of a 'Toblerone' packet (ii) of a school protractor.

16 A circular pool of diameter 35 feet has a path $3\frac{1}{2}$ feet wide round it. Find the area of the path. How many gallons of water are required to fill the pool to a depth of 4 feet? Give your answer to the nearest 10 gallons, taking 1 $ft^3 = 6\frac{1}{4}$ gal, and $\frac{22}{7}$ as an approximation for π.

17 A sheet of metal 10 cm square has 16 circular holes, each of diameter 0·50 cm, bored in it. Find the surface area of the metal remaining. If the metal is 2 mm thick, find the weight of metal remaining if 1 cm^3 weighs 7·6 g.

18 A garden roller is in the shape of a cylinder with radius 1 foot 3 inches and length 2 feet. What area of ground is rolled in one revolution of the roller?
If 10% of the rolling is wasted through overlapping, how many revolutions will be necessary in rolling a lawn 40 yards long and 20 yards broad (to the nearest whole number)?

19 Mark off on a large sheet of paper a set of parallel lines 4 cm apart. Cut a large number of sticks (e.g. matchsticks) each 2 cm long. Now place the sheet of paper on a flat surface and drop the matches one by one on to it from several feet above. Count the number of sticks which cross or touch the parallel lines. Tabulate your results thus:

Number of sticks dropped	Number of sticks touching or crossing a line

Evaluate the ratio $\dfrac{\text{number of sticks dropped}}{\text{number touching or crossing a line}}$

Your answer should be a good approximation to π!

Revision Exercise on Chapter 4

Statistics

1 The numbers of eggs collected daily over a period of six weeks by a smallholder were:

76	80	93	84	88	97	83	100	94	77	97
80	88	90	79	85	99	100	96	91	82	88
93	98	99	89	81	86	95	94	102	94	
88	92	101	80	90	81	91	95	87	93	

Construct a frequency table with a class interval of 5, starting at 76. What would the frequencies be if a class interval of 10 were chosen?

2 From a survey made on a new housing estate, the distribution of the ages of the children under 5 years is shown in the accompanying histogram (Figure 3 on page 244).

(i) How many children under 5 years of age are there on the estate?
(ii) Calculate, to the nearest whole number, the percentage of the children born in the twelve months preceding the survey.
(iii) Represent the information given in the histogram on a pie chart, of radius 30 mm, labelling each compartment with the number denoting the age, next birthday, of the children in the group.

3 A business has 50 employees who work a five-day week. The manager compiled the following data of the number of days lost through illness in one period of six months:

Number of days lost	1	2	3	4	5	9	22
Number of employees who lost this number of days	8	5	7	0	6	1	1

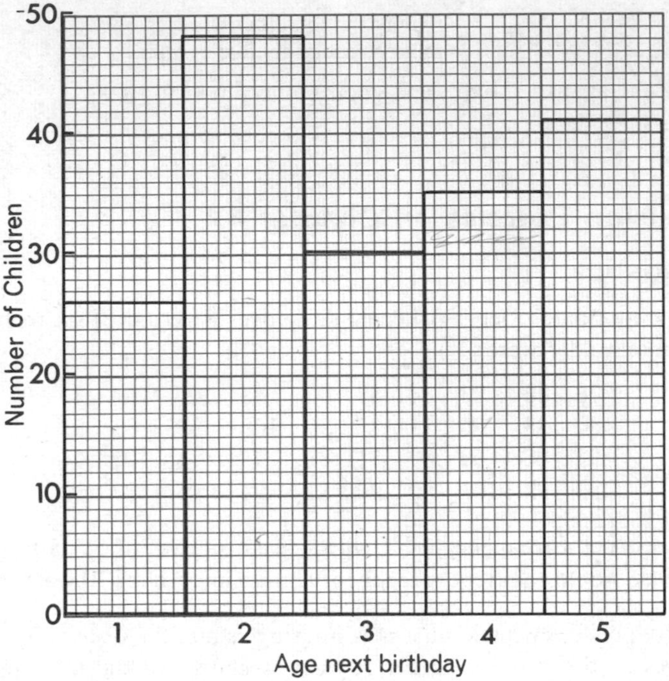

FIG. 3

(*a*) How many employees had no absence due to illness over the period?

(*b*) What percentage of employees were absent for less than 4 days?

4 In an archery tournament each competitor in a York Round shoots 72 arrows at the target 100 yards distant. Gold scores 9 points, red 7, blue 5, black 3, white 1, and a miss 0. A competitor's scores are:

0	3	1	0	5	3	3	0	1	3	3	1	5	0	0	3	1	3
5	3	0	7	3	3	1	3	5	9	5	7	0	3	1	1	3	3
1	0	3	5	1	3	1	5	3	0	3	1	3	3	5	3	7	3
0	1	3	3	0	5	3	9	5	3	0	1	5	3	1	7	3	3

(i) Make a frequency table and calculate his mean score.

(ii) Assuming this to be a typical sample of his shooting, what is the probability that if he shoots another arrow it will score 5?

5 In an experiment dealing with the fertility of hens' eggs, an Agricultural Research Institute issued batches of 100 eggs to a number of farms to be hatched in incubators. The following table gives the results:

Number of eggs hatched per batch	91	90	89	88	87	86	85	84	83	82
Number of batches	3	1	1	5	12	11	9	9	9	9
Number of eggs hatched per batch		81	80	79	78	77	76	75		70
Number of batches		9	3	5	4	4	3	1		2

(*a*) Draw a histogram to illustrate these results.
(*b*) Find the total number of batches issued, and the mean number of eggs hatched per batch.
(*c*) Find the percentage of batches for which (i) more than 86% of the eggs hatched (ii) less than 80% of the eggs hatched.

6 Each of the two books *Alice in Wonderland* and *Gulliver's Travels* was opened at random, and the numbers of letters in each of the first hundred words on the page were counted. The results of this survey are shown in Figure 4; (*a*) refers to *Alice* and (*b*) to *Gulliver*.

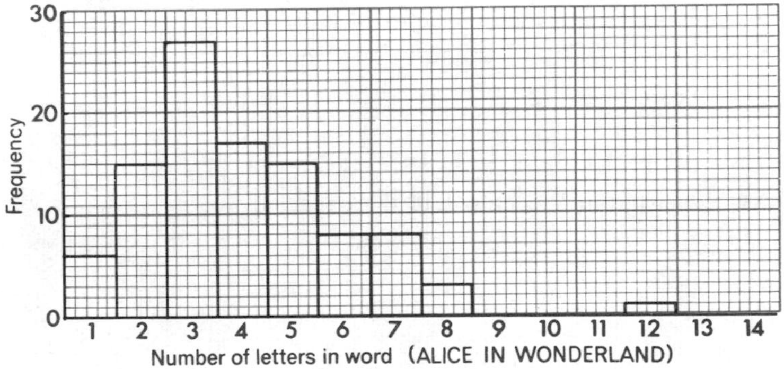

FIG. 4*a*

Calculate, for the chosen sample in each book:

(i) The modal number of letters per word.
(ii) The mean number of letters per word.

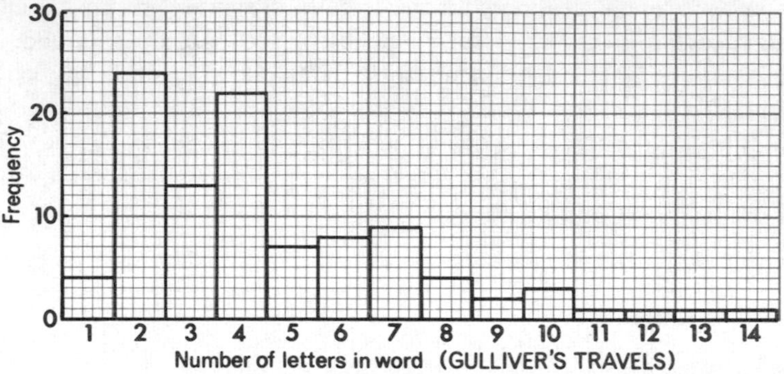

FIG. 4*b*

(iii) The percentage of words which contain 2, 3, or 4 letters.
(iv) The percentage of words which have more than 6 letters.
Which of these books would you judge (from these statistics) to be the easier to read?

7 Write out as an array the set of all possible outcomes of throwing two dice simultaneously. Hence calculate the probabilities of scoring 2, 3, 4, . . . , 12, in throwing two dice simultaneously. Now complete the following table showing the expected frequency of each score in throwing two dice simultaneously 144 times:

Score	2	3	4	5	6	7	8	9	10	11	12
Frequency											

Draw a histogram and calculate the expected mean score.

General Revision Exercises (Books 1–4)

General Revision Exercise 1

Whole Numbers, Fractions, and Decimals

1 Express as a product of prime factors (i) 42 (ii) 24 (iii) 120.

2 Write down (i) the set of multiples of 13 which are less than 200 (ii) the set of multiples of 14 which are less than 200. Hence find the LCM of 13 and 14.

3 The symbol $\odot$ denotes the operation 'double the first number and then add the second number', and the symbol $*$ denotes the operation 'double the first number and then multiply by the second number'.

Evaluate (i) $7 \odot 5$ and $5 \odot 7$ (ii) $(3 \odot 5) \odot 2$ and $3 \odot (5 \odot 2)$
(iii) $7 * 5$ and $5 * 7$ (iv) $(3 * 5) * 2$ and $3 * (5 * 2)$

Does it seem that the commutative and associative properties are true for the operations $\odot$ and $*$?

4 Make a table of addition for 'clock arithmetic' for numbers in the set $\{0, 1, 2, 3, 4\}$.
Notice that there are 5 elements in the set, and that the sum of any two elements is given by the remainder on dividing the sum by 5. For example, $4+3 = 2$ (from your table); $(4+3)\div 5=7\div 5=1$, r2. Can you explain why this is?
Use this method for the set $\{0, 1, 2, 3, 4, 5, 6, 7\}$ and the sums

(i) $5+4$ (ii) $7+5$ (iii) $1+4$ (iv) $5+6+7$ (v) $6+6+6+6$

5 Arrange in order, using the symbol $<$,

(*a*) $\frac{5}{12}, \frac{3}{8}, \frac{1}{3}$ (*b*) $\frac{7}{31}, \frac{7}{33}, \frac{7}{32}$

6 Multiply $1\frac{3}{4}$ by (i) 4 (ii) 20 (iii) 60 (iv) $1\frac{3}{4}$ (v) $\frac{1}{8}$

7 One way to simplify $\dfrac{\frac{7}{8}}{1\frac{1}{2}}$ is to multiply numerator and denominator by 8, obtaining $\frac{7}{12}$.

In the same way, a 'complex' fraction like $\dfrac{\frac{1}{2}+\frac{1}{3}}{\frac{1}{4}-\frac{1}{6}}$ can be simplified by multiplying each term in the numerator and denominator by 12. Why do we choose 12? Simplify the fraction.

Now simplify (i) $\dfrac{\frac{3}{4}-\frac{1}{6}}{\frac{5}{6}+\frac{2}{3}}$ (ii) $\dfrac{\frac{3}{5}-\frac{1}{4}}{\frac{7}{10}+\frac{1}{2}}$ (iii) $\dfrac{\frac{2}{3}+\frac{3}{5}}{\frac{1}{6}+\frac{3}{15}}$

8 Express in scientific notation, correct to three significant figures
(*a*) 42·79 (*b*) 91,500,000 (*c*) 0·314 (*d*) 0·005723

9 The marks scored in a skating contest were 27·75, 29·50, 22·25, 34·50, 49·25, 51·75, 46·00, 41·50. Calculate the average score.

10 In Figure 1, four towns are represented by A, B, C, and D, and the distances between them in kilometres are shown.

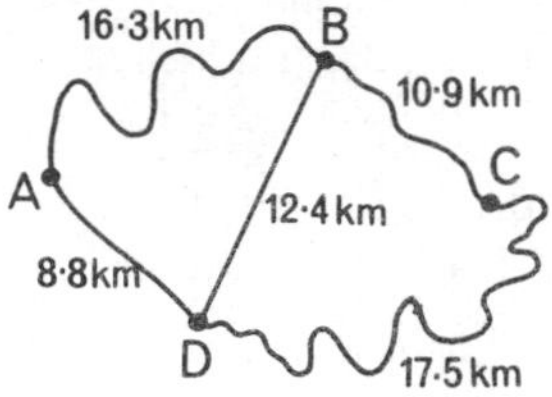

FIG. 1

(i) How many possible routes are there from A to C, no town being included more than once in any route?

(ii) What is the difference in distance between the longest and the shortest route from A to C?

11 How many pieces of wire each 7·8 cm long can be cut from a coil containing 10 m of wire? What length will be left over?

12 Find the average of £6·85, £7·93, £8·84, £5·69, and £9·04.

13 A school received a consignment of twelve calculating machines, each packed in a box weighing 1·1 kg. The total weight of the machines and boxes was 69·6 kg. Calculate the weight of each machine.

14 Use a slide rule to calculate:

(*a*) $\dfrac{7{\cdot}69 \times 11{\cdot}2}{19{\cdot}7}$ (*b*) $\dfrac{0{\cdot}423 \times 0{\cdot}650}{0{\cdot}821}$

(*c*) $43{\cdot}2 \times 46{\cdot}3 \times 0{\cdot}124$ (*d*) $4{\cdot}19 \times 2{\cdot}5^3$

General Revision Exercise 2

Rectangular Areas and Volumes; Square Roots

1 A rectangular sheet of pegboard 5 ft 6 in long and 4 ft 6 in broad costs 99 pence. How much is this per ft^2?
What would be the cost of a sheet three times as long and half as broad?

2 A rectangular plot 27 ft 3 in long and 14 ft 10 in broad is to be made into a lawn. Grass seed is to be sown at the rate of 2 oz per yd^2, and can be bought in $\frac{1}{2}$-lb bags. How many bags should be bought? (You should not calculate the area exactly.)

3 A rectangular panel 6 ft by 1 ft 8 in is to be tiled with square tiles of side $4\frac{1}{4}$ in. How many tiles will be required, and how many of these will have to be cut in order to cover the panel completely?
If tiles cost 85 pence per box of 36, or $2\frac{1}{2}$ pence each if bought separately, find the total cost.

4

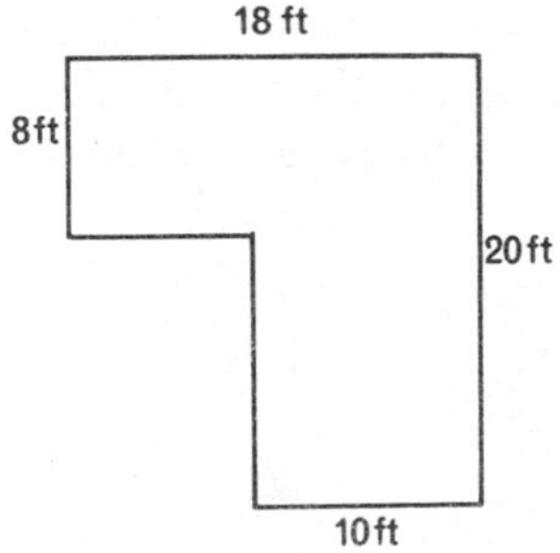

FIG. 2

Figure 2 shows the shape of the floor of a room. Calculate the cost of covering it with carpet at £3·20 per yd^2.

5 The perimeter of a rectangle is 28 mm and the ratio of the length to the breadth is 4 : 3. Find its area.

6 Calculate, to three significant figures, the volume of a cuboid 16·8 cm long, 11·8 cm broad, and 7·8 cm high.

7 A rectangular water tank has a base $3\frac{1}{2}$ ft by 3 ft, and holds 175 gal. If 1 ft^3 is equivalent to $6\frac{1}{4}$ gal, calculate the depth of the water.

8 A brick wall is to be 6 ft long, 3 ft high, and 9 in thick. How many bricks, each 9 in by $4\frac{1}{2}$ in by 3 in, will be required for the wall? (Ignore the thickness of cement.)

9 Find the weight of a cuboid of lead 21·3 cm by 12·4 cm by 3·5 cm, assuming that 1 cm^3 of lead weighs 11·2 g. Convert the weight to lb, given that 1 kg is approximately equal to 2·20 lb.

10 Which of the following are approximations for $\sqrt{745}$?
(*a*) 27·3 (*b*) 86·3 (*c*) 8·63 (*d*) $2{\cdot}73 \times 10$

11 Which of the following are approximations for $\sqrt{0{\cdot}745}$?
(*a*) 0·273 (*b*) 0·863 (*c*) $2{\cdot}73 \times 10^{-2}$ (*d*) $8{\cdot}63 \times 10^{-1}$

12 A rectangle measures 6·5 cm by 2·6 cm. Calculate the perimeter of a square equal in area to the rectangle.

13 Express the square root of $3{\cdot}45 \times 10^{-7}$ in standard form.

14 Use tables to find the square roots of 75·6 and of 0·000346, correct to three significant figures. Then calculate the square roots to five significant figures (by one division in each case).

15 One cubic foot of copper is drawn into wire one mile long. Calculate the area of cross-section of the wire as a fraction of a square inch.

General Revision Exercise 3

Proportion

1 Find the rate for each of the following, in the units given:

(i) I travelled 2,500 miles and used 75 gallons of petrol (miles per gallon).

(ii) An electric fire used 84 units of electricity in 168 hours (units per hour).

(iii) A hose delivered 1,008 gallons of water in 42 minutes (gallons per minute).

2 When petrol cost 24 pence a gallon the cost of filling a tank was £1·26. What would the cost be if the price of petrol rose by 4 pence a gallon?

3 The cost of spraying a field of $1\frac{1}{2}$ acres is £4·20. Find the cost of spraying a rectangular field 200 yards by 154 yards. (1 acre = 4,840 square yards.)

4 A slow train averaging 32 mph takes 3 hours for a journey. How long would an express averaging 60 mph take? What is the length of the journey?

5 When three boys stand on a weighing machine platform, the machine registers 18 stones. What would it show if five boys stood on the platform?

6 A car is 14 ft 6 in long and 5 ft 3 in wide. If a model of the car is to be 19 cm long, how wide should it be?

7 14·4 Swedish kronor are worth 11·2 German marks. How many marks are equivalent to 87·5 kronor?

8 When planting strawberry plants, I require 6 rows if I place the plants 15 in apart. How many rows would I require if I set the plants 10 in apart?

9 A boy answered the first six questions in a mathematics test in 20 minutes. How long will it take him to finish the paper, which contains ten questions?

10 A 'slow motion' camera takes pictures at 72 frames per second, and these are projected on a screen at 16 frames per second. How long will a shot of a golfer's swing take when projected if it actually takes 0·45 second to complete?

11 A rectangular park measures 0·35 in by 0·15 in on a map whose scale is 4 miles to 1 in. Calculate its area in acres (1 acre = 4840 yd^2).

12 A plan is drawn to a scale of 6 inches to 1 mile. What area of the ground is represented by 1 in^2 on the map? What area is represented by a square of side 1·8 in?

13 A transparency 2·5 cm long and 1·9 cm broad is projected on a screen. If the picture is 6 ft long, calculate its breadth.

14 If 1·75 litres of gas weigh 0·630 grams, what is the weight of 22·5 litres?

15 12 Swiss francs are approximately equal to 100 British pence. Draw a graph for converting francs to pence (up to 100p). Use it to convert (*a*) 5 francs, 7 francs, 3·50 francs to pence; (*b*) 80 pence, $27\frac{1}{2}$ pence, 56 pence to francs.

General Revision Exercise 4

Binary Numbers

1 Express all the prime numbers between 30_{ten} and 40_{ten} in binary notation.

2 Write down all the pairs of binary numbers whose sum is 10_{ten}.

3 Calculate $1+11$, $1+11+111$, and $1+11+111+1111$, all the numbers being in the scale of two.

4 Calculate (i) the perimeter of a rectangle of length 11011_{two} feet and breadth 1010_{two} feet.

(ii) the length of the side of a square of perimeter 10100_{two} feet.

5 Write down the next two terms of each of the following sequences of binary numbers. Then express all the terms in the denary (decimal) scale:

(*a*) 1, 10, 100, 1000, . . . (*b*) 1, 10, 101, 1010, . . .

6 Arrange in ascending order of magnitude:

100110, 101010, 101100, 110001, 100011

7 Calculate the volume of a cuboid of dimensions 101 cm, 110 cm, and 11 cm, the numbers being in the scale of two.

8 How many pieces of wire each 1101_{two} cm long can be cut from a length of 110110_{two} cm of wire? Check your working by converting all the numbers to base ten.

9 In base ten, we know that $0·1 = \frac{1}{10}$, and $0·01 = \frac{1}{100}$. What then must be the meaning of 0·1 and 0·01 in base two notation? Express 0·11 and 0·101 in the same way, and then convert them to base ten numbers. (These are sometimes called 'bicimals'.)

General Revision Exercise 5
Social Arithmetic

1 Calculate the total cost of:

6,000 sheets of loose-leaf paper at 40 sheets for 7 pence.
1,500 exercise books at 25 pence per dozen.
200 textbooks at $47\frac{1}{2}$ pence each.

2 A householder used 900 gallons of oil for central heating. The oil cost $7{\cdot}82\frac{1}{2}$ pence per gallon and annual servicing of the boiler cost £4·20. Find the total annual cost of the heating system, and the monthly payment necessary to meet it.

3 Parcel post rates are as follows:
Not more than 2 lb, $13\frac{1}{2}$ pence.
Over 2 lb but not over 3 lb, 15 pence; over 3 lb but not over 4 lb, $16\frac{1}{2}$ pence; over 4 lb but not over 6 lb, 18 pence; over 6 lb but not over 8 lb, 20 pence. In the course of a day a firm sent out 200 parcels equally divided among the above categories. What was the total cost of postage?

4 Two successive readings of an electricity meter were 4,783 and 5,153. The first 36 units are charged at 2·5 pence per unit, the next 78 units at 1·25 pence per unit, the rest at 0·55 pence per unit. Calculate the cost.

5 During one year a car travelled 7,500 miles, using 220 gallons of petrol costing 26 pence a gallon and 15 pints of oil costing 14 pence per pint. The vehicle licence cost £17·50, insurance £15, and repairs £12·20. In addition, the value of the car fell by £120. Calculate the total cost of owning and running the car during the year, and also the cost per mile, to the nearest penny.

6 A football team played 24 games and scored an average of 1·83 goals per game. How many goals had they scored altogether?

7 The average weight of 8 oarsmen in a boat-race crew is 13 st 10 lb. The average weight of the 9 crew members, including the cox, is 13 st 6 lb. What is the weight of the cox?

8 A car normally travels 30 to 35 miles per gallon of petrol (depending on traffic, speed, etc.), but when towing a caravan it covers between

20 and 25 miles per gallon. The owner planned to travel 650 miles on holiday, towing a caravan for 400 of the miles. Estimate the maximum and minimum quantities of petrol he will use.

9 Calculate what percentage the first is of the second in the following:

(i) 37; 150 (ii) £5·50; £73·20 (iii) 2·25 cm; 1·5 m

10 A shop advertises a discount of 5% for all cash payments. How much (to the nearest penny) would be paid for purchases totalling:

(*a*) £17 (*b*) £15·60 (*c*) £23·82?

11 One dozen articles cost £2·90. If they are sold for 27 pence each, calculate the profit as a percentage of the selling price.

12 A dealer buys 12 tons of potatoes at £25 a ton. It costs him ½p per lb to clean them and pack them in 3-lb bags, which he then sells at 5p a bag. What is his percentage profit or loss, reckoned on his total outlay?

13 A salesman is paid 2½% commission on all sales over £5,000 per annum, together with a basic wage of £7·50 per week. How much does he earn in a year when his sales total £48,700?

14 A Trustee Savings Bank pays interest of 2½% per annum on ordinary accounts, and 5½% per annum on special accounts, both paid on complete £s in the account. How much interest is paid in a year when a person had £57·37 in the ordinary account and £145·59 in the special account?

15 Calculate the simple interest on £112·50 at 3½% per annum from 20th January to 3rd July 1966, interest being payable on complete pounds and for complete calendar months.

16 A space probe travelling at 8,350 mph took 243 days to reach the planet Venus. How many miles did it travel?

17 The distance from Prestwick to New York is 3,200 miles. On the westward journey an aircraft flew at an average speed of 550 mph, and on the eastward journey at 650 mph. Find the difference in duration of the journeys, to the nearest minute.

18 A man lived 42 miles from Inverness. He motored there in daylight at an average speed of 45 mph and returned after dark at an average speed of 30 mph. Calculate his overall average speed.

19 Calculate the cost of the following hotel bill in Paris:

11 days room and breakfast at 32·40 francs per day
10 lunches at 9·85 francs each
22 dinners at 15·60 francs each.

If there is a service charge of $12\frac{1}{2}\%$, what change is given for a 1,000-franc note?

20 In 1964 the internal National Debt was £27,801 million. How much interest, at an average rate of 5·6% per annum, had to be paid?

General Revision Exercise 6

Probability

1 A number is chosen at random from the sequence 2, 3, 5, 8, 12, 17. Find the probability that it is (i) even (ii) odd (iii) prime (iv) odd and prime (v) odd or prime or both.

2 A box contains one red, one yellow, one blue, and one white disc. If a disc is selected at random, what is the probability that (i) it is blue (ii) it is not blue?
The disc is replaced and another disc is drawn. By drawing up an array of all possible outcomes, find the probability that a red and a blue disc have been selected (not necessarily in that order) in two successive draws.

3 In a school of 1,095 pupils how many are likely to have a birthday (i) in December (ii) on Christmas day?

4 A number is selected from the set {1, 3, 5, 7} and added to a number selected from the set {2, 4, 6, 8}; show all possible sums in an array. From this draw up a frequency table showing how often each sum occurs. Calculate (i) the most likely sum, and its probability (ii) the probability that the sum is (*a*) 13 (*b*) odd (*c*) even (*d*) divisible by 3.

5 If a number is selected at random from each of the sets {1, 2, 3} and {3, 4, 5}, what is the probability that (i) the sum of the two numbers will be greater than 5 (ii) the product of the numbers will be greater than 5?

6 In a certain country the number of men in the 55–64 age group is 3·456 million. On the basis of past statistics it is estimated that the probability that any one man in this group will be alive ten years later is 0·68; estimate the number of men in the 65–74 age group ten years later.

7 Of 80 pupils in a certain year, 20 are specializing in mathematics and 30 are members of the athletic club; 40 of the pupils neither specialize in mathematics nor are members of the athletic club. Show these facts in a Venn diagram. If a pupil is selected at random, what is the probability that he (i) both specializes in mathematics and is a member of the athletic club (ii) specializes in mathematics and is not a member of the athletic club?

General Revision Exercise 7

True—False

State whether each of the following is true (T) or false (F).

1 $11011_{two} = 29_{ten}$

2 $3{\cdot}75^2 = 14{\cdot}1$, by slide rule.

3 $\sqrt{47{\cdot}0} = 21{\cdot}7$ to three significant figures.

4 $1\frac{1}{2}\%$ of £2,300 = £34.

5 $4\frac{1}{2}$ dozen wallflowers at 17p per dozen cost $76\frac{1}{2}$p.

6 The length, breadth, height, and volume of a cuboid are 0·8 cm, 0·6 cm, 0·3 cm, and 1·44 cm^3 respectively.

7 Cycling at 8 mph I take 36 minutes for a journey, so cycling at 12 mph I should take 24 minutes.

8 The circumference of a circle of radius 2 m is approximately 6·28 m.

9 The probability that a number selected at random from the set $\{1, 2, 3, 4, 5\}$ is greater than 3 is 0·6.

10 Travelling for $2\frac{1}{2}$ hours at an average speed of 46 mph, I should cover 115 miles.

11 A square playground 70 yd long has an area of slightly more than 1 acre (1 acre = 4840 yd^2).

12 A rectangle 1·2 m by 98 cm has an area greater than 1 m^2.

13 (i) $\sqrt{3\frac{1}{16}} = 1\frac{3}{4}$ (ii) $\sqrt{0{\cdot}5} \doteqdot 0{\cdot}7$ (iii) $\sqrt{239}$ lies between 15 and 16

14 (i) $52{\cdot}3 \times 0{\cdot}03 = 15{\cdot}69$ (ii) $9{\cdot}43 \div 0{\cdot}471 \doteqdot 2$
(iii) $7{\cdot}6 \times 10^{-2} = 0{\cdot}076$
(iv) If $a = 0{\cdot}8$ and $b = 0{\cdot}02$, $a+\frac{5}{2}b = \frac{17}{20}$

15 If a train travelled for 3 h 15 min at an average speed of 48 mph, then
(*a*) the distance travelled was 156 miles;
(*b*) if the train stopped in stations for 15 min, the average running speed was 60 mph;
(*c*) if the length of the journey was doubled, and the speed halved, the time would be four times as long.

General Revision Exercise 8

Miscellaneous

1 Calculate (i) $(2\frac{1}{3}-1\frac{1}{2}) \div 6\frac{2}{3}$ (ii) $3{\cdot}02 \times 0{\cdot}009$

2 Find $7\frac{1}{2}\%$ of £5·50.

3 Express the product of $1{\cdot}5 \times 10^3$ and $3{\cdot}7 \times 10^{-5}$ in the form $a \times 10^n$, with a correct to two significant figures.

4 How many tiles each 4 in square are required to cover a rectangular floor 4 yd 2 ft long and 3 yd wide?

5 Calculate the simple interest on £720 for 7 months at $3\frac{1}{2}\%$ per annum.

6 What decimal fraction of one acre is a rectangular area 88 yd long and 33 yd broad?

7 A train departs at 2234 hours and reaches its destination 210 miles away at 0219 hours the next day. Calculate its average speed.

8 A portable typewriter is described as being $13\frac{1}{2}$ in (34·29 cm) deep and weighing 13 lb 6 oz (6·02 kg). How many cm does this assume per in, and how many lb per kg?

9 Give the *n*th term of each of the following sequences:
(i) 5, 10, 15, 20, . . . (ii) $\frac{1}{2}, \frac{1}{4}, \frac{1}{8}, \frac{1}{16}, \ldots$

10 The population of Canada in 1951 was 14,009,000 (to the nearest thousand) and it increased by 30% over the following ten years. Of this growth in population, natural increase, i.e. the excess of births over deaths, contributed 75% and immigration the rest. What increases (to the nearest thousand) were due to each of these two factors?

General Revision Exercise 9

Miscellaneous

1 Evaluate (i) $(0{\cdot}2)^2 \times 0{\cdot}09$ (ii) $9{\cdot}65 - 12{\cdot}83 + 7{\cdot}76$

2 The reading on a barometer is 760 mm. Taking 1 m = 39·37 in, express the reading in inches.

3 From a square sheet of acetate of side 35 cm are cut a square of side 12·2 cm, a rectangle 10·2 cm by 7·8 cm, and a circle of radius 5·0 cm. Taking 3·14 as an approximation for π, calculate the area of acetate left.

4 18 girls enter for a singles knockout tennis tournament. How many matches does the winner play if she receives a bye in the first round?

5 When a metal bar 2·500 cm long is heated, its length becomes 2·507 cm. What percentage increase in length does this represent?

6 In throwing a die, what is the theoretical probability of obtaining a number greater than 2?

7 A man is paid $37\frac{1}{2}$ pence an hour for a 40-hour week. One week he works 49 hours and is paid £19·72$\frac{1}{2}$. Find the hourly payment for overtime.

8 Oxford beat Cambridge in the 1966 Boat Race by $3\frac{3}{4}$ lengths. If 1 length was rowed in $3\frac{1}{2}$ seconds, and the winning time was 19 minutes 12 seconds, what was the loser's time?

9 A rectangular field of area $\frac{1}{2}$ acre has length 110 yd. Find its breadth (1 acre = 4840 yd²).

10 The petrol tank in a car made in France holds 50 litres, and the car can travel 9·6 km on a litre of petrol. Calculate (*a*) the number of

miles it can travel per litre of petrol, (*b*) the number of miles it can travel per gallon of petrol (approximately, 8 km = 5 miles, and 1 gallon = 4·5 litres).

General Revision Exercise 10

Miscellaneous

1 Calculate the cost of 180 books at 34 pence each.

2 Divide £7·48 by 12 to the nearest halfpenny.

3 The average age of 4 boys is 12 years 1 month, and of another 5 boys is 12 years 10 months. What is the average age of all the boys?

4 An account of £15 is settled by a payment of £13·72½ in cash. Calculate the discount per £, and the percentage discount.

5 A circular disc of radius 5 cm weighs 300 g. Find its weight when ½ cm is cut off all round the edge.

6 The time for a 100-m race was 10·4 sec. At the same speed, what would be the time for a 100-yd race? (1 m ≑ 39·37 in)

7 After his wages are increased by 5% a man earns £13·12½ per week. Calculate his weekly wage before the increase.

8 One inch of rain fell on an area of 160 yd². Find the volume of water which fell, in ft³.

9 A city savings bank, in conjunction with 90 school groups, carried through 158,630 transactions in one year involving £26,668. Calculate (i) the average number of transactions per group, (ii) the average sum of money involved in each transaction.

10 A chemical mixture consists of three elements A, B, and C in the ratio 4 : 3 : 2 by weight. 24 g of B and 10 g of C are in stock. What weight of A and C should be added to the quantities in stock of B and C to make the mixture, and what weight of mixture is obtained?

Square Roots: 1—10

	0	1	2	3	4	5	6	7	8	9
1·0	1·00	1·00	1·01	1·01	1·02	1·02	1·03	1·03	1·04	1·04
1·1	1·05	1·05	1·06	1·06	1·07	1·07	1·08	1·08	1·09	1·09
1·2	1·10	1·10	1·10	1·11	1·11	1·12	1·12	1·13	1·13	1·14
1·3	1·14	1·14	1·15	1·15	1·16	1·16	1·17	1·17	1·17	1·18
1·4	1·18	1·19	1·19	1·20	1·20	1·20	1·21	1·21	1·22	1·22
1·5	1·22	1·23	1·23	1·24	1·24	1·24	1·25	1·25	1·26	1·26
1·6	1·26	1·27	1·27	1·28	1·28	1·28	1·29	1·29	1·30	1·30
1·7	1·30	1·31	1·31	1·32	1·32	1·32	1·33	1·33	1·33	1·34
1·8	1·34	1·35	1·35	1·35	1·36	1·36	1·36	1·37	1·37	1·37
1·9	1·38	1·38	1·39	1·39	1·39	1·40	1·40	1·40	1·41	1·41
2·0	1·41	1·42	1·42	1·42	1·43	1·43	1·44	1·44	1.44	1·45
2·1	1·45	1·45	1·46	1·46	1·46	1·47	1·47	1·47	1·48	1·48
2·2	1·48	1·49	1·49	1·49	1·50	1·50	1·50	1·51	1·51	1·51
2·3	1·52	1·52	1·52	1·53	1·53	1·53	1·54	1·54	1·54	1·55
2·4	1·55	1·55	1·56	1·56	1·56	1·57	1·57	1·57	1·57	1·58
2·5	1·58	1·58	1·59	1·59	1·59	1·60	1·60	1·60	1·61	1·61
2·6	1·61	1·62	1·62	1·62	1·62	1·63	1·63	1·63	1·64	1·64
2·7	1·64	1·65	1·65	1·65	1·66	1·66	1·66	1·66	1·67	1·67
2·8	1·67	1·68	1·68	1·68	1·69	1·69	1·69	1·69	1·70	1·70
2·9	1·70	1·71	1·71	1·71	1·71	1·72	1·72	1·72	1·73	1·73
3·0	1·73	1·73	1·74	1·74	1·74	1·75	1·75	1·75	1·75	1·76
3·1	1·76	1·76	1·77	1·77	1·77	1·77	1·78	1·78	1·78	1·79
3·2	1·79	1·79	1·79	1·80	1·80	1·80	1·81	1·81	1·81	1·81
3·3	1·82	1·82	1·82	1·82	1·83	1·83	1·83	1·84	1·84	1·84
3·4	1·84	1·85	1·85	1·85	1·85	1·86	1·86	1·86	1·87	1·87
3·5	1·87	1·87	1·88	1·88	1·88	1·88	1·89	1·89	1·89	1·89
3·6	1·90	1·90	1·90	1·91	1·91	1·91	1·91	1·92	1·92	1·92
3·7	1·92	1·93	1·93	1·93	1·93	1·94	1·94	1·94	1·94	1·95
3·8	1·95	1·95	1·95	1·96	1·96	1·96	1·96	1·97	1·97	1·97
3·9	1·97	1·98	1·98	1·98	1·98	1·99	1·99	1·99	1·99	2·00
4·0	2·00	2·00	2·00	2·01	2·01	2·01	2·01	2·02	2·02	2·02
4·1	2·02	2·03	2·03	2·03	2·03	2·04	2·04	2·04	2·04	2·05
4·2	2·05	2·05	2·05	2·06	2·06	2·06	2·06	2·07	2·07	2·07
4·3	2·07	2·08	2·08	2·08	2·08	2·09	2·09	2·09	2·09	2·10
4·4	2·10	2·10	2·10	2·10	2·11	2·11	2·11	2·11	2·12	2·12
4·5	2·12	2·12	2·13	2·13	2·13	2·13	2·14	2·14	2·14	2·14
4·6	2·14	2·15	2·15	2·15	2·15	2·16	2·16	2·16	2·16	2·17
4·7	2·17	2·17	2·17	2·17	2·18	2·18	2·18	2·18	2·19	2·19
4·8	2·19	2·19	2·20	2·20	2·20	2·20	2·20	2·21	2·21	2·21
4·9	2·21	2·22	2·22	2·22	2·22	2·22	2·23	2·23	2·23	2·23
5·0	2·24	2·24	2·24	2·24	2·25	2·25	2·25	2·25	2·25	2·26
5·1	2·26	2·26	2·26	2·26	2·27	2·27	2·27	2·27	2·28	2·28
5·2	2·28	2·28	2·28	2·29	2·29	2·29	2·29	2·30	2·30	2·30
5·3	2·30	2·30	2·31	2·31	2·31	2·31	2·32	2·32	2·32	2·32
5·4	2·32	2·33	2·33	2·33	2·33	2·33	2·34	2·34	2·34	2·34

Square Roots: 1—10

	0	1	2	3	4	5	6	7	8	9
5·5	2·35	2·35	2·35	2·35	2·35	2·36	2·36	2·36	2·36	2·36
5·6	2·37	2·37	2·37	2·37	2·37	2·38	2·38	2·38	2·38	2·39
5·7	2·39	2·39	2·39	2·39	2·40	2·40	2·40	2·40	2·40	2·41
5·8	2·41	2·41	2·41	2·41	2·42	2·42	2·42	2·42	2·42	2·43
5·9	2·43	2·43	2·43	2·44	2·44	2·44	2·44	2·44	2·45	2·45
6·0	2·45	2·45	2·45	2·46	2·46	2·46	2·46	2·46	2·47	2·47
6·1	2·47	2·47	2·47	2·48	2·48	2·48	2·48	2·48	2·49	2·49
6·2	2·49	2·49	2·49	2·50	2·50	2·50	2·50	2·50	2·51	2·51
6·3	2·51	2·51	2·51	2·52	2·52	2·52	2·52	2·52	2·53	2·53
6·4	2·53	2·53	2·53	2·54	2·54	2·54	2·54	2·54	2·55	2·55
6·5	2·55	2·55	2·55	2·56	2·56	2·56	2·56	2·56	2·57	2·57
6·6	2·57	2·57	2·57	2·57	2·58	2·58	2·58	2·58	2·58	2·59
6·7	2·59	2·59	2·59	2·59	2·60	2·60	2·60	2·60	2·60	2·61
6·8	2·61	2·61	2·61	2·61	2·62	2·62	2·62	2·62	2·62	2·62
6·9	2·63	2·63	2·63	2·63	2·63	2·64	2·64	2·64	2·64	2·64
7·0	2·65	2·65	2·65	2·65	2·65	2·66	2·66	2·66	2·66	2·66
7·1	2·66	2·67	2·67	2·67	2·67	2·67	2·68	2·68	2·68	2·68
7·2	2·68	2·69	2·69	2·69	2·69	2·69	2·69	2·70	2·70	2·70
7·3	2·70	2·70	2·71	2·71	2·71	2·71	2·71	2·71	2·72	2·72
7·4	2·72	2·72	2·72	2·73	2·73	2·73	2·73	2·73	2·73	2·74
7·5	2·74	2·74	2·74	2·74	2·75	2·75	2·75	2·75	2·75	2·75
7·6	2·76	2·76	2·76	2·76	2·76	2·77	2·77	2·77	2·77	2·77
7·7	2·77	2·78	2·78	2·78	2·78	2·78	2·79	2·79	2·79	2·79
7·8	2·79	2·79	2·80	2·80	2·80	2·80	2·80	2·81	2·81	2·81
7·9	2·81	2·81	2·81	2·82	2·82	2·82	2·82	2·82	2·82	2·83
8·0	2·83	2·83	2·83	2·83	2·84	2·84	2·84	2·84	2·84	2·84
8·1	2·85	2·85	2·85	2·85	2·85	2·85	2·86	2·86	2·86	2·86
8·2	2·86	2·87	2·87	2·87	2·87	2·87	2·87	2·88	2·88	2·88
8·3	2·88	2·88	2·88	2·89	2·89	2·89	2·89	2·89	2·89	2·90
8·4	2·90	2·90	2·90	2·90	2·91	2·91	2·91	2·91	2·91	2·91
8·5	2·92	2·92	2·92	2·92	2·92	2·92	2·93	2·93	2·93	2·93
8·6	2·93	2·93	2·94	2·94	2·94	2·94	2·94	2·94	2·95	2·95
8·7	2·95	2·95	2·95	2·95	2·96	2·96	2·96	2·96	2·96	2·96
8·8	2·97	2·97	2·97	2·97	2·97	2·97	2·98	2·98	2·98	2·98
8·9	2·98	2·98	2·99	2·99	2·99	2·99	2·99	2·99	3·00	3·00
9·0	3·00	3·00	3·00	3·00	3·01	3·01	3·01	3·01	3·01	3·01
9·1	3·02	3·02	3·02	3·02	3·02	3·02	3·03	3·03	3·03	3·03
9·2	3·03	3·03	3·04	3·04	3·04	3·04	3·04	3·04	3·05	3·05
9·3	3·05	3·05	3·05	3·05	3·06	3·06	3·06	3·06	3·06	3·06
9·4	3·07	3·07	3·07	3·07	3·07	3·07	3·08	3·08	3·08	3·08
9·5	3·08	3·08	3·09	3·09	3·09	3·09	3·09	3·09	3·10	3·10
9·6	3·10	3·10	3·10	3·10	3·10	3·11	3·11	3·11	3·11	3·11
9·7	3·11	3·12	3·12	3·12	3·12	3·12	3·12	3·13	3·13	3·13
9·8	3·13	3·13	3·13	3·14	3·14	3·14	3·14	3·14	3·14	3·14
9·9	3·15	3·15	3·15	3·15	3·15	3·15	3·16	3·16	3·16	3·16

Square Roots: 10—100

	0	1	2	3	4	5	6	7	8	9
10	3·16	3·18	3·19	3·21	3·22	3·24	3·26	3·27	3·29	3·30
11	3·32	3·33	3·35	3·36	3·38	3·39	3·41	3·42	3·44	3·45
12	3·46	3·48	3·49	3·51	3·52	3·54	3·55	3·56	3·58	3·59
13	3·61	3·62	3·63	3·65	3·66	3·67	3·69	3·70	3·71	3·73
14	3·74	3·75	3·77	3·78	3·79	3·81	3·82	3·83	3·85	3·86
15	3·87	3·89	3·90	3·91	3·92	3·94	3·95	3·96	3·97	3·99
16	4·00	4·01	4·02	4·04	4·05	4·06	4·07	4·09	4·10	4·11
17	4·12	4·14	4·15	4·16	4·17	4·18	4·20	4·21	4·22	4·23
18	4·24	4·25	4·27	4·28	4·29	4·30	4·31	4·32	4·34	4·35
19	4·36	4·37	4·38	4·39	4·40	4·42	4·43	4·44	4·45	4·46
20	4·47	4·48	4·49	4·51	4·52	4·53	4·54	4·55	4·56	4·57
21	4·58	4·59	4·60	4·62	4·63	4·64	4·65	4·66	4·67	4·68
22	4·69	4·70	4·71	4·72	4·73	4·74	4·75	4·76	4·77	4·79
23	4·80	4·81	4·82	4·83	4·84	4·85	4·86	4·87	4·88	4·89
24	4·90	4·91	4·92	4·93	4·94	4·95	4·96	4·97	4·98	4·99
25	5·00	5·01	5·02	5·03	5·04	5·05	5·06	5·07	5·08	5·09
26	5·10	5·11	5·12	5·13	5·14	5·15	5·16	5·17	5·18	5·19
27	5·20	5·21	5·22	5·22	5·23	5·24	5·25	5·26	5·27	5·28
28	5·29	5·30	5·31	5·32	5·33	5·34	5·35	5·36	5·37	5·38
29	5·39	5·39	5·40	5·41	5·42	5·43	5·44	5·45	5·46	5·47
30	5·48	5·49	5·50	5·50	5·51	5·52	5·53	5·54	5·55	5·56
31	5·57	5·58	5·59	5·59	5·60	5·61	5·62	5·63	5·64	5·65
32	5·66	5·67	5·67	5·68	5·69	5·70	5·71	5·72	5·73	5·74
33	5·74	5·75	5·76	5·77	5·78	5·79	5·80	5·81	5·81	5·82
34	5·83	5·84	5·85	5·86	5·87	5·87	5·88	5·89	5·90	5·91
35	5·92	5·92	5·93	5·94	5·95	5·96	5·97	5·97	5·98	5·99
36	6·00	6·01	6·02	6·02	6·03	6·04	6·05	6·06	6·07	6·07
37	6·08	6·09	6·10	6·11	6·12	6·12	6·13	6·14	6·15	6·16
38	6·16	6·17	6·18	6·19	6·20	6·20	6·21	6·22	6·23	6·24
39	6·24	6·25	6·26	6·27	6·28	6·28	6·29	6·30	6·31	6·32
40	6·32	6·33	6·34	6·35	6·36	6·36	6·37	6·38	6·39	6·40
41	6·40	6·41	6·42	6·43	6·43	6·44	6·45	6·46	6·47	6·47
42	6·48	6·49	6·50	6·50	6·51	6·52	6·53	6·53	6·54	6·55
43	6·56	6·57	6·57	6·58	6·59	6·60	6·60	6·61	6·62	6·63
44	6·63	6·64	6·65	6·66	6·66	6·67	6·68	6·69	6·69	6·70
45	6·71	6·72	6·72	6·73	6·74	6·75	6·75	6·76	6·77	6·77
46	6·78	6·79	6·80	6·80	6·81	6·82	6·83	6·83	6·84	6·85
47	6·86	6·86	6·87	6·88	6·88	6·89	6·90	6·91	6·91	6·92
48	6·93	6·94	6·94	6·95	6·96	6·96	6·97	6·98	6·99	6·99
49	7·00	7·01	7·01	7·02	7·03	7·04	7·04	7·05	7·06	7·06
50	7·07	7·08	7·09	7·09	7·10	7·11	7·11	7·12	7·13	7·13
51	7·14	7·15	7·16	7·16	7·17	7·18	7·18	7·19	7·20	7·20
52	7·21	7·22	7·22	7·23	7·24	7·25	7·25	7·26	7·27	7·27
53	7·28	7·29	7·29	7·30	7·31	7·31	7·32	7·33	7·33	7·34
54	7·35	7·36	7·36	7·37	7·38	7·38	7·39	7·40	7·40	7·41

Square Roots: 10—100

	0	1	2	3	4	5	6	7	8	9
55	7·42	7·42	7·43	7·44	7·44	7·45	7·46	7·46	7·47	7·48
56	7·48	7·49	7·50	7·50	7·51	7·52	7·52	7·53	7·54	7·54
57	7·55	7·56	7·56	7·57	7·58	7·58	7·59	7·60	7·60	7·61
58	7·62	7·62	7·63	7·64	7·64	7·65	7·66	7·66	7·67	7·67
59	7·68	7·69	7·69	7·70	7·71	7·71	7·72	7·73	7·73	7·74
60	7·75	7·75	7·76	7·77	7·77	7·78	7·78	7·79	7·80	7·80
61	7·81	7·82	7·82	7·83	7·84	7·84	7·85	7·85	7·86	7·87
62	7·87	7·88	7·89	7·89	7·90	7·91	7·91	7·92	7·92	7·93
63	7·94	7·94	7·95	7·96	7·96	7·97	7·97	7·98	7·99	7·99
64	8·00	8·01	8·01	8·02	8·02	8·03	8·04	8·04	8·05	8·06
65	8·06	8·07	8·07	8·08	8·09	8·09	8·10	8·11	8·11	8·12
66	8·12	8·13	8·14	8·14	8·15	8·15	8·16	8·17	8·17	8·18
67	8·19	8·19	8·20	8·20	8·21	8·22	8·22	8·23	8·23	8·24
68	8·25	8·25	8·26	8·26	8·27	8·28	8·28	8·29	8·29	8·30
69	8·31	8·31	8·32	8·32	8·33	8·34	8·34	8·35	8·35	8·36
70	8·37	8·37	8·38	8·38	8·39	8·40	8·40	8·41	8·41	8·42
71	8·43	8·43	8·44	8·44	8·45	8·46	8·46	8·47	8·47	8·48
72	8·49	8·49	8·50	8·50	8·51	8·51	8·52	8·53	8·53	8·54
73	8·54	8·55	8·56	8·56	8·57	8·57	8·58	8·58	8·59	8·60
74	8·60	8·61	8·61	8·62	8·63	8·63	8·64	8·64	8·65	8·65
75	8·66	8·67	8·67	8·68	8·68	8·69	8·69	8·70	8·71	8·71
76	8·72	8·72	8·73	8·73	8·74	8·75	8·75	8·76	8·76	8·77
77	8·77	8·78	8·79	8·79	8·80	8·80	8·81	8·81	8·82	8·83
78	8·83	8·84	8·84	8·85	8·85	8·86	8·87	8·87	8·88	8·88
79	8·89	8·89	8·90	8·91	8·91	8·92	8·92	8·93	8·93	8·94
80	8·94	8·95	8·96	8·96	8·97	8·97	8·98	8·98	8·99	8·99
81	9·00	9·01	9·01	9·02	9·02	9·03	9·03	9·04	9·04	9·05
82	9·06	9·06	9·07	9·07	9·08	9·08	9·09	9·09	9·10	9·10
83	9·11	9·12	9·12	9·13	9·13	9·14	9·14	9·15	9·15	9·16
84	9·17	9·17	9·18	9·18	9·19	9·19	9·20	9·20	9·21	9·21
85	9·22	9·22	9·23	9·24	9·24	9·25	9·25	9·26	9·26	9·27
86	9·27	9·28	9·28	9·29	9·30	9·30	9·31	9·31	9·32	9·32
87	9·33	9·33	9·34	9·34	9·35	9·35	9·36	9·36	9·37	9·38
88	9·38	9·39	9·39	9·40	9·40	9·41	9·41	9·42	9·42	9·43
89	9·43	9·44	9·44	9·45	9·46	9·46	9·47	9·47	9·48	9·48
90	9·49	9·49	9·50	9·50	9·51	9·51	9·52	9·52	9·53	9·53
91	9·54	9·54	9·55	9·56	9·56	9·57	9·57	9·58	9·58	9·59
92	9·59	9·60	9·60	9·61	9·61	9·62	9·62	9·63	9·63	9·64
93	9·64	9·65	9·65	9·66	9·66	9·67	9·67	9·68	9·69	9·69
94	9·70	9·70	9·71	9·71	9·72	9·72	9·73	9·73	9·74	9·74
95	9·75	9·75	9·76	9·76	9·77	9·77	9·78	9·78	9·79	9·79
96	9·80	9·80	9·81	9·81	9·82	9·82	9·83	9·83	9·84	9·84
97	9·85	9·85	9·86	9·86	9·87	9·87	9·88	9·88	9·89	9·89
98	9·90	9·90	9·91	9·91	9·92	9·92	9·93	9·93	9·94	9·94
99	9·95	9·95	9·96	9·96	9·97	9·97	9·98	9·98	9·99	9·99

Answers

Algebra—Answers to Chapter 1

Page 2 Exercise 1

1. (i) (ii) (iv) (v) (vi) are well defined

5. $A = \{0, 1, ..., 10\}$, $B = \{2, 3, 5, 7\}$, $C = \{2, 4, 6, 8, 10\}$, $D = \{3, 6, 9\}$
$2 \in A, B, C$; $3 \in A, B, D$; $5 \in A, B$; $7 \in A, B$; $10 \in A, C$
$2 \notin D$; $3 \notin C$; $5 \notin C, D$; $7 \notin C, D$; $10 \notin B, D$

Page 3 Exercise 2

1. $F = \{1, 3, 5, 7, 9, 11, 13\}$ $G = \{11, 13, 17, 19, 23\}$
$H = \{7, 14, 21, 28, 35, 42, 49\}$ $n(F) = 7$, $n(G) = 5$, $n(H) = 7$

2. $5 \notin A$, $n(A) = 4$, $n(B) = 5$

3. $C = \{9{,}530,\ 9{,}531, ..., 9{,}536\}$ $n(C) = 7$

4. No; yes

5. $X = \{2, 3, 5\}$, $Y = \{2, 3, 4, 5, 6, 10, 12, 15, 20, 30\}$
$n(X) = 3$, $n(Y) = 10$ $X \neq Y$

6. $\{541, 514, 451, 415, 154, 145\}$ $n(S) = 6$

7. $n(R) = 4$, $n(S) = 8$, $n(P) = 2$, $n(I) = 2$, $n(T) = 6$, $n(H) = 12$

8. $\{35, 14, 10, 7, 5, 4, 2\}$

9. No

10. $P = \{2, 3, 5, 7, 11\}$, $Q = \{2, 3, 5, 7, 11\}$. Hence $P = Q$

Page 5 Exercise 3

1. (*a*) $\{3, 6, 9, ..., 99\}$ (*b*) $\{-1, -2, -3, ...\}$
(*c*) $\{1, 9, 25, 49, ...\}$ (*d*) $\{-24, -23, -22, ..., -1\}$
(*e*) $\{5, 7, 9, 11, ...\}$

2. The set of (*a*) even numbers, (*b*) even numbers less than 100, (*c*) squares of natural numbers up to 20, (*d*) multiples of 5 up to 100, (*e*) cubes of natural numbers, (*f*) powers of 2, (*g*) reciprocals of

natural numbers, (h) decimal fractions of the form $\frac{1}{10^n}$, $n = 1, 2, \ldots$

49, 20, 20

4. The set of (a) odd numbers less than 100, (b) odd numbers, (c) multiples of 4, with zero, (d) numbers of the form $7n-6$, $n = 1, 2, 3, \ldots$. (b), (c), (d)

Page 6 Exercise 4

1. (a) $\{4, 5, 6\}$ (b) $\{2, 4\}$ (c) $\{7, 9, 11\}$ (d) $\{4\}$ (e) $\emptyset$
(f) $\{(2,2), (4,4), (6,6)\}$ (g) $\{(6,3), (10,5)\}$
(h) $\{(1,3), (2,5), (3,7), (4,9), (5,11), (6,13)\}$

2. $A = \{3, 4, 5, \ldots\}$ $B = \{1, 2, 3, 4, 5\}$
$C = \{1, 2, 3\}$ $D = \{-2, -1, 0, 1\}$

3. (i) F (ii) F (iii) T (iv) F (v) T (vi) T (vii) F (viii) F

4. (a) $\{x : x > 5, x \in N\}$ (b) $\{x : x < 10, x \in N\}$
(c) $\{x : 3 < x < 11, x \in N\{$ (d) $\{x : -3 < x < 11, x \in N\}$
(e) $\{x : -5 < x < 5, x \in N\}$ (f) $\{x : x = 5y, y \in N\}$
(g) $\{x : x = 5y+1, y \in N\}$ (h) $\{x : x = 5y-2, y \in N\}$

Page 7 Exercise 5

1. The set of (i) even numbers, odd numbers, etc.,
(ii) warships, steamers, etc.,
(iii) Scots, Americans, etc.,
(iv) triangles, pentagons, etc.

2. The set of (i) Presidents of the U.S.A., (ii) solids, (iii) equations in one variable

3. (i) $\{0, 1, 2\}$ (ii) $\{4\}$ (iii) $\emptyset$ (iv) $\{1, 2, 3, 4\}$

4. (i) $\{1\}$ (ii) $\{1, 2, 3, 7\}$ (iii) $\emptyset$

Page 8 Exercise 6

1. $\emptyset$, {red}, {white}, {blue}, {red, white}, {red, blue}, {white, blue}, {red, white, blue}

2. 4, 1

3. $C = D$, $C \subset D$, $D \subset C$, $E \subset A$, $E \subset B$, $E \subset C$, $E \subset D$, $E \subset F$, $B \subset A$, $C \subset A$, $D \subset A$, $C \subset F$, $D \subset F$

4. (i) $\emptyset$ (ii) $A = B$

5. (i) Two (ii) $\emptyset$ (iii) A Formula is $2^{n(A)}$

6. (i) $S \subset R$ (ii) $P \subset Z$ (iii) $S \subset C$

Page 13 Exercise 7

Within a rectangle representing the appropriate universal set are circles or ovals representing the various sets as follows:

1. (*a*) Two non-intersecting circles, A and B, (*b*) three intersecting circles A, B, C with B inside A, and C intersecting A and B, (*c*) two intersecting circles A and C with circle B inside A, not intersecting C, (*d*) three intersecting circles A, B, C
2. Three intersecting circles A, B, C
3. Three intersecting circles A, B, C
4. (i) Three non-intersecting circles C, P, N; (ii) three intersecting circles M, S, F

Page 14 Exercise 8

1. (i) $\{3,5\}$ (ii) $\emptyset$ (iii) $\{2,7\}$ (iv) $\emptyset$ (v) $\{3,5\}$

2. $\{3\}$

3. Yellow roses in a flower shop. If the shop has no yellow roses

4. Two intersecting circles I, K. Some right-angled triangles are isosceles.

5. (*a*) $\{a,e,g\}$ $\{a,e,g\}$. $A \cap B = B \cap A$. $C \cap B$. $A \cap C$. The commutative law. (*b*) $\{e,g\}$ $\{e,g\}$. The sets are equal. Yes. The associative law. (*c*) Yes, in both cases

6. HCF $= 6$.

7. $\{1,5,9\}$ $\{1,6,8\}$ $\{2,4,9\}$ $\{2,5,8\}$ $\{2,6,7\}$ $\{3,4,8\}$ $\{3,5,7\}$ $\{4,5,6\}$; $\{1,5,9\}$ $\{2,5,8\}$ $\{3,5,7\}$ $\{4,5,6\}$; $\{1,6,8\}$, $\{3,5,7\}$

8. $\{1,2,3,4\}$, $\emptyset$, $\emptyset$, $\{0\}$

10. 9

11. 11

12. 5 take maths but not science; 2 take science but not maths; 3 take neither maths nor science.

13. (i) 8 (ii) 40

14. (i) 15% (ii) 40%

Page 18 Exercise 9

1. $n(A \cup B) = 5$ 2. $n(P \cup Q) = 8$
4. (i) {letters in the alphabet} (ii) 26 (iii) $\emptyset$ (iv) 0
5. No. {2, 3, 5, 7} and {2, 3, 5} 6. (*a*) R (*b*) S.
7. (*a*) $\{1, 2, 3, 4, 5, 6, 8, 10\}$. $A \cup B = B \cup A$. $\{2, 3, 4, 6, 8, 9, 12\}$. Yes. $A \cup C$. The commutative law. (*b*) $\{1, 2, 3, 4, 5, 6, 8, 9, 10, 12\}$. Yes. The associative law
8. (*a*) 86. 26 in the intersection, also 24 in A and 36 in B. (*b*) 18 (*c*) 25
9. (i) $A \cup B$ (ii) $B \cup C$ (iii) $A \cup B \cup C$ (iv) $B \cap C$ (v) $(A \cap B) \cup C$ (vi) $C \cap (A \cup B)$ or $(C \cap A) \cup (C \cap B)$

Page 20 Exercise 10

1. $\{q, s, t\}$ 2. $\{1, 4, 6, 8, 9, 10, 12, 14, 15, 16, 18, 20\}$
3. Odd numbers; $\{x : x = 2n - 1, n \in N\}$
4. Zero and the positive integers.
5. $\{x : x < 0 \text{ and } x \geqslant 2, x \in R\}$.
6. The set of triangles with no two sides equal
7. (i) $\{5, 6, 7, 8\}$ (ii) $\{1, 2, 3, 5, 7\}$ (iii) $\{4, 5, 6, 7, 8\}$ (iv) $\{1, 2, 3, 4, 5, 7\}$ (v) E (vi) $\emptyset$ (vii) $\{5, 7\}$ (viii) $\{5, 7\}$ (ix) $\{1, 2, 3, 5, 6, 7, 8\}$ (x) $\{1, 2, 3, 5, 6, 7, 8\}$ (xi) $\{1, 2, 3, 4, 6, 8\}$
8. $\{4, 6, 8, 9, 10\}$, $\{2, 4, 6, 8, 9, 10\}$, $\{1, 3, 5, 7, 9, 10\}$. $B \subset A$, $B \subset C'$
10. A', B', $(A \cup B)'$ or $A' \cap B'$, $A' \cup B'$ or $(A \cap B)'$

Algebra—Answers to Chapter 2

Page 25 Exercise 1

3. $x + 2y = 10$ 4. $a + b = 90$ 5. $P = 4l$ 6. $C = 20 + \frac{1}{100}n$
7. $S = 2n - 4$ 8. $W = 16 + 4n \leqslant 64$

Page 26 Exercise 2

1. All except (1, 3), (5−3) 2. (12, 2), (10, 0), (5, −5), ($8\frac{1}{2}$, $-1\frac{1}{2}$)
4. y: 10, 8, 6, 4, 2, 0, −2, 20, 18, $4\frac{1}{2}$

5. y: 6, 4, 2, 0, −2, −4, −6, 16, 14, $\frac{1}{2}$

6. y: 9, 8, 7, 6, 5, 4, 3, 14, 13, $6\frac{1}{4}$

Page 29 Exercise 4

1. $5x+8y \leqslant 40$ 2. $5x+4y \leqslant 40$ 3. $5x+3y \leqslant 20$

4. $12x+20y \leqslant 100$ 5. $4x+5y \leqslant 20$ 6. $2x+3y \leqslant 45$

Algebra—Answers to Chapter 3

Page 33 Exercise 1

1. Rectangle 2. Right-angled isosceles triangle 3. As 2

4. Infinite strip 5. Square 6. As 2 7. As 2

8. Right-angled triangle 9. Parallelogram 10. Rectangle

11. Triangle

Page 37 Exercise 2

1. {(3, 3)} 2. {(4, 3)} 3. {(−3, −3)} 4. {(1, −1)}

5. {(3, 4)} 6. {(1, 3)} 7. {(2, 2)} 8. {(3, 4)} 9. $\emptyset$

10. $\emptyset$ 11. {(−0·4, 3·6)} 12. {(3·33, 1·33)}

13. {(−1·33, 0·67)} 14. {(1·5, 3·0)} 15. {(−1·5, 1·5)}

16. {(0·5, −3·5)} 17. {(−1·33, −2·67)} 18. {(0, 0)}

19. $\emptyset$ 20. $\emptyset$

Page 41 Exercise 3

1. {(0, 2)} 2. {(2, 3)} 3. {(2, −3)} 4. $\{(\frac{1}{2}, 2)\}$

5. $\{(\frac{1}{3}, \frac{1}{2})\}$ 6. $\{(\frac{1}{2}, 1\frac{1}{2})\}$ 7. {(5, 3)} 8. {(0, 2)}

9. {(2, 3)} 10. {(1, 0)} 11. {(2, 1)} 12. {(−1, 2)}

13. $\{(1\frac{1}{3}, -2\frac{1}{3})\}$ 14. $\{(3\frac{3}{4}, 2\frac{1}{2})\}$ 15. $\{(\frac{7}{10}, \frac{7}{15})\}$ 16. $\emptyset$

17. {(0, 5)} 18. {(4, 0)} 19. {(7, 13)} 20. {(2, 5)}

Page 43 Exercise 4

1. {(4, 7)} 2. {(6, 2)} 3. {(−7, −21)} 4. {(5, 1)}

5. {(10, 5)} 6. {(2, 3)} 7. {(3, 4)} 8. {(5, −2)}

9. $\{(-1, -2)\}$ 10. $\{(0, 3)\}$ 11. $\{(1\frac{1}{2}, -3)\}$ 12. $\{(-\frac{1}{3}, \frac{2}{3})\}$
13. $\{(-2, -2)\}$ 14. $\{(-4, 2)\}$ 15. $\{(\frac{1}{2}, 2)\}$ 16. $\{(1\frac{4}{7}, 1\frac{2}{7})\}$

Page 44 Exercise 5

1. $\{(6, 6)\}$ 2. $\{(2, 4)\}$ 3. $\{(5, 0)\}$ 4. $\{(4, 4)\}$
5. $\{(3, -1)\}$ 6. $\{(5\frac{1}{2}, -2\frac{1}{2})\}$ 7. $\{(5, 18)\}$ 8. $\{(-1, 8)\}$
9. $\{(4, 7)\}$ 10. $\{(7, 5)\}$ 11. $\{(11, 5)\}$ 12. $\{(0{\cdot}5, 0{\cdot}25)\}$

Page 45 Exercise 6

1. 74 and 38 2. $37\frac{1}{2}$ and $25\frac{1}{2}$ 3. 73·5° and 16·5°
4. 124° and 56° 5. 51 and 33 6. $3\frac{1}{2}$ and $30\frac{1}{2}$
7. 30p and 40p 8. 25p and 10p 9. 16, $\frac{1}{2}$; $23\frac{1}{2}$, 8
10. $-1\frac{1}{4}$, 40; $27\frac{1}{2}$, $12\frac{4}{5}$ 11. -1, 6; 59 12. £52, £60

Algebra—Answers to Chapter 4

Page 50 Exercise 1

1. $P = 2(x+y)$; 30 2. $P = 4x$; 24 3. $P = 3m$; (i) 48 (ii) 8
4. $d = x+y$; 814 5. $P = 2x+2y+z$; (i) 155 (ii) 20
6. $W = t-fh$; $11\frac{1}{4}$
7. (i) $2x$ (ii) $3x+2y$ (iii) $4x+2y$ (iv) $4x+3y$
150 m, 325 m, 400 m, 450 m
8. 3, 4, 5, 7, 17, $n-3$; $d = n-3$; 97
9. (i) $P = 6x+\pi x$ (ii) $A = 4x^2+\frac{1}{2}\pi x^2$; 91·4, 557
10. (i) $\frac{1}{n^2}$ (ii) $\frac{n}{(n+1)(n+2)}$; $\frac{1}{400}$, $\frac{20}{21\times 22}$
11. $\{a\}$, $\emptyset$, 2; $\{a\}$, $\{b\}$, $\{a, b\}$, $\emptyset$, 4; $\{a\}$, $\{b\}$, $\{c\}$, $\{b, c\}$, $\{a, c\}$, $\{a, b\}$, $\{a, b, c\}$, $\emptyset$, 8; 16; 2^n
12. 18; $n(P \cup Q) = n(P)+n(Q)-n(P \cap Q)$ 13. 21

Page 54 Exercise 2

1. $\frac{8}{3}$ 2. 3 3. 72 4. -4 5. 12 6. $6\frac{1}{2}$
7. $\frac{4}{3}$ 8. $\frac{3}{4}$ 9. $3\frac{1}{3}$ 10. $-\frac{2}{3}$ 11. $-\frac{3}{4}$ 12. $-\frac{3}{7}$

13. $\frac{2}{3}$ **14.** 34 **15.** $-\frac{3}{5}$ **16.** $\frac{1}{2}$ **17.** -30 **18.** $-\frac{1}{2}$
19. 2 **20.** -1 **21.** 1

Page 56 Exercise 3

1. $5-a$ **2.** $b-a$ **3.** $4+a$ **4.** $p+q$ **5.** $\frac{1}{2}c$
6. $\frac{7}{p}$ **7.** $\frac{b}{a}$ **8.** $4p$ **9.** $10h$ **10.** mn
11. $\frac{ab}{c}$ **12.** $\frac{1}{2}(p-4)$ **13.** $\frac{1}{2}(1-a)$ **14.** $\frac{b-3}{a}$ **15.** $\frac{r-q}{p}$
16. $\frac{4}{3}h$ **17.** $\frac{5b}{a}$ **18.** $\frac{pq}{c}$ **19.** $\frac{c}{a+b}$ **20.** $(r+1)q$
21. $\frac{1}{2}(d-e)$ **22.** $\frac{k-n}{m}$ **23.** $\frac{1}{2}(b-a)$ **24.** $a-b$ **25.** 20
26. $a(b-1)$ **27.** $k(m+n)$ **28.** -1 **29.** $b-a$ **30.** $bc-a$
31. $\frac{rs+q}{p}$ **32.** 6 **33.** $\frac{c}{a}-b$ **34.** $\frac{s-pr}{pq}$ **35.** $2a+ab$
36. $\frac{d-b}{a}+c$ **37.** $a\left(1-\frac{y}{b}\right)$ **38.** $\frac{ab}{a-c}$ **39.** $\frac{ab}{a+b}$ **40.** $\frac{pqr}{q-p}$
41. $\frac{abc}{c-a}$ **42.** $\frac{2ab}{a-b}$

Page 59 Exercise 4

1. (i) 15 lbf (ii) 25 lbf (iii) 8 (iv) $11\frac{1}{5}$, $p=\frac{4}{5}w$ (v) $6\frac{2}{5}$ (vi) $7\frac{1}{5}$

2. (*a*) (i) 66 ft/s (ii) 1,760 ft/s (*b*) $M = \frac{15}{22}F$ (i) $22\frac{1}{2}$ mph (ii) 750 mph

3. $l=\frac{A}{b}$; $7\frac{1}{2}$ **4.** (i) $s = vt$ (ii) $t=\frac{s}{v}$ **5.** $R=\frac{V}{I}$; 48 ohms

6. $r=\frac{C}{2\pi}$; $26\frac{1}{4}$ **7.** $h=\frac{2A}{b}$; 5 m **8.** $b=\frac{1}{2}p-a$; 4 ft

9. $n=\frac{1}{2}R+2$; 7; no **10.** (i) $C = Id^2$ (ii) $d=\sqrt{\frac{C}{I}}$

11. $c = \sqrt{(a^2 - b^2)}$; 8·94 **12.** $x = \sqrt{A}$; 9·47 **13.** $r = \sqrt{\dfrac{A}{\pi}}$; 7

14. (i) $h = \dfrac{V}{\pi r^2}$; (ii) $r = \sqrt{\dfrac{V}{\pi h}}$; 0·866

Page 61 Exercise 5

Note: Different versions of the answer are possible in some of the following:

1. (*a*) (i) $36\frac{2}{3}$°C (ii) 100°C (iii) $18\frac{1}{3}$°C (iv) $-17\frac{7}{9}$°C
(*b*) $F = \frac{9}{5}C + 32$ (i) 212°F (ii) $80\frac{3}{5}$°F (iii) 32°F (iv) -40°F

2. (i) $s = c + \frac{1}{100}pc$ (ii) $c = \dfrac{s}{1 + \frac{1}{100}p}$

3. (i) $\frac{7}{2}(4+22) = 91 = 4+7+10+13+\ldots+22$ (ii) 1,302
(iii) $l = \dfrac{2S}{n} - a$; 17 **4.** $h = \dfrac{A}{2\pi r} - r$ **5.** $m = \sqrt{(ab)}$

6. (i) $f = \dfrac{v-u}{t}$ (ii) $u = \dfrac{1}{t}(s - \frac{1}{2}ft^2)$ (iii) $t = \dfrac{2s}{v+u}$
(iv) $s = \dfrac{v^2 - u^2}{2f}$ (v) $f = \dfrac{2(s-ut)}{t^2}$ (vi) $u = \sqrt{(v^2 - 2fs)}$

7. (i) 64 (ii) 60, 62, 63, $63\frac{1}{2}$, $63\frac{3}{4}$, $63\frac{7}{8}$, $63\frac{15}{16}$ (iii) $r = 1 - \dfrac{a}{S}$; $\frac{1}{3}$

8. $n = \dfrac{IR}{E - Ir}$; 4

Algebra—Answers to Revision Exercises

Page 63 Revision Exercise on Chapter 1

1. (*a*) Yes. Finite (*b*) Yes. Finite or empty (*c*) Yes. Infinite
(*d*) No (*e*) Yes. Empty (*f*) No

2. $\{B, C, D, E, H, I, K, O, X\}$; $\{A, H, I, M, O, T, U, V, W, X, Y\}$;
$\{H, I, O, X\}$

3. (*a*) $\{10, 11, 12, \ldots, 99\}$ (*b*) $\{-24, -23, -22, \ldots, -1\}$
(*c*) $\{2, 4, 8, \ldots\}$ (*d*) $\{5, 8, 11, 14, \ldots\}$

4. (*a*) $B = D$ (*b*) No; Yes; No; 45°, 45°, 90°; sides equal

5. $\bar{0} = \{4, 8, 12, ..., 32\}$, $\bar{1} = \{1, 5, 9, ..., 29\}$, $\bar{2} = \{2, 6, 10, ..., 30\}$ and $\bar{3} = \{3, 7, 11, ..., 31\}$

6. $P = T,\ P \subset R,\ T \subset R$; $Q = S,\ Q \subset V,\ S \subset V$

7. (*a*) $\{x : x = 2n \text{ and } n \in N\}$ (*b*) $\{x : x = 2n+1 \text{ and } n \in N\}$
(*c*) $\{x : x = 4n \text{ and } n \in N\}$ (*d*) $\{x : x = 5n+3 \text{ and } n \in N\}$
(*e*) $\{x : x = 10n-2 \text{ and } n \in N\}$ (*f*) $\{x : x = n^2+1 \text{ and } n \in N\}$
(*g*) $\{x : x = n^3+3 \text{ and } n \in N\}$

9. (i) A (ii) E (iii) $\{a, c, f, g, k\}$ (iv) K (v) K (vi) A (vii) A' (viii) $\emptyset$ (ix) $\{a, b, c, d, e, f, g, h\}$ (x) $\{a, b, c, f, g, h\}$ (xi) $\{b\}$ (xii) $\{b\}$ (xiii) $\emptyset$ (xiv) E (xv) $\{a, b, c, e, f, g, k\}$ (xvi) $\{d, h\}$ (xvii) $\{d, h\}$ (xviii) C (xix) $\{a, c, e, g, k\}$ (xx) $\{a, c, e, g, k\}$ (xxi) B (xxii) B (xxiii) $\{c, f\}$ (xxiv) $\{c, f\}$

15. (i) 90 (ii) 100 (iii) 69 (iv) 192

16. Subsets of E are $A = \{a\}$, $B = \{b\}$, $\emptyset$ and $\{a, b\} = E$

$\cup$	$\emptyset$	A	B	E
$\emptyset$	$\emptyset$	A	B	E
A	A	A	E	E
B	B	E	B	E
E	E	E	E	E

$\cap$	$\emptyset$	A	B	E
$\emptyset$	$\emptyset$	$\emptyset$	$\emptyset$	$\emptyset$
A	$\emptyset$	A	$\emptyset$	A
B	$\emptyset$	$\emptyset$	B	B
E	$\emptyset$	A	B	E

Symmetrical about the leading diagonal

17. 18

Page 68 Revision Exercise on Chapter 3

2. $\{(0, 2)\}$ 3. (i) $2y \geqslant 3x$ (ii) $x \leqslant 6-3y$ (iii) $y < 3$ (iv) $x > 8-3y$

4. $x < 2,\ y > 2,\ 4y < 5x+18$ 5. (i) $x \leqslant 5$ (ii) $y \geqslant -6$

7. (i) $\{(-3, 4)\}$ (ii) $\{(4, -7)\}$ (iii) $\{(\frac{4}{3}, 1)\}$ (iv) $\{(1, 3)\}$

8. $2\frac{1}{2}$ 9. $a = \frac{5}{4}$, $b = -10$ (i) 65 (ii) 40

10. 12 hours and 6 hours

Page 70 Revision Exercise on Chapter 4

1. (i) $x = \dfrac{c-a}{b}$ (ii) $x = \dfrac{r}{p+q}$ (iii) $x = \dfrac{b^2}{a^2}$

(iv) $x = \frac{1}{2}(a+b)$ (v) $x = \dfrac{a+b}{abc}$ (vi) $x = (a+b)(c+d)$

(vii) $x = \dfrac{c-b}{a-1}$ (viii) $x = \dfrac{a+b}{c}$ (ix) $x = \dfrac{1}{a}$

(x) $x = \dfrac{ab}{a+b}$ (xi) $x = a(b-1)+1$ (xii) $x = 0$

2. (i) $(n-1)$ (ii) n^2+1 (iii) $\dfrac{1}{n^2+n}$; (i) 11 (ii) 145 (iii) $\frac{1}{156}$

3. $n(P \cap Q) = n(P)+n(Q)-n(P \cup Q)$

4. (i) $l = a+(n-1)d$ (ii) $n = \dfrac{d+l-a}{d}$; $a = 7$

5. (i) $S = \dfrac{lr-a}{r-1}$ (ii) $l = \dfrac{a+rS-S}{r}$

6. 91·44 cm; 1 cm $= \dfrac{1}{30{\cdot}48}$ ft

7. 1 gal $= \dfrac{50}{11}$ litres

8. $d = \dfrac{2A}{a+b}$; $3\frac{1}{5}$ ft

9. (i) $h = \dfrac{3V}{\pi r^2}$ (ii) $r = \sqrt{\dfrac{3V}{\pi h}}$; $r = 4{\cdot}89$

10. $r = \sqrt{\dfrac{S}{4\pi}}$; $r = 0{\cdot}892$

11. $20\frac{1}{4}$; $132\frac{1}{4}$; $12\frac{1}{4}$; $90\frac{1}{4}$; 5,625; 3,025

12. 5·0625; 39·0625; 18·0625; 10·5625; 390,625; 1,500,625

Algebra—Answers to General Revision Exercises

Page 73 General Revision Exercise 1

1. (i) T (ii) T (iii) F (iv) F

2. (*a*) {2, 4, 6, 8, 10, 12, 14}
(*b*) $\{x : x$ is a positive integer divisible by 3 and $x < 18\}$
(*c*) $\emptyset$, $\{p\}$, $\{q\}$, $\{r\}$, $\{s\}$, $\{p,q\}$, $\{p,r\}$, $\{p,s\}$, $\{q,r\}$, $\{q,s\}$, $\{r,s\}$, $\{p,q,r\}$, $\{p,q,s\}$, $\{p,r,s\}$, $\{q,r,s\}$, $\{p,q,r,s\}$

3. (*a*) {2, 3, 5, 7} (*b*) {1, 3, 5, 7, 9} (*c*) {2, 3, 4, 6, 12}
$B \cap C = \{3\}$, $A \cap C = \{2, 3\}$, $A \cap B \cap C = \{3\}$, $X = \{2\}$

4. (i) {5, 6, 7, 8} (ii) 21 (iii) 1

5. (*a*) (i) $P \cap Q = Q$ (ii) $H \cap K = \emptyset$ (iii) $X \cap E = X$

7. (*a*) {2, 3, 4, 5, 8, 9} (*b*) {2, 5} (*c*) {5, 9} (*d*) {2, 5, 9}
(*e*) {2, 5, 9} The distributive law for intersection over union

8. {8, 9, 10, ...} **9.** 8 **10.** (i) 10 (ii) 6

11. (i) T (ii) F (iii) F (iv) T

12. (i) {5, 6, 7, 8} (ii) {1} (iii) {5, 8} (iv) {5, 8}

Page 76 General Revision Exercise 2

1. (i) $3k$ (ii) k^3 (iii) $45a$ (iv) $24ab$ (v) $36a^3$ (vi) $6a^2b^3$

2. (i) 7 (ii) -10 (iii) -7 (iv) $-5a$ (v) $6a^2$
(vi) $-a^3$ (vii) $5m$ (viii) $12p^2q^2$ (ix) $-7a^2$ (x) $\dfrac{6m}{n^2}$
(xi) $-5x$ (xii) $32a^2$ (xiii) $5p^2$ (xiv) $4y(4x^2-3)$
(xv) $-6a^2+8ab$

3. (i) 25 (ii) $\frac{1}{6}(x+13)$ (iii) $14x$
(iv) $-2x(x+5)$ (v) $2\frac{1}{6}$ (vi) $\dfrac{1}{n+1}$

4. (i) 10 (ii) $2\sqrt{2}$

5. (i) 1,300 (ii) 700 (iii) 29,253 (iv) 7

6. (*a*) 0 (*b*) $2x+6y-12z$ (*c*) (i) $7(p-q)$ (ii) $-3(p+q)$

7. (i) C (ii) C (iii) C (iv) B

8. (i), (ii), (iii)

9. (*a*) 1 (*b*) No (*c*) (i) 2 (ii) -10 (iii) -24 (iv) $\frac{3}{2}$

11. (i) 8 (ii) 8 (iii) 38 (iv) 46 (v) 50 (vi) -10 (vii) -10
(viii) 2 (ix) 32. No. Associative Law

12. (i) $\frac{4}{5}x$ (ii) $-\dfrac{a}{12}$ (iii) $\frac{1}{15}x$
(iv) $\frac{1}{6}(9a+8b)$ (v) $\frac{1}{30}(20x-6y+15)$ (vi) $\dfrac{25}{12p}$
(vii) $\dfrac{3y-4x}{xy}$ (viii) $\dfrac{25b+12a}{20ab}$

Page 78 General Revision Exercise 3

1. (i) 16 (ii) 7 (iii) 40 (iv) 14 (v) 24 (vi) 11
2. (i) 7 (ii) 28 (iii) $-\frac{1}{4}$ (iv) 4 (v) $1\frac{1}{3}$ (vi) $12\frac{1}{2}$ (vii) $2\frac{1}{2}$ (viii) $11\frac{1}{2}$
3. (i) {5, 6, 7} (ii) 19 (iii) 2
4. $14\frac{2}{5}$
5. (*a*) ± 3 (*b*) $a = 1, b = -4$
6. (*a*) $3\frac{1}{4}$ (*b*) 37 (*c*) $2{\cdot}2 \times 10^5$
7. (i) 3 (ii) (*a*) F (*b*) T (*c*) T (*d*) T
8. (i) T (ii) F (iii) T (iv) T
9. (*a*) $s = 27$ (*b*) $v = 15$
10. (*a*) (i) $2t^2+7t+3$ (ii) $6t^3+8t^2+4t+2$ (iii) $8t^3+5t+1$
    (*b*) (i) 304 (ii) 5,207 (iii) 7,647
11. (*a*) $\frac{1}{3}$ (*b*) (i) 2, 7, 16, 29 (ii) 46, 67
12. (i) 19 (ii) $-5a$

Page 80 General Revision Exercise 4

1. (i) {11} (ii) $\{17\frac{3}{5}\}$ (iii) {−7} (iv) {10} (v) $\{6\frac{3}{4}\}$ (vi) {−1}
2. (i) T (ii) F (iii) F (iv) T (v) T (vi) T
3. (i) $x = 2$, $y = 3$ (ii) No
4. (i) {2, 3, 4, ...} (ii) {4, 5, 6, ...} (iii) {2, 3, 4, ...}
   (iv) {2, 3, 4, 5, 6, 7, 8, 9, 10} (v) {4, 5, 6, 7, 8} (vi) ∅
5. (i) Yes. Table is symmetrical about leading diagonal
   (ii) ⊙ (iii) (*a*) △ (*b*) ⊙ (*c*) □ (*d*) □
6. (*a*) (i) $x = 5$ (ii) $x = 3$ (iii) No solution
   (*b*) (i) $x = 1\frac{1}{2}$ (ii) $x = 2\frac{1}{2}$ (iii) $x = 9$
7.

*	1	2	3	4
1	1	2	3	4
2	2	4	1	3
3	3	1	4	2
4	4	3	2	1

(*a*) Yes. Table is symmetrical about leading diagonal
(*b*) Yes
(*c*) (i) $x = 4$ (ii) $y = 2$

8. (i) {30} (ii) {12} (iii) $\{x : x \geqslant -6, x \in R\}$
   (iv) $\{x : x > -4\frac{1}{2}, x \in R\}$

9. (i) $\{x : 1 \leqslant x \leqslant 3, x \in R\}$ (ii) $\{x : x \geqslant 2, x \in R\}$ (iii) $\emptyset$

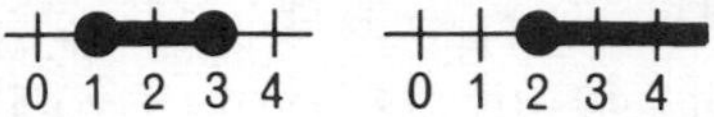

FIG. 1

10. (i) $\{4\}$ (ii) $\{-1\}$ (iii) $\{x : x < 3\frac{3}{4}, x \in R\}$
(iv) $\{x : x \geqslant 9, x \in R\}$ (v) $\{0{\cdot}75\}$

11. (i)

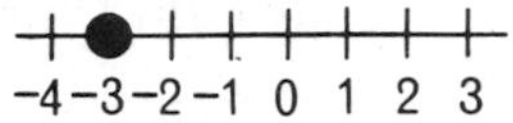

(ii)

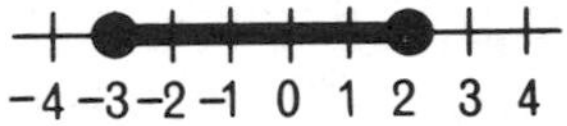

(iii)

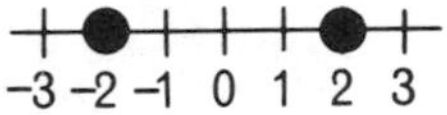

FIG. 2

12. (i) F (ii) F (iii) F

13. (i) $(-2, 3)$ (ii) $(4, -1)$ (iii) $(2\frac{4}{13}, -\frac{6}{13})$

Page 82 General Revision Exercise 5

1. (i) $6\frac{1}{2}$ (ii) $12\frac{1}{2}$ **2.** $x < 100$ and $x > 48$ **3.** $y > 1$ and $y < 8$

4. $A = 8x + 4$ **5.** (i) $S = \frac{1}{2}n(n+1)$ (ii) 500, 500

6. (i) $\frac{1}{2}(a+b) < 49$ or $a+b < 98$ (ii) $2x - 5 > 2$ (iii) $(y+3)^2 \leqslant 42$

7. $D = d^3\left(1 - \frac{\pi}{4}\right)$ **8.** 90, 120, 150 units

9. (i) 56; 57 (ii) 94; 96 (iii) 863; 865 **10.** $\pi r = 2x$

11. (i) $r = \dfrac{3V + \pi d^3}{3\pi d^2}$ (ii) $r = 5$; 4 cm **12.** $h = \dfrac{A - 2\pi r^2}{2\pi r}$; $h = 3\frac{1}{2}$

13. $12SR$ and $3CM$ *or* $48SR$ and $2CM$ *or* $84SR$ and $1CM$

14. $R = \dfrac{r_1 r_2}{r_1 + r_2}$; 18 **15.** (i) $\dfrac{m_2 x + m_1 y}{m_1 m_2}$ (ii) $\dfrac{m_1 m_2(x+y)}{m_2 x + m_1 y}$

Page 86 General Revision Exercise 6

2. (*a*) (i) 8 (ii) -8

3. (i) $\{(2,2), (2,6), (2,8), (3,3), (3,6), (3,9), (6,6), (8,8), (9,9)\}$
(ii) $\{(2,2), (3,3), (6,6), (8,8), (9,9), (6,2), (8,2), (6,3), (9,3)\}$

4. (i) T (ii) F (iii) T

5. (i) B (ii) C, D (iii) C (iv) A, D   6. (iii) $\frac{1}{5}$ (iv) $\frac{3}{5}$

7. (ii) More than one arrow leaves each element of A and terminates on B (iii) $\{(1,1), (3,1), (3,2), (3,3), (5,1), (5,2), (5,3)\}$

8. (iv) $\{(x, y): x \in T \text{ and } y > -4+1\frac{1}{2}x\}$

10. (i) AB (ii) (*a*) C(2, 3) (*b*) E(2, −1)
(iii) (*a*) $\{(x, y): x > 2 \text{ and } y \in R\}$ (*b*) $\{(x, y): y \leqslant x+1, 0 \leqslant x \leqslant 2\}$

Geometry—Answers to Chapter 1

Page 90 Section 2

1. (*c*) $a+b < 180, p+q \geqslant 180$
(*f*) (i) T (ii) F (iii) F (iv) T (v) F (vi) T (vii) F

Page 92 Section 3

2. (*c*) $p = 5+q$ (*d*) $p > 5+q$ and $q > 5+p$ (*e*) $s+5 > r$

Page 96 Section 5

3. $x > 5{\cdot}0$ 4. Greater than 5·0   5. $r > 5{\cdot}0$; $s > 5{\cdot}0$ 6. $t = 2{\cdot}5$

Page 98 Section 6

3. 1·4 km   4. From A, 46½°E of N

Geometry—Answers to Chapter 2

Page 101 Section 1

4. (i) 75 yd to 97½ yd (ii) 3·1 in; 42 yd   5. 6 in

6. $1\frac{1}{8}$ in; 1:48; $2\frac{1}{4}$ in; 1 in; 5 ft

Page 104 Section 2

1. (*b*)   2. (*a*), (*c*), (*d*)   3. (*b*), (*d*)

4. No   5. 6 cm   6. (i) Yes (ii) No

7. (*a*) Yes (*b*) Similar   8. 62°   9. 68°

Page 106 Section 3

6. $\frac{3}{4}$ in, $\frac{1}{2}$ in (i) 6:1 (ii) 36:1 (iii) 216:1 (iv) 1:2, 1:4, 1:8 (v) $1:m$, $1:m^2$, $1:m^3$ **7.** (ii) 59°

Page 109 Section 4

4. (*a*) Similar (*c*) Similar, 5·4 in, 4·4 in (*d*) Similar, 5 in

5. (*a*), (*c*) **6.** 16 in **7.** 52 ft **8.** 13 ft 6 in

9. 8 cm and 10 cm **10.** $37\frac{1}{2}$ and $62\frac{1}{2}$ ft

11. (ii) $\frac{2}{3}$, AD = 6 in, BD = 2 in (iii) AC = 6 in, AE = 9 in

12. 9 in, 10 in **13.** 25 ft

Page 114 Section 5

8. (i) +4 (ii) −3 (iii) +10 (iv) +3 (v) 0 (vi) No answer

9. (i) $y = 2x$ (ii) +3 **10.** (i) $y = -\frac{1}{2}x$ (ii) −2

11. (i) 8, 17, 62, −10, $y = 3x+2$ (ii) $\frac{1}{2}$

12. (i) −5, −3, −1, 1, 5, $y = -\frac{2}{3}x+3$ (ii) −1

13. (i) $y = 4x$ (ii) $y = \frac{2}{3}x$ (iii) $y = \frac{3}{2}x$
(iv) $y = -4x$ (v) $y = -\frac{2}{3}x$ (vi) $y = -\frac{3}{2}x$
(vii) $y = 0$

14. (i) $y = 4x+4$ (ii) $y = \frac{2}{3}x+4$ (iii) $y = \frac{3}{2}x+4$
(iv) $y = -4x+4$ (v) $y = -\frac{2}{3}x+4$ (vi) $y = -\frac{3}{2}x+4$
(vii) $y = 4$

15. (*a*) (i) $y = 2x+4$ (ii) $y = 2x$ (iii) $y = 2x+1$ (iv) $y = 2x-4$
(*b*) (i) $y = -x+4$ (ii) $y = -x$ (iii) $y = -x+1$ (iv) $y = -x-4$

16. (i) 2, (0, 5) (ii) −1, (0, 3) (iii) −2, (0, −4)
(iv) $\frac{3}{4}$, (0, −3) (v) 1, (0, 2) (vi) 3, (0, 4)
(vii) −2, (0, 5) (viii) 5, (0, 7) (ix) $\frac{1}{2}$, (0, 3)

Geometry—Answers to Chapter 3

Page 119 Section 1

7. (i) False (ii) True

8. (i) Equilateral (ii) Acute-angled
(iii) Could be acute- or obtuse-angled (iv) No

9. (*b*) Diameter AB, chord CD. A nearest, B farthest.
(*c*) HA = 11 in, OC = 13 in, OH + HC > OC, HC > 11 in
(*d*) HB = 15 in, OD = 13 in, HD < OH + OD, HD < 15 in
(*e*) (ii) OH + HC > OC, $h+c>r$ (iii) $h+c>h+a$, $c>a$
(iv) OH + OD > HD, $h+r>d$ (v) $h+r=b$, $b>d$

13. (i) $2x$, $3x$, $2x$, $5x$ cm (ii) $2y°$, $3y°$, $2y°$, $5y°$
(iii) (*a*) 2:3:2:5 (*b*) 2:3:2:5 (iv) No.

14. (i) True (ii) True (iii) True (iv) True
(v) False (vi) True (vii) False (viii) False

15. (i) 135° (ii) $\frac{2}{15}$ (iii) 30° per hour; 360° per minute
(iv) 60 times as fast; less than 60 times as fast
(v) Same angular rate (vi) 200°/s; no

Page 128 Section 2

1. 40°; $\frac{1}{9}$; 70°, 70°, 40°; 140°

2. 45° 3. 72°, 54°, 54°

5. (*a*) 144°, 150° (*b*) $128\frac{4}{7}°$, $147\frac{3}{11}°$, 176·4° (*c*) $180 - \left(180 - \frac{360}{n}\right)°$

6. (i) 8 (ii) 12 (iii) 4 (iv) 3 (v) n
(vi) 0; bilateral symmetry

Page 129 Section 3

2. 4, 8

3. (i) 3, 6; 3, 6; 3 (ii) 5, 10; 5, 10; 5

4. (i) Reflection in OA
(ii) Anticlockwise rotation of 200° (or 160° clockwise)

(iii) Reflection in OH

(iv) Anticlockwise rotation of 240° (or 120° clockwise) *or* reflection in OD

8. One; chord BD; arc AC; angle BDC; ABC, BCD, BAD

9. One; PT, QT; PTX, QTY, TPQ, TQP

10. LM is bisected at right angles by diameter perpendicular to AB

13. (*b*) An infinite number; on perpendicular bisector of AB. No; yes; two

Page 134 Section 4

1. 13 cm 2. 11·7 cm 3. 10 cm

4. 0·8 inches 5. 16 yards 6. 2 feet 7. 3 feet

8.

0	1·0	2·0	3·0	4·0	5·0	6·0	7·0	8·0	9·0	10·0
20	19·9	19·6	19·1	18·3	17·3	16·0	14·3	12·0	8·72	0

Page 136 Section 5

1. (i) False (ii) True (iii) False (iv) True (v) False

2. (i) On the circumference (ii) Outside the circle (iii) Inside the circle

3. (i) $x^2+y^2=9$ (ii) $x^2+y^2>100$ (iii) $x^2+y^2<36$

4. (*b*) Empty set

5. (i) 5 units, $x^2+y^2=25$
   (ii) $p=-4$, $q=-3$ (iii) $(-3, -4)$
   (iv) $r=3$ or -3, $s=3$ or -3, $t=4$ or -4, $u=4$ or -4
   (v) Four axes. Rotations through multiples of 90°

7. (i) (4, 3), (−4, 3), 8 (ii) (3, 4), (−3, 4), 6
   (iii) (0·995, 4·9), (−0·995, 4·9), 1·99
   (iv) (0·316, 4·99), (−0·316, 4·99), 0·632
   (v) (0, 5), 0 (vi) No point of intersection

Page 138 Section 6

2. Four 5. 24 cm 6. 41 cm

Page 139 Topics to Explore

2. $3r^2$
3. (*c*) X and Y are either both inside, or both outside, the closed curve
   (*d*) One point is inside, the other outside, the closed curve

Geometry—Answers to Revision Exercises

Page 144 Revision Exercise on Chapter 1

2. N $23\frac{1}{2}$°E or N$23\frac{1}{2}$°W 3. 54·7 m, 31·6 m, 38·2 m
4. 8·7 cm 5. 7·4 cm, 7·1 cm 6. '6·1 cm^2

Page 145 Revision Exercise on Chapter 2

4. 1:3 5. 9:11, ∠A = ∠Q, ∠B = ∠T, ∠C = ∠H
6. ΔXHD, 9:10; ΔFTY, 6:5
7. 3:1, $r = 9$, $p = 12$ 8. 3:2, $c = 8$, $d = 6$
9. 2:1, 1:2, $a = 6$, $b = 9$, $x = 3{\cdot}5$ 10. 1 cm
11. 1·3 in, 25 ft 12. $x = 6{\cdot}4$, $y = 4{\cdot}8$, $p = 10$, $q = 7{\cdot}5$
13. (ii) 16·8 ft (iii) $7\frac{1}{2}$ ft
14. (i) 4:1 (ii) 1:9 (iii) 16:1 (iv) 4:9 (v) 16:9 (vi) 4:25 (vii) $m^2:1$ (viii) $1:n^2$ (ix) $m^2:n^2$
16. 120 mm, 96 pence 17. 50 cm^2
18. (i) 8:1 (ii) 1:27 (iii) 27:8 (iv) 64:1 (v) 27:125 (vi) $m^3:1$ (vii) $1:n^3$ (viii) $m^3:n^3$
19. (i) 8:1 (ii) 1:27 (iii) 64:27 (iv) 27:125 (v) $h^3:1$ (vi) $1:k^3$ (vii) $h^3:k^3$
20. (i) 1:1,728 (ii) 1:27 (iii) $1:36^3$ (iv) 1:1,000,000 (v) $1:2{\cdot}54^3$
21. 2:1 22. (i) 1·5 ft (ii) 1:100 (iii) 2·6 pounds
23. $n^3:1$

Page 151 Revision Exercise on Chapter 3

1. $\frac{1}{3}$, 240° 2. A; 600° per min 3. $7\frac{1}{2}$ min 6. 50 in 7. 50·5 m

Geometry—Answers to General Revision Exercises

Page 154 General Revision Exercise 1

2. (i) $(-1, 3)$ (ii) $(25, 3)$ (iii) $(29, 2)$ (iv) $(-62, 6)$ (v) $(7, 10)$ (vi) $(-4, -1)$

3. T, (i), (iv), (v), (vii)

4. (i) $(a, 20-b)$ (ii) $(24-a, b)$ (iii) $(a, -10-b)$ (iv) $(-14-a, b)$ (v) $(-a, b)$ (vi) $(a, -b)$ (vii) $(a, 2m-b)$ (viii) $(2n-a, b)$

5. (*a*) $(-5, -4), (-6, 3), (-3, 6), (8, 1), (0, 7), (0, 0)$
(*b*) $(9, 6), (8, 13), (11, 16), (22, 11), (14, 17), (14, 10)$
(*c*) $(14-u, 10-v)$

6. (*a*) (i) $x = 13$ (ii) $x = 8$ (iii) $x = -2$ (iv) $x = 23$ (v) $y = 0$ (vi) $y = 7$ (vii) $y = -8$
(*b*) (i) $x = 5$ (ii) $x = 10$ (iii) $x = 20$ (iv) $x = -5$ (v) $y = 14$ (vi) $y = 7$ (vii) $y = 22$

8. (i) O (ii) A (iii) AB (iv) OP (v) QR (vi) QS
square, parallelogram, square

9. 72°, 144°, 216°, 288°, 360°; 72°, 216°, 288°; 72°, 36°, 72°

10. (i) $(-1, 3)$ (ii) $(2, 5)$ (iii) $(-2, -6)$ (iv) $(7, -4)$ (v) $(-y, x)$

11. $P_1(-1, 3), Q_1(-2, 6), R_1(-3, 7), S_1(-4, 4)$
$P_2(1, 3), Q_2(2, 6), R_2(3, 7), S_2(4, 4)$; $y = x$

12. $P_1(-3, 1), Q_1(-6, 2), R_1(-7, 3), S_1(-4, 4)$
$P_2(-1, -3), Q_2(-2, -6), R_2(-3, -7), S_2(-4, -4)$; $y = -x$

15. $A_1(0, 5), B_1(-3, 8), A_2(-5, 5), B_2(-8, 5), A_3(-5, 0), B_3(-5, -3), A_4(0, -5), B_4(3, -8), A_5(5, -5), B_5(8, -5)$

16. (*b*) $(a, 2a)$ (*c*) $(-a, -2a)$ (*d*) $(a, -2a)$ (*e*) $(-a, 2a)$

17. (*a*) $(a, 6+\frac{1}{2}a)$ (*b*) $(-a, 6-\frac{1}{2}a), y = 6+\frac{1}{2}x$;
(*c*) $(-a, -6-\frac{1}{2}a), y = -6+\frac{1}{2}x$; (*d*) $(-a, 6+\frac{1}{2}a), y = 6-\frac{1}{2}x$
(*e*) $(a, 6-\frac{1}{2}a), y = 6-\frac{1}{2}x$ (*f*) $(a, -6-\frac{1}{2}a), y = -6-\frac{1}{2}x$

Page 158 General Revision Exercise 2

1. C, H, K, a parallelogram

2. R(3, 4); (2, 2); 14 **3.** EDA, 24 in^2, *bh*

4. (i) rhombus (ii) rectangle (iii) rhombus (iv) square
5. Rectangle, rhombus 6. 3, 3
9. (2, −3), (6, −3), (4, 2) 11. N, −5·3; E, −5·8
12. (i) 80°, 100° (ii) 80°, 100° (iii) $180° - (x+y)°$, $(x+y)°$
14. 70° 15. 90° 16. 150°
19. 31°, 31°, 31°, 31°; isosceles; rhombus
20. E, mid-point of FD 21. (i) 234 (ii) 13 (iii) 18

Page 166 General Revision Exercise 4

1. AB = 6·40, BC = 1·41, CA = 6·40, (11, 11)
2. 3 cm^2 3. $y = 2x + 12$, (5, 22) 4. (i) 45° (ii) 25°
5. (i) 35 (ii) 420 (iii) 22·7 6. 1, 2 units 8. 60°, 120°
9. 32°, 132° 10. 40°, S, D
11. (i) 108°, 126°, 54°, 63° (ii) 6·2, 15, 5·3 cm

Page 169 General Revision Exercise 5

1. 25°, 77½°, 77½° 2. No, $0 < a < 8$ 3. DE > 1·25
5. 3·66 cm; 5 cm; AC > 5; 3·66 < AC < 5 6. 1 in, 9 in
10. 3·9 miles, 1·95 miles, 6·0 miles, N 19°E 11. 1,080, 1,200 yd
13. 1,850 yd

Arithmetic—Answers to Chapter 1

Page 177 Exercise 3

1. 6	2. 15	3. 16	4. 14
5. 15	6. 6	7. 12	8. 6·25
9. 3	10. 2	11. 3	12. 2
13. 1·6	14. 4	15. 4	16. 5·2

Page 178 Exercise 4

1. 1·1; 1·25; 1·4; 1·6; 1·74 2. 3·2; 3·32; 3·66; 3·85
3. 7·05; 7·2; 7·45; 7·78
4. 3·2; 6·2; 9·0; 2·48; 4·44; 9·8. Multiplying by 2

Page 179 Exercise 5

1. 6·00	2. 10·0	3. 7·50	4. 3·60
5. 10·0	6. 6·40	7. 10·0	8. 9·00
9. 3·50	10. 9·00	11. 4·84	12. 9·86

Page 180 Exercise 6

1. 2·00	2. 2·00	3. 3·50	4. 2·50
5. 4·00	6. 1·33	7. 1·14	8. 1·60
9. 1·67	10. 1·40	11. 1·57	12. 1·05

Page 180 Exercise 7

1. 5·48	2. 8·12	3. 1·73	4. 1·24
5. 4·47	6. 9·38	7. 81·0	8. 13·0
9. 26·0	10. 51·8	11. 3·61	12. 1·17

Page 181 Exercise 8

1. 1,000	2. 80	3. 20	4. 0·9
5. 0·02	6. 900	7. 6	8. 10
9. 0·03	10. 0·07	11. 40	12. 100
13. 400	14. 6,000	15. 20 cm^2	16. 0·04 cm^2
17. 8 ft^3	18. 800 yd	19. 6 miles; 8 miles	

20. 20,000 miles; 6,000 miles

Page 181 Exercise 8 (by slide rule)

1. 1,070	2. 93·4	3. 15·2	4. 0·609
5. 0·0230	6. 882	7. 6·02	8. 14·4
9. 0·0257	10. 0·0696	11. 47·4	12. 166
13. 396	14. 4,790	15. 16·2 cm^2	16. 0·0529 cm^2
17. 7·47 ft^2	18. 750 yd	19. 5·50 miles; 6·85 miles	

20. 24,800 miles; 6,780 miles

Page 182 Exercise 9

1. 200; 209	2. 200; 234	3. 400; 378	4. 90; 80·0
5. 800; 779	6. 8; 7·77	7. 6; 6·53	8. 6; 6·58
9. 700; 757	10. 80; 92·2	11. 1; 0·936	12. 50,000; 56,100

Page 182 Exercise 10

1. 20; 14·6	2. 20; 21·1	3. 20; 18·0	4. 4; 3·39
5. 20; 20·2	6. 2; 1·89	7. 20; 22·7	8. 20; 20·1
9. 0·2; 0·245	10. 2; 2·26	11. 0·001; 0·00113	12. 30; 29·6

Page 183 Exercise 11

1. 35·0	2. 6,470	3. 47·0	4. 0·622
5. 261	6. 7·88	7. 0·500	8. 3·00
9. 9·46	10. 0·0353	11. 0·0634	12. 0·0382

Page 184 Exercise 12

1. 5·45 2. 12·2 3. 10·5 cm^2 4. (i) 5·39 (ii) 40·6

5. (i) 57·1% (ii) 62·5% (iii) 88·9% (iv) 15·6% (v) 56·2%

6. 4·59	7. 0·579	8. 77·4 in^2	9. 4·30 in
10. $1,910	11. £892	12. £830	13. 21·9
14. 1·51	15. 1·57 m^3	16. 0·500 in	17. 413 mph
18. 10 h 12 min		19. 8·91 kg	20. 535
21. 2·28	22. See page 284		

Arithmetic—Answers to Chapter 2

Note.—Where a Slide Rule has been used, answers obtained may not be exactly the same as those given.

Page 191 Exercise 2

1. 88 ft, 11 ft, 63 yd, 22 cm, 154 m, 12·6 cm
2. 330 yd, 11 ft, 88 cm, 12·6 in, 31·4 m, 629 cm
3. 70 yd, 10·5 in, 28 cm, 2·55 m, 280 yd, 1·91 cm

4. 3·14 in	5. 62·9 yd	6. 50·2 yd
7. 210 ft	8. 70 yd	9. 63·6 cm

10. (i) 31·4 cm, 50·2 in, 628 yd (ii) 25,000 miles (iii) $5·8 \times 10^8$

11. 491 yd **12.** 1·75 yd **13.** 14·3 cm **14.** 60°, $\frac{1}{6}$, $\frac{1}{6}$, 1·05 cm

15. 88 cm, 7·33 cm, 9·78 cm, 29·3 cm, 66 cm

Page 196 Exercise 4

1. 154 yd², 616 in², 12·6 cm², 616 m², 7·07 ft², 28·3 cm² **2.** 402 yd²

3. 0·786 in² **4.** 7 in, 1·75 yd, 2·65 cm, 39·2 m

5. 14,600 yd², 12·6 cm² **6.** 3·22 ft², 9·54 m², 3·4 in², 42 cm²

7. 321 ft² **8.** 21·4% **9.** (i) 314 cm², 78·5 yd² (ii) 254 in²

10. 1·60 cm **11.** 11·3 ft **12.** 2:1, 4:1

Page 199 Exercise 5

1. 462 in³, 2 ft³ 240 in³, 12·6 m³, 113 cm³, 14 cm, 3·9 ft, 3 ft

2. 33·7 in³ **3.** 48 **4.** 12·8 cm, 10·8 cm **5.** 550 gal

6. $6{\cdot}28 \times 10^4$ ft³ **7.** 3·32 cm **8.** 24 cm

Page 200 Exercise 6

1. 11 in, 11 in by 3 in **2.** $52\frac{1}{4}$ in², $42\frac{5}{8}$ in²

3. 37·7 cm, 37·7 cm by 6 cm, 453 cm², 339 cm²

4. $2\pi rh + 2\pi r^2$, $2\pi rh + \pi r^2$, $2\pi rh$

5. 440 in², 126 cm², 528 cm², 3·14 yd² **6.** 2,992 cm² **7.** 2,266 in²

8. 203 ft²

Arithmetic—Answers to Chapter 3

Page 203 Exercise 1

1. (*a*) $\frac{1}{5}$ (*b*) $1\frac{17}{20}$ (*c*) $\frac{1}{400}$ (*d*) $\frac{1}{40}$ (*e*) $\frac{1}{8}$ (*f*) $\frac{3}{40}$ (*g*) $\frac{1}{250}$ (*h*) $\frac{1}{12}$

2. (*a*) 75 (*b*) 16 (*c*) $233\frac{1}{3}$ (*d*) $1\frac{1}{4}$ (*e*) $62\frac{1}{2}$ (*f*) 80 (*g*) 3 (*h*) 117

3. $\frac{11}{20}$, 0·55, 55%; $\frac{17}{100}$, 0·17, 17; $\frac{21}{50}$, 0·42, 42; $\frac{1}{125}$, 0·008, $\frac{4}{5}$;
$\frac{1}{3}$, 0·333, $33\frac{1}{3}$; $\frac{11}{9}$, 1·22, $122\frac{2}{9}$

4. 76%, 65% **5.** 8 units²; 25%, $12\frac{1}{2}$%, $6\frac{1}{4}$%, $12\frac{1}{2}$%, $43\frac{3}{4}$%

6. 5, $2\frac{1}{2}$, $12\frac{1}{2}$ p **7.** £14·02$\frac{1}{2}$ **8.** $81\frac{1}{4}$%

9. 28p per week **10.** £78

Page 205 Exercise 2

1. 70 2. 180 3. £1·68 4. 1 lb 4 oz
5. £10 6. 50p 7. 160 8. 50p
9. £580 10. 180 miles 11. £1,740 12. £3,460

Page 207 Exercise 3

1. 40, $12\frac{1}{2}$, $16\frac{2}{3}$, $3\frac{1}{3}$, $1\frac{1}{4}$ pence 2. 25, 12, $1\frac{1}{2}$, 14, 40
3. £15·16 4. £0·45, £2·61, 33 pence 5. $1\frac{1}{4}$% 6. £11·50
7. £15·50 8. £12, £1·30 9. £40·95, £13·16, £62
10. £25·50 11. £2,340 12. $\frac{1}{4}$%

Page 209 Exercise 4

1. 15%, 115% 2. $12\frac{1}{2}$%, $16\frac{2}{3}$%, $3\frac{1}{3}$%, 5%
3. 9·95 cm and 10·05 cm 4. 605, 363, 121, 121 yd^2
5. 30 oz, 27 oz, 3 oz 6. 115% 7. 28 oz, 14 oz, 14 oz
8. 94%, 107%, 90% 9. 16·2, 5·4, 5·4 ft^3
10. $62\frac{1}{2}$%, $37\frac{1}{2}$% 11. £1,260, £1,050, £105, £315
12. 26,000, 4,680 13. 16,524 14. (i) 58% (ii) 54%, 52%

Page 211 Exercise 5

1. £40 2. £1·70 profit 3. 50 pence 4. £17·80 5. £4·45

Page 213 Exercise 6

1. $16\frac{2}{3}$% 2. 8% 3. $68\frac{3}{4}$% 4. 12%
5. $17\frac{1}{3}$% 6. 15% 7. 12% 8. 14·3%
9. 20%, $16\frac{2}{3}$% 10. $8\frac{1}{3}$% 11. £897 12. $16\frac{2}{3}$%

Page 214 Exercise 7

1. £16·50 2. $72\frac{1}{2}$ pence 3. 95 pence 4. 96 pence
5. £1·$27\frac{1}{2}$ 6. 6 pence 7. £572 8. £118·80
9. $37\frac{1}{2}$ pence 10. £57·60, $21\frac{1}{4}$%, 27%
11. $4\frac{1}{2}$ pence, £2·$62\frac{1}{2}$, 14·3%

Page 216 Exercise 8

1. £15, £9, £1, £65, £2·19 **2.** £205·50, £73·50, £2,425·80
3. £5,325 **4.** £150

Page 217 Exercise 9

1. £2·25 **2.** £2·50 **3.** £4·22 **4.** £5·31
5. £313·50 **6.** £2·40 **7.** £40,625·00
8. £2·08, £5·50, £2·92

Page 219 Exercise 10

1. £40·80 **2.** £48·96 **3.** £20·70 **4.** £58·90
5. £122·58 **6.** £60·51 **7.** £100·73 **8.** £41·79
9. £167·02 **10.** £193·93

Arithmetic—Answers to Chapter 4

Page 221 Exercise 1

1. 3·2% **2.** 3,428, 1·4% **4.** 225,000, 29%

Page 225 Exercise 2

1. 1 **2.** 37 **4.** 75

Page 227 Exercise 3

4. 37–39

Page 229 Exercise 4

1. $\frac{11}{23}$

Page 231 Exercise 5

3. $\frac{7}{22}$, $\frac{1}{5}$ **4.** 120, 3, $\frac{3}{10}$, $\frac{17}{30}$ **5.** $\frac{1}{50}$, $\frac{17}{50}$

Page 235 Exercise 6

1. 5·85, 7·15 **3.** 225 **4.** 4·9 h **5.** 20 **6.** 7·1 min

Page 236 Exercise 7

2. 100, 20·0oz, $\frac{27}{100}$ 5. 5·7 6. 2·32in 7. 6·4, 29%, 47%

9. 300, 7·9, 10, 18%, 11%, 1·8

Arithmetic—Answers to Revision Exercises

Page 240 Revision Exercise on Chapter 2

1. 62·4 in^2, 33 in
2. 9·8 cm^2, 13·9 cm
3. (*a*) 367 ft (*b*) 1,440
4. 1,500,000 miles
5. 15,700 mph
6. 6,540 miles
7. 323 ft^2
8. 371 cm^2
9. 241 gal
10. (*a*) 0·28 cm (*b*) 0·92 cm
11. 3,130 cm^3, 847 cm^2
12. 352 yd/min, 264 yd/min
13. $10\frac{1}{2}$ ft
14. 180, 21·4%
16. 424 ft^2, 24,100 gal
17. 96·9 cm^2, 147 g
18. 15·7 ft^2, 509

Page 244 Revision Exercise on Chapter 4

1. 12, 20, 10 2. (i) 180 (ii) 14% 3. (*a*) 22 (*b*) 84%

4. (i)

Score	0	1	2	3	4	5	6	7	8	9
Frequency	12	14	0	29	0	11	0	4	0	2

Mean Score = 2·8 (ii) $\frac{11}{72}$

5. (*b*) 100, 83·15 (*c*) (i) 22% (ii) 19%

6. (i) 3, 2 (ii) 4, 4·55 (iii) 59%, 59% (iv) 12%, 22%

7.

Score	2	3	4	5	6	7	8	9	10	11	12
Probability	$\frac{1}{36}$	$\frac{1}{18}$	$\frac{1}{12}$	$\frac{1}{9}$	$\frac{5}{36}$	$\frac{1}{6}$	$\frac{5}{36}$	$\frac{1}{9}$	$\frac{1}{12}$	$\frac{1}{18}$	$\frac{1}{36}$
Frequency in 144 throws	4	8	12	16	20	24	20	16	12	8	4

Mean = 7

Arithmetic—Answers to General Revision Exercises

Page 247 General Revision Exercise 1

1. (i) $2\times3\times7$ (ii) $2^3\times3$ (iii) $2^3\times3\times5$ **2.** 182

3. (i) 19; 17 (ii) 24; 18 (iii) 70; 70 (iv) 120; 120

4. (i) 1 (ii) 4 (iii) 5 (iv) 2 (v) 0

5. (*a*) $\frac{1}{3}<\frac{3}{8}<\frac{5}{12}$ (*b*) $\frac{7}{33}<\frac{7}{32}<\frac{7}{31}$

6. (i) 7 (ii) 35 (iii) 105 (iv) $3\frac{1}{16}$ (v) $\frac{7}{32}$

7. (i) $\frac{7}{18}$ (ii) $\frac{7}{24}$ (iii) $3\frac{5}{11}$

8. (*a*) $4{\cdot}28\times10$ (*b*) $9{\cdot}15\times10^7$ (*c*) $3{\cdot}14\times10^{-1}$ (*d*) $5{\cdot}72\times10^{-3}$

9. 37·81 **10.** (i) 4 (ii) 19·9 km **11.** 128; 1·6 cm

12. £7·67 **13.** 4·7 kg

14. (*a*) 4·37 (*b*) 0·335 (*c*) 248 (*d*) 65·5

Page 249 General Revision Exercise 2

1. 4 pence, £1·48½ **2.** 12 **3.** 85; 21; £2·02½ **4.** £93·86½

5. 48 mm^2 **6.** 1,550 cm^3 **7.** 2 ft 8 in **8.** 192

9. 22·8 lb **10.** *a*, *d* **11.** *b*, *d* **12.** 16·44 cm

13. $5{\cdot}87\times10^{-4}$ **14.** 8·6948; 0·018601 **15.** $\frac{3}{110}$ in^2

Page 250 General Revision Exercise 3

1. (i) $33\frac{1}{3}$ mpg (ii) ½ unit per hour (iii) 24 gal per min

2. £1·47 **3.** £17·82 **4.** 1 hr 36 min; 96 miles

6. 6·9 cm **7.** 68·1 marks **8.** 4 rows **10.** 2·025 s

11. 537·6 acres **12.** 17·8 acres; 57·6 acres **13.** 4·56 ft

14. 8·1g **15.** (*a*) 42, 58, 29 pence (*b*) 9·60, 3·30, 6·72 fr

Page 252 General Revision Exercise 4

1. 31 = 11111; 37 = 100101

2. 1 + 1001; 10 + 1000; 11 + 111; 100 + 110; 101 + 101

3. 100; 1011; 11010 **4.** (i) 1001010 ft (ii) 101 ft

5. (*a*) 10000, 100000; 1, 2, 4, 8, 16, 32
   (*b*) 10101, 101010; 1, 2, 5, 10, 21, 42

6. 100011, 100110, 101010, 101100, 110001

7. $1011010\,\text{cm}^3$ 8. 100

9. $\frac{1}{10}_{\text{two}}$; $\frac{1}{100}_{\text{two}}$; $\frac{11}{100}_{\text{two}}$; $\frac{101}{1000}_{\text{two}}$; $\frac{3}{4}$; $\frac{5}{8}$

Page 253 General Revision Exercise 5

1. £136·75 2. £74·62$\frac{1}{2}$; £6·22 3. £33·20

4. £3·28 5. £224; 3 pence 6. 44 7. 11 st 2 lb

8. 28$\frac{1}{3}$; 23$\frac{1}{7}$ gal 9. (i) 24$\frac{2}{3}$ (ii) 7·51 (iii) 150

10. (*a*) £16·15 (*b*) £14·82 (*c*) £22·63 11. 10·5%

12. 3% profit 13. £1,482·50 14. £9·40 15. £1·63

16. $4{\cdot}87 \times 10^7$ miles 17. 54 min 18. 36 mph

19. 102·14 fr 20. £1,557 million

Page 255 General Revision Exercise 6

1. (i) $\frac{1}{2}$ (ii) $\frac{1}{2}$ (iii) $\frac{2}{3}$ (iv) $\frac{1}{2}$ (v) $\frac{2}{3}$ 2. (i) $\frac{1}{4}$ (ii) $\frac{3}{4}$; $\frac{1}{8}$

3. (i) 93 (ii) 3 4. (i) 9; $\frac{1}{4}$ (ii) (*a*) $\frac{1}{8}$ (*b*) 1 (*c*) 0 (*d*) $\frac{3}{8}$

5. (i) $\frac{2}{3}$ (ii) $\frac{2}{3}$ 6. 2·350 million 7. (i) $\frac{1}{8}$ (ii) $\frac{1}{8}$

Page 256 General Revision Exercise 7

1. F 2. T 3. F 4. F 5. T 6. F

7. T 8. F 9. F 10. T 11. T 12. T

13. (i) T (ii) T (iii) T 14. (i) F (ii) F (iii) T (iv) T

15. (*a*) T (*b*) F (*c*) T

Page 257 General Revision Exercise 8

1. (i) $\frac{1}{8}$ (ii) 0·02718 2. £0·41 3. $5{\cdot}6 \times 10^{-2}$

4. 1,134 5. £14·70 6. 0·6 7. 56 mph

8. 2·54; 2·22 9. (i) $5n$ (ii) $1/2^n$ 10. 3,152,000; 1,051,000

Page 258 General Revision Exercise 9

1. (i) 0·0036 (ii) 4·58
2. 29·92 in
3. 918·1 cm^2
4. 4
5. 0·28 %
6. $\frac{2}{3}$
7. $52\frac{1}{2}$ pence
8. 19 min $25\frac{1}{8}$ s
9. 22 yd
10. (*a*) 6 miles (*b*) 27 miles

Page 259 General Revision Exercise 10

1. £61·20
2. $62\frac{1}{2}$ pence
3. 12 yr 6 months
4. $8\frac{1}{2}$ pence, $8\frac{1}{2}$%
5. 243 g
6. 9·51 s
7. £12·50
8. 120 ft^3
9. (i) 1,763 (ii) £0·17
10. 32 g; 6 g; 72 g